COMPUTERS IN MATHEMATICAL RESEARCH

Editors

R. F. CHURCHHOUSE
J.-C. HERZ

Atlas Computer Laboratory,
IBM-France and University of Lille

computers

in mathematical

research

1968

NORTH-HOLLAND PUBLISHING COMPANY - AMSTERDAM

Library of Congress Catalog Card Number 67-25032

Publishers:

NORTH-HOLLAND PUBLISHING CO. – AMSTERDAM

PRINTED IN THE NETHERLANDS

CONTENTS

PREFACE

This book is based mainly on a Symposium on Utilisation of Computers in Mathematical Research held at the IBM World Trade European Education Centre, Blaricum, Netherlands, August 29-31, 1966. D. H. Lehmer's paper is the actual text of his talk in that Symposium. Papers by A. O. L. Atkin, R. F. Churchhouse, J. H. Conway, A. J. W. Duijvestijn, J. C. P. Miller, S. M. Ulam, have been written after their talks in Blaricum. C. E. Fröberg, J. -C. Herz and A. Liulevicius have presented their results from the International Congress of Mathematicians, Moscow, August 1966. G. Glaeser and Y. Siret discussed their works at the AFIRO Congress, Lille, June 1966. P. Deussen, J. -J. Duby and J. K. S. McKay's papers are presented here for the first time.

We have to acknowledge, in addition to the contributors, many mathematicians who made possible the realization of this survey, by their advice or encouragement, especially H. G. ApSimon, F. L. Bauer, P. Belgodère, J. -P. Benzecri, B. J. Birch, P. Braffort, J. W. S. Cassels, C. Coatmelec, P. Erdös, N. Gastinel, F. Genuys, A. Ghizzetti, H. H. Goldstine, D. Hirschberg, A. J. Hoffman, P. L. Ivanescu, S. Kuroda, J. Leech, F. Le Lionnais, J. H. van Lint, J. -L. Lions, G. Poitou, J. A. van der Pool, T. Rus, E. S. Selmer, J. -P. Serre, H. P. F. Swinnerton-Dyer, H. Werner, A. van Wijngaarden. The bibliography owes much to Prof. J. Dénes, who communicated an unpublished extensive list of references on non-numerical applications of computers.

We are grateful to Prof. J. Dieudonné for his authoritative introduction and to North-Holland for their excellent work.

R. F. Churchhouse
J. -C. Herz

INTRODUCTION

Les mathématiciens purs sont en général aussi peu informés des possibilités des ordinateurs que le grand public. Ils sont même assez enclins à la méfiance, ne serait-ce qu'en raison des articles "à sensation" que la grande presse ne cesse de publier régulièrement sur les merveilles des "machines à penser". En contact journalier avec les difficultés de la recherche mathématique, conscients de la primauté de l'imagination créatice, seul vrai moteur de la science, connaissant bien les longs cheminements à-demi conscients et les rares illuminations de l' "intuition", ils sont à bon droit sceptiques lorsqu'on vient péremptoirement leur affirmer que sous peu, par sa seule rapidité à examiner en quelques millisecondes une multitude de possibilités, un robot sera en mesure de s'égaler aux meilleurs d'entre eux.

Il est bon de savoir que, sans exclure totalement *a priori* une telle possibilité dans un avenir lointain, les spécialistes sérieux du Calcul numérique sont loin de tomber dans ce genre de "science fiction". Ils savent trop bien que, si complexe et ingénieux que soit un programme, la machine qui l'exécute ne fait qu'effectuer des opérations qui sont certes en très grand nombre, mais ont toutes été prévues d'avance. La véritable création, l'idée qui fait choisir une méthode parmi une *infinité* d'autres possibles, n'est pas concevable chez un robot. J'aime à prendre pour exemple concret, dans ce genre de débat, une méthode élémentaire d'Analyse qui a d'innombrables applications, l'idée d'itération. Le jour où, placée devant le problème de la résolution d'une équation $x = g(x)$, une machine, sans aide apparente ou cachée de son cornac, sera parvenue à l'idée de former la suite $x_0, x_1 = g(x_0), x_2 = g(x_1)$, etc., je ne serai pas loin de croire, moi aussi, à la possibilité de faire "penser" les ordinateurs.

En attendant, les mathématiciens les plus "purs" auraient tort de négliger l'aide que les robots peuvent leur apporter, et c'est pour les en convaincre qu'a été écrit ce volume. Il devrait persuader les plus réticents que dans ce domaine on n'en est encore qu'aux premiers pas, et il est fort probable que des mathématiciens imaginatifs sauront multiplier les applications des ordinateurs dans bien d'autres domaines que ceux qui sont abordés ici.

Les divers textes rassemblés dans ce volume se répartissent assez inégalement en plusieurs familles. Il y a d'abord le type d'application le plus universellement connu, la fabrication de tables; celles dont il s'agit ici sont toutefois d'un type peu habituel, qui surprendra peut-être le mathématicien non familier avec l'algèbre et la topologie modernes. Il y verra apparaître, à côté de structures algébriques déjà classiques comme les groupes finis et leurs caractères (McKay) et les corps finis (Conway), des objets algébriques beaucoup plus complexes comme les anneaux de vecteurs de Witt

(Duby) et les algèbres de Steenrod (Liulevicius), où les moindres essais de calcul algébrique "à la main" deviennent rapidement inextricables; il est clair que l'ordinateur doit ici prendre la relève, et en fait il s'agit de structures si complexes que, même avec les machines les plus modernes, on risque de ne pouvoir aller très loin dans les tabulations, à moins de trouver de nouvelles méthodes de programmation utilisant de meilleure façon leurs capacités.

Un second type d'utilisation déjà classique des ordinateurs concerne ce qu'on pourrait appeler les mathématiques énumératives. Il s'agit d'ensembles finis doués d'une certaine structure, et parmi tous les ensembles de ce type ayant un nombre donné d'éléments, on cherche ceux qui possèdent une ou plusieurs propriétés additionnelles. La théorie des graphes est fertile en de tels problèmes, et les articles de Duijvestijn, Herz, Miller et Ulam donnent une idée de leur variété et de l'aide efficace que peut encore apporter ici un ordinateur convenablement programmé. On peut aussi ranger dans cette famille le travail de Deussen sur les classes d'isomorphismes de semi-groupes finis.

Des mathématiques "finies" le passage est presque insensible à la Théorie des nombres, et bien avant l'arrivée des machines électroniques cette partie des mathématiques était celle où les essais de calcul numérique avaient été les plus nombreux et les plus persistants. L' "induction simple" chère à Euler et à ses contemporains n'était pas autre chose que la vérification d'une loi pour un nombre raisonnablement élevé de cas, permettant de la poser comme conjecture plausible. C'est vraisemblablement ainsi qu'a dû naître la conjecture de Goldbach; Euler lui-même a formulé un grand nombre de telles hypothèses (plus ou moins solidement fondées); et l'on sait que c'est grâce à sa remarquable habileté de calculateur que Gauss avait pu conjecturer de profonds résultats comme la loi asymptotique de répartition des nombres premiers. La tentation était donc grande de se servir de la puissance des ordinateurs pour poursuivre à une bien plus grande échelle l'exploration numérique des conjectures anciennes restées ouvertes, et on n'y a pas manqué. A vrai dire, comme le souligne l'article de Lehmer, les résultats obtenus dans cette direction sont assez maigres: sans doute, nous connaissons des centaines de nouveaux cas d'impossibilité de l'équation de Fermat $x^n + y^n = z^n$, et on sait factoriser beaucoup plus de nombres de Mersenne $2^n - 1$ qu'il y a 50 ans; mais on peut difficilement soutenir que cela nous ait beaucoup avancés, et il en est de même dans d'autres problèmes moins célèbres, comme ceux mentionnés dans l'article de Fröberg. Parfois on a la chance que l'ordinateur fournisse par hasard un contre-exemple démolissant une vieille conjecture: c'est ce qui s'est passé pour celle d'Euler sur l'impossibilité de résoudre l'équation $x^5 + y^5 + z^5 + t^5 = u^5$ en nombres entiers > 0; on soupçonne qu'Euler n'avait pas de raisons bien sérieuses pour étayer cette hypothèse.

Ce qui est beaucoup plus intéressant, c'est qu'on voit s'amorcer, en Théorie des nombres, une collaboration entre le mathématicien et la machine, l'analyse des résultats d'un programme pouvant suggérer des lois qui autrement seraient restées insoupçonnées; on en a des exemples très suggestifs avec les problèmes de congruence traités dans les articles de

Atkin et de Churchhouse, et on en garde l'impression que l'on touche peut-être là au début d'une série de féconds développements en Théorie des nombres.

C'est la même impression qui se dégage du très intéressant article de Glaeser, le seul (avec celui de Martinet et Siret sur la méthode de Runge-Kutta) qui soit consacré aux applications à l'Analyse: c'est le récit, fait avec esprit et humour, d'un travail de trois années de l'auteur et de son équipe sur des problèmes difficiles d'approximation de fonctions différentiables. On y reconnaît la démarche habituelle de la recherche, le passage progressif de conjectures naïves à une compréhension en profondeur de la situation; mais ce qui est remarquable, c'est que cet apprentissage des difficultés, au bout duquel se trouvera peut-être l'illumination créatrice, est ici encore magnifié de telle façon par la machine qu'il permet d'effectuer cette pénétration du problème dans des cas où les calculs "à la main" rebuteraient le plus persévérant. Il est bien certain que cette utilisation intelligente des possibilités de l'ordinateur n'est pas limitée aux problèmes assez particuliers étudiés par l'auteur, et il faut espérer que son exemple suscitera de nombreux projets analogues, pour le plus grand bien de l'Analyse.

J. Dieudonné

MACHINES AND PURE MATHEMATICS

D. H. LEHMER
University of California, Berkeley

1. INTRODUCTION

Today opportunities exist, as never before, for the pure, as well as the applied, mathematician, to avail himself of the large scale computing system to further his research. There are even a goodly number of young computer people who are working at smoothing the path the mathematician must tread in approaching the computer. Special purpose software (but no hardware) is being created to help the mathematician communicate with the machine with a minimum of knowledge. Inevitably, some decisions are being made that tell the mathematician what is good for him. As one might expect, these hardworking, conscientious, young people are really not those who are supposed to benefit from their own software creations. Nor is their's a task of self-denying service to their cousins, the pure mathematicians. In reality one feels that instead their real devotion is to the laudable purpose of automating basic mathematical procedures. In the back of their collective mind is the thought of eliminating the human being as far as possible, replacing him by the machine. They are fascinated by the problems created by the machine in teaching it to perform still more elaborate tricks. They leave to others the missionary work of acquainting the great unwashed multitudes of mathematicians with the prospects of a new era in research activity.

Even if we were to embark on this great missionary effort, I believe that the response would be less than enthusiastic. After all, the great majority of pure mathematicians are concerned with questions and concepts that a mere digital computer cannot comprehend fully, such as compactness, limits, measure, to name the first three that come to mind. Another point to remember is that a mathematician prides himself on the simplicity of his work and results. He naturally rejects things than are not easily done by hand. If our missionary were to reveal his hidden purpose, that of replacing the mathematician's handwork, he would be received even less enthusiastically.

When one reads, for example, "The computer can and should carry out the entire process", one wonders whether this is not becoming automation for automation's sake.

It seems to me that what really matters is the search for truth. In some cases, and certainly not in other cases, real strides forward can be made by involving, not replacing, the pure mathematician with the computer. One must realize that this general program is immeasurably more prolix than merely assisting the mathematician with his arithmetic. Opportunities for such involvement are, even now, not too numerous, considering the nature of the man and his interests and the limitations of the computer. I should like to discuss with you a few of these opportunities, arranged in order of increasing involvement.

2. COUNTER-EXAMPLES

Computing machines have been of service to mathematics in pointing out, by an example, the falsity of a conjectured result. The Theory of Numbers is a good branch of mathematics to look for these counter-examples, not only because of its discrete variable nature but also because the subject abounds with easily stated propositions whose truth values are very difficult to establish.

A very recent discovery of Lander and Parkin and the CDC 6600 is a case in point. Euler (circa 1769), in discussing the Fermat Problem, declared that it is also impossible to find three fourth powers whose sum is a fourth power or to find four fifth powers whose sum is a fifth power. Two centuries later, this summer, the 6600 came up with the undisputable fact that

$$27^5 + 84^5 + 110^5 + 133^5 = 144^5 .$$

This not only demolishes Euler's assertion about fifth powers but even raises hopes that the equation

$$x^4 + y^4 + z^4 = w^4$$

may also be solvable. I know three different computing establishments where this equation is now under scrutiny.

Not all searches for counter-examples have triumphal endings. In fact, in the case of some famous unsolved problems, it would seem foolhardy to invest much good machine time in such a search. Examples are the Four Color Problem and the Goldbach Conjecture that every even number (>2) is the sum of two primes.

3. VERIFICATION OF CONJECTURES

When one has been unsuccessful in finding a counter-example, one can sometimes report that one's machine time was well spent in verifying the truth of N cases of the general proposition one secretly was hoping to demolish. If N is pretty large, one can say that the proposition is now more plausible than before. A metric for plausibility has never been proposed, as far as I know, but if we had one we may be sure that it would not be a linear function of N.

Although we cannot prove a proposition that begins, "For every positive integer K", by merely verifying it for $K = 1(1)N$, no matter how large N is taken, there are two possibilities still open to us:

a) We may succeed in recasting the proposition so that it reads, "For every positive integer $K \leq N \ldots$". This reformulation can be done by proving the original proposition for all sufficiently large K by an asymptotic approach that exploits the largeness of K and determines that "sufficiently large K" means $K > N$, or it can be done by a transformation in which infinitely many cases of the original proposition become a single case of the transformed proposition, reducing an infinite problem to a finite one.

To illustrate this last technique, consider the infinite class S of all positive integers divisible by no prime greater than 7. That is

$$S:\ 2^{a_1}3^{a_2}5^{a_3}7^{a_4} \qquad (a_i \geq 0)\ .$$

Let S' be the set

$$S':\ 2^{b_1}3^{b_2}5^{b_3}7^{b_4} \qquad (0 \leq b_i \leq 4)\ .$$

Then S' is finite, having indeed 625 members. These may be represented in an obvious way by the vector

$$[b_1, b_2, b_3, b_4]\ .$$

If we write

$$a_i = 5c_i + b_i\ ,$$

we see at once that every member s of S is of the form

$$s = t^5 s'$$

where s' belongs to S' and t belongs to S. In this sense s' represents s.

If we are concerned with the elements of S taken with respect to a prime modulus $p = 10\,n + 1$ in such a way that their "quintic characters" are involved, as, for example, in the case in which the solvability of the congruence

$$x^5 \equiv s \pmod{p} \tag{1}$$

is in question, then we may confine ourselves to the elements s' of the finite class S' since this congruence (1) is solvable in exactly those cases in which the corresponding congruence

$$x^5 \equiv s' \pmod{p}$$

is solvable.

Not only this, the infinite class of all primes p of the form $10\,n + 1$ breaks up into 625 infinite subclasses according to the quintic characters mod p of the first four primes 2, 3, 5, 7. For each prime p in the same subclass the answer to the question whether the congruence

$$x^5 \equiv s' \pmod{p}$$

has solutions is identical. Accordingly, the doubly infinite number of questions raised by the congruence (1) can be answered by considering $(625)^2 = 390625$ cases only.

b) We may discover, by a detailed analysis of the verified cases, why the original proposition is generally true (i.e., for all K) and thus come up with a proof. This analysis need not be wholly a hand job. We should not hesitate to call upon the speed and flexibility of the computer to do most of the work.

Both processes have been successful in the recent past.

4. EXPLORATION OF MATHEMATICAL SYSTEMS

The preceding uses of the machine are examples of exploration or search over the one dimensional space of propositions p_k, the kth example of our general proposition. More generally, the computer can make searches over higher-dimensional spaces of mathematical objects and in many cases the search can be exhaustive when a reasonably finite number of objects is involved. For example, all free semi-groups of, say, 10 elements can be generated, analyzed, classified, catalogued, collated, concorded, enumerated and all but published, within the present state of the art. This kind of work is worse than drudgery, it is simply unsafe to do by hand. A systematic exploration of certain parts of pure mathematics, if ever undertaken seriously, would be a project to end all projects. Full use would have to be made of a list processing language such as LISP or SNOBOL. The somewhat tragic fact about this hypothetical mechanized scrutiny is that the computer would fail to discover those features of the landscape that it had not been told to look for.

5. MANIPULATION OF MATHEMATICAL SYSTEMS

The current (August, 1966) number of the *Communications of the ACM* is devoted to Symbol Manipulation and contains 11 complete papers on the subject. Although many papers are somewhat oriented towards applied mathematics, much of the material has application to pure mathematics.

In writing and using a symbol manipulation system, or even a modest number of manipulation subroutines, one must be on one's guard against the explosive tendencies induced by generality, iteration and combinatorics.

One does not call on a computer to do an amount of manipulation that could possibly be done by hand work, even though a five-minute hand job could be done in a millisecond. One needs the computer for extensive non-linear iterative procedures involving several variables. Unless there is a great deal of input and output, much space and time is required. One of the first discoveries from experience with early manipulatory systems was the necessity of variable precision, fixed point, integer and rational arithmetic; an arithmetic package in which the number of words devoted to a number rises and falls as the calculations proceed. Unless there is some special reason why the coefficients in the resulting expansions are not too large, they will become so large as to make floating-point arithmetic wholly inadequate. One must in some cases be prepared to use a push-down storage system, not only for the terms of the expansion but even for the coefficients of these terms.

An example of the explosive nature of the general approach may be cited.

It is desired to make a study of a large class of quintic equations

$$f(x) = x^5 + a_1x^4 + a_2x^3 + a_3x^2 + a_4x + a_5 = \prod_{i=1}^{5} (x - p_i) = 0 .$$

in which the discriminant

$$D = D(f) = \prod_{i<j} (p_i - p_j)^2$$

plays a role. One can design a fairly short program for the numerical cal-culation of D when the coefficients a_i are given exact integer values.

The more general approach would be to produce D, once for all, as a polynomial in the literals $(a_1, a_2, a_3, a_4, a_5)$, as the resultant of $f(x)$ and $f'(x)$. More generally, using symbol manipulation, one could construct the resultant of any two quintics f and g as a polynomial in their two sets of co-efficients, from which D can be obtained as a very special case.

The result of this disarmingly general approach turns out to be a poly-nomial in 10 variables with thousands of terms having huge coefficients. Printing out these terms on several sheets of paper, even with a clever for-mat, is no answer. The alternative of storing this enormous polynomial in memory and substituting into it whenever necessary is much too expensive when compared with the direct numerical approach.

To combat combinatorial explosion, much attention must be given to re-duction by methodical grouping, collecting and simplifying terms when pos-sible. To do this with full generality takes a large number of instructions that can be called "executive", "supervisory", or "custodial", depending on one's viewpoint. No wonder there are large demands for space and time.

There is some question in my mind whether a large complete system for symbol manipulation is the answer to problems in pure mathematics. Such systems are designed and written by experts whose interest in the results of manipulation extend no further than their output on the printed page (or pages) in some reasonable readable format. One detects here a kind of "you asked for it" attitude. Again, what we need is an internal analysis of the large volume of generated information to boil it down to something compre-hensible by the mathematician. Such an analysis will depend very strongly on the type of problem being run and will require still more space. There is therefore, I believe, a good case for replacing the large manipulatory system by an old-fashioned library of a dozen subroutines, a selection of which is made for each problem to be run.

6. SPECIAL PURPOSE HARDWARE

In conclusion I would like to submit that there is still a case for the de-sign and construction of special purpose hardware for application to mathe-matics and to cite an example to prove my point, even on grounds of eco-nomics.

Any special purpose device, in order to compete with the combined hardware and software of the large scale computing system, must perform some set of operations more efficiently. If, in addition, it can operate without tying up the large system, a distinct economic advantage is gained. At the same time there must be a wide general class of problems to which the equipment is applicable, in order to make the unusual effort of construction worthwhile.

The example I wish to cite is a modest solid-state device called the Delay Line Sieve (DLS-127). It was built as an unsponsored educational project of the Departments of Mathematics and Electrical Engineering at the Berkeley campus of the University of California.

One large class of problems to which the DLS-127 is applicable is the solution of diophantine equations of the form

$$f(x, y) = 0 \tag{2}$$

where $f(x, y)$ is a polynomial of any degree in x and y with arbitrarily large integer coefficients. The DLS-127 solves this and other problems by reducing them to the general sieve problem; namely:

Find the least integer $x \geq 0$ such that

$$x \equiv a_{i1} \text{ or } a_{i2} \text{ or } \dots , \text{ or } a_{ik_i} (\text{mod } m_i) \ (i = 1(1)w) \tag{3}$$

where a_{ij} are given integers and the moduli m_i are relatively prime in pairs.

The DLS uses delay lines with feedback to produce the cyclic binary pulse patterns demanded by (3) and a coincidence circuit to render the conditions (3) simultaneous. The moduli m_i are fixed at

$$m_1 = 64, \ m_2 = 81, \ m_3 = 25, \ m_4 = 49, \ m_5 = 11, \ \dots , \ m_{31} = 127$$

so that $w = 31$. The search for x proceeds over consecutive integers at the modest rate of a million per second without attention, so that problems with $x < 10^{11}$ are within easy reach.

To reduce the problem (2) to one of type (3) one simply replaces (2) by the necessary condition

$$f(x, y) \equiv 0(\text{mod } m_i) \quad (i = 1(1)w) \ . \tag{2'}$$

Output from DLS-127 is then fed into (2) for verification.

Apparently uninteresting diophantine equations (1) sometimes lead to significant output from the DLS-127. For example, the equation

$$xy = 1 \tag{4}$$

has only the solution (1, 1) in positive integers. The output from the sieve gives in this case, in addition, the integers x not divisible by any of the primes ≤ 127. For problems of this sort, that have a great many solutions, the DLS-127 has an alternative mode of operation that only counts but does not put out the solutions. This mode is useful in studying the density of solutions of problems. In the above example we thus obtain values of the Legendre Cross Classification Sum

$$N - \sum_{i \le 31} \left[\frac{N}{P_i} \right] + \sum_{i < j \le 31} \left[\frac{N}{P_i P_j} \right] - \sum_{i < j < k \le 31} \left[\frac{N}{P_i P_j P_k} \right] + \dots , \tag{5}$$

which figures in formulas for the exact number of primes $\le N$, but is expensive to compute by (5).

If one wishes to omit from the summation in (5) any subset of primes P_i, one only has to replace (4) by

$$xy = m$$

where m is the product of the omitted primes.

Another interesting special case of (2) is

$$x - P(y) = 0$$

where $P(y)$ is a polynomial of arbitrarily high degree with integer coefficients that may be arbitrarily large in absolute value. In this case the DLS-127 is deciding during the N-th microsecond whether $P(n)$ represents N for integers n. This speed is independent of $P(y)$ and is many times faster than that obtainable from "all purpose" types of computers.

There is a small software package for the offline preparation of input and for processing the output. This uses the 7094 and even a Bendix G-15 for the preparation of paper input tape by means of which a new problem can be presented to the DLS-127 in a few seconds. Contact with human beings is confined to the specification of the coefficients of $f(x, y)$.

The choice of the moduli m_i was based on the fact that many interesting sieve problems are of "quadratic" type, i.e., that k_i in (3) is approximately $\frac{1}{2} m_i$. This makes the probability 2^{-w} that any x is solution of (3). At a megacycle, this makes 2000 seconds as the expected time between solutions when $w = 31$. An example of such a problem is the respresentation of a large integer by an arbitrary binary quadratic form which arises in factorization problems. A recent solution of such a sieve problem proposed by J. D. Brillhart and J. L. Selfridge resulted in the complete factorization into primes of the number

$$2^{330} + 1 = 5^2.13.41.61.397.661.1321.2113.3301.8581.312709 .$$

$$4327489.391249826881.415878438361.36301055201 41 .$$

$$12127627350301.13379250952981.$$

In competition with the IBM 7094 the DLS-127 makes a good showing, especially on economic grounds. It is roughly 10 times faster than the 7094 and costs about 2 cents an hour to operate.

The problems that have been run on the DLS-127 since last December would take another seven years to complete at our University Computer Center, supposing that the time were available, and would cost upwards of 15 million dollars, at the going rate.

CONGRUENCES FOR MODULAR FORMS

A. O. L. ATKIN

Atlas Computer Laboratory

1. INTRODUCTION

This paper describes in general terms my attempts to extend and generalise congruence properties of modular forms with the aid of a computer (the ICT Atlas 1 computer of the Science Research Council at Chilton). The main practical conclusion can be stated simply: working in continuous direct contact with a large and powerful computer establishment has led to results far beyond my original expectations. Accordingly it seems worthwhile to try and give here some account of the actual process of the discovery as it appeared to me at the time, which involves in effect a description of the work in reverse logical order; and to publish elsewhere the full mathematical details and a "logical" exposition based on the work in reverse order of time.

I have used Atlas to obtain a number of results, some of which are more interesting computationally than the present work. But in so far as the computer's function is to assist research, what matters is the final mathematical result rather than (to be fanciful) the machine's personal enjoyment of the tasks it has been ordered to perform. I am perfectly clear that the work described in this paper represents the most significant use I have made of Atlas. It might in theory have been possible to arrive at some of these results by *a priori* reasoning; certainly the cases where the proofs are complete require in the event no more computation than a few hours' hand work. But I would not myself have been able to conjecture the possibility of such results without the evidence provided by the computer.

I should like to thank the Director, Dr. J. Howlett, and my other colleagues at the Atlas Computer Laboratory for the frequent help they have given me. In particular I have had many valuable discussions with Dr. R. F. Churchhouse, both a number theorist and a veteran programmer, and Mr. E. B. Fossey and Miss Barbara Stokoe have constantly assisted me with the Atlas Hartran (Fortran) system.

It is intended that this account shall be intelligible to the reader with no knowledge of modular theory, provided that he is prepared to accept that the coefficient $c(n)$ which we mainly consider is mathematically significant. However at some points we give brief additional explanations for the reader who has such knowledge.

2. RAMANUJAN CONGRUENCES FOR PRIMES $q \leqslant 11$

The general theory of elliptic and modular functions had been in the process of development for about a century before Ramanujan[1919] conjectured his remarkable congruences for the partition function $p(n)$, defined combinatorially as the number of distinct ways of expressing n as the sum of integral parts, where the order of the parts is immaterial. His conjecture was

$$\text{if } 24n - 1 \equiv 0 \ (\text{mod } 5^a 7^b 11^c) \text{ then } p(n) \equiv 0 \ (\text{mod } 5^a 7^b 11^c) . \tag{1}$$

The curious appearance of $24n - 1$ in (1) is due to the fact that, writing

$$x = e^{2\pi i \tau} \quad (|x| < 1, \ \text{Im } \tau > 0) ,$$
$$f(x) = (1 - x)(1 - x^2)(1 - x^3) \dots , \tag{2}$$
$$\eta(\tau) = e^{\pi i \tau / 12} f(x) ,$$

we have

$$\sum_{n=0}^{\infty} p(n) \, x^n = 1/f(x) ,$$

and $\eta(\tau)$ is a modular form of half-integral dimension and complicated multiplier system. Thus the congruence properties are naturally associated not with $f(x)$ whose reciprocal enumerates $p(n)$, but with $x^{1/24} f(x)$; that is, they are essentially modular and not combinatorial *. Ramanujan himself was of course well aware of this, as his proofs of some particular cases show.

However this conjecture (1), originally found from the evidence of hand computed tables, was found to fail for the case of 7^3 by Chowla [1934] who observed that $p(243)$, computed by Gupta [1935], is not divisible by 7^3. This provides a simple illustration of the value of computers; had Ramanujan lived 50 years later he would surely have tested his conjecture extensively and probably found the correct form for 7. Watson [1938] proved the conjecture for all powers of 5, and a suitably modified form for all powers of 7, while Atkin [1967] proved the conjecture for all powers of 11. Thus the true form of (1) is

$$\text{if } 24n - 1 \equiv 0 \ (\text{mod } 5^a 7^b 11^c) \text{ then } p(n) \equiv 0 \ (\text{mod } 5^a 7^\beta 11^c) , \tag{3}$$

where $\beta = [\frac{1}{2}(b + 2)]$.

It might be argued that for Ramanujan to have obtained the correct form (3) would have been relatively unimportant; that the *idea* of such a property is all that matters short of actual proof. But this is far from true in this kind of work, since the exact numerical form of such results can often provide important clues as to a possible method of proof.

Despite the early recognition of the modular nature of these congruences, it was not until 1949 that Lehner [1949a, 1949b] considered the analogous properties of $c(n)$, where

---

* But see Dyson [1944] and Atkin and Swinnerton-Dyer [1954] for an exception.

$$j(\tau) = j(x) = \sum_{n=-1}^{\infty} c(n) \, x^n = \{1 + 240 \sum_{n=1}^{\infty} \sigma_3(n) \, x^n\}3 / x \, f\,24(x) - 744 \ * \qquad (4)$$

and

$$\sigma_3(n) = \sum_{d\,|\,n} d^3 \ .$$

This function $j(\tau)$ is essentially the simplest of all modular forms, being in fact the Hauptmodul of the full modular group so that

$$j\left(\frac{a\tau + b}{c\tau + d}\right) = j(\tau) \text{ for all integral } a, b, c, d \text{ with } ad - bc = 1 \ .$$

The results for $c(n)$ are

$$\text{if } n \equiv 0 \ (\text{mod } 2^a 3^b 5^c 7^d 11^e) \text{ then } c(n) \equiv 0 \ (\text{mod } 2^{3a+8} 3^{2b+3} 5^{c+1} 7^d 11^e) \ . \quad (5)$$

These are all due to Lehner [1949a, 1949b, 1950] except the cases $e > 3$ due to Atkin [1967]. They represent what are perhaps the simplest and most natural "Ramanujan-type" congruences. The general possibilities are not confined to the coefficients $c(n)$ and $p(n)$, and many other modular forms have Fourier coefficients ** with similar properties. The work described in this paper was in fact conducted simultaneously with $c(n)$ and $p(n)$, the former being the simplest case and the latter an example of the most difficult type of case; but we confine ourselves to $c(n)$ from now on in the present account.

3. CONGRUENCES FOR $q = 13$

3.1. It might have been hoped that results similar to (5) would exist for primes $q > 11$, but this is (by now) extremely improbable (there are strong theoretical grounds for this assertion which is not merely based on the fact that no properties have been found). The first results for $q > 11$, of an entirely different kind from those described in §2, are due to Newman [1958], who proved that

$$c(13^2 n) \equiv 8c(13n) \ (\text{mod } 13) \ , \qquad (6)$$

and †

$$\text{if } t(n) = -c(13n) \text{ and } p \neq 13 \text{ is prime, then}$$
$$t(np) - t(n) \, t(p) + p^{11} t(n/p) \equiv 0 \ (\text{mod } 13) \qquad (7)$$

---

* We choose the arbitrary constant in $j(x)$ to make $c(0) = 0$ and thus avoid tiresome exceptions to our results.
** That is, the coefficients of the expansion of a form $F(\tau)$ in powers of $x = e^{2\pi i \tau}$.
† For any number-theoretic coefficient $t(n)$ we write $t(n) = 0$ if n is not an integer.

From these Newman deduces, using the computed "accident" that $c(7.13) \equiv 0 \pmod{13}$, that

$$c(7.13^n) \equiv 0 \pmod{13} \text{ if } n \geq 1 \tag{8}$$

and

$$c(91n) \equiv 0 \pmod{13} \text{ if } (n,7) = 1 . \tag{9}$$

The first of these results shows that $c(n)$ is divisible by 13 infinitely often; the second shows more, that $c(n)$ is divisible by 13 in positive density of n.

Newman proves (7) by observing that $t(n) \equiv \tau(n) \pmod{13}$, where * $\tau(n)$ is defined by

$$\sum_{n=1}^{\infty} \tau(n) \, x^n = x f^{24}(x) .$$

Now $\tau(n)$ satisfies the *identical* relation

$$\tau(np) - \tau(n) \, \tau(p) + p^{11} \tau(n/p) = 0 \tag{10}$$

as conjectured by Ramanujan [1916] and proved by Mordell [1919], so that (6) and (7) are immediate. We may remark here that Ramanujan probably found this conjecture also by inspection of his own table of values of $\tau(n)$ and his extraordinary intuition for algebraic form in this subject. It is a consequence of (10) that $\tau(n)$ is multiplicative, i.e.,

$$\tau(mn) = \tau(m) \, \tau(n) \text{ if } (m,n) = 1 . \tag{11}$$

Glaisher [1907] had previously obtained a number of results similar to (11) for coefficients relating to the expression of a number as sums of squares, but he did not obtain the crucial third term (analogous to $p^{11}\tau(n/p)$ in (10)) in his equations to obtain the full result similar to (10). Glaisher's results have been completed and fully proved by Rankin [1967].

3.2. In 1962 ** O'Brien and I obtained a result which generalises Newman's (6):

> *For all $\alpha \geq 1$ there exists a constant k_α not divisible*
>
> *by 13 such that for $n \geq 1$ we have* (12)
>
> $c(13^{\alpha+1}n) \equiv k_\alpha c(13^\alpha n) \pmod{13\alpha} .$

Specifically, we had at this stage proved (12) for $\alpha \leq 4$ by detailed hand computation using the irrational modular equation for 13, and conjectured it for all α. It appeared to us at the time that the proof might depend on

---

* We apologise to the reader for the two uses of τ. Both are well established, and there is no real danger of confusion.

** The results of §3.2 appear in Atkin and O'Brien (1967). In the present context it seems natural to use real time.

some very deep properties of certain numerical coefficients of the form $a_i.13^{bi}$, and our subsequent proof of (12) for all α in 1963 arose from a fortunate numerical mistake. In fact one of us used some incorrect values of the a_i and still obtained (12), suggesting that only the values of b_i were relevant. This turned out to be the case. It thus appears that occasionally it is better *not* to have a reliable computer; but this is the only instance I can quote from personal experience.

It is clear from (12) that if we can find an "accident" of the form $c(13^\alpha n_0) \equiv 0 \pmod{13^\beta}$ for some $\beta \leqslant \alpha$, then $c(13^{\alpha+n} n_0) \equiv 0 \pmod{13^\beta}$ for $n \geqslant 0$, so that $c(n)$ is divisible by 13^β infinitely often. After my appointment to Atlas in 1964 I computed $c(13^6 n)$ modulo 13^6 for $1 \leqslant n \leqslant 40960$ with output of the form

$$n \qquad a(n) \qquad b(n)$$

denoting that $c(13^6 n) \equiv a(n).13^{b(n)} \pmod{13^6}$, with $a(n)$ prime to 13. The largest $b(n)$ found was a disappointing 3; there seemed a priori to be a reasonable chance of 4 if the values of $c(13^6 n)$ were random $\pmod{13^4}$ since $40960/13^4 \simeq 1.4$. However an inspection of the results exposed some very interesting features. Thus $b(7) = b(11) = 1$, $b(77) = 2$, and $b(154) = 2$; also $b(757) = 2$ and $b(5299 = 7.757) = 3$. We knew already from (7) that if $(m,n) = 1$ and $b(m) \geqslant 1$ then $b(mn) \geqslant 1$, but the above instances suggested immediately a multiplicative property modulo at least 13^3. In fact a few further hand calculations using the values of $a(n)$ as well as $b(n)$ led us to the following conjecture:

Let $t(n) = c(13^6 n)$. Then if $(m,n) = 1$ we have

$$t(1)t(mn) \equiv t(m)t(n) \pmod{13^6} . \qquad (13)$$

Since $c(13^6)$ is prime to 13, we may properly divide by it in the residue class ring modulo 13^6; rewriting $t(n) = c(13^6 n)/c(13^6)$ we have (13) with $t(1) = 1$, and it was now natural to look for the precise detail analogues to (7). The natural power of p in the third term is p^{-1}, and since $p^{11} \equiv p^{-1}$ $\pmod{13}$ this agrees with (7). Thus finally, replacing 6 by a general α, we conjectured the following:

Let $\alpha \geqslant 1$, and $p \neq 13$ be prime. Then if $t(n) = c(13^\alpha n)/c(13^\alpha)$ we have, for all $n \geqslant 1$,

$$t(np) - t(n)t(p) + p^{-1}t(n/p) \equiv 0 \pmod{13^\alpha} . \qquad (14)$$

This conjecture I tested successfully on Atlas for $\alpha \leqslant 8$, $p \leqslant 97$, and $pn \leqslant 1000$, and have recently proved in general. We may now regard (12) as the ramified form which (14) takes for the exceptional prime $p = 13$, and in fact we can rewrite (12) as

$$t(13n) \equiv t(13)t(n) \pmod{13^\alpha} . \qquad (15)$$

We shall in future refer to multiplicative congruence properties similar to

(14) as M-results, and to their ramified cases similar to (15) as R-results.

Now it is easy to show from (7) by the theory of second order linear difference equations that for each $p \neq 13$ there exists some θ such that $c(13.p^\theta) \equiv 0 \pmod{13}$. Thus from (14) we have for any $\alpha \geq 1$ the result

$$c(13^\alpha.P.n) \equiv 0 \pmod{13^\alpha} \text{ if } (n,P) = 1 \tag{16}$$

where

$$P = \prod_{i=1}^{\alpha} p_i{}^{\theta_i} \, ,$$

so that (since there are infinitely many primes) $c(n)$ is divisible by 13^α in positive density of n for every $\alpha \geq 1$. Hence in the final analysis the extensive computation of $c(13^6 n)$ becomes unncessary but without it we could not have found (14).

However in this connection there is a subtle difference in the corresponding work for $p(n)$, and generally for the Fourier coefficients of forms of half-integral dimension. In these cases there are results of M- and R-type, but they contain an unknown constant which is not a value of the coefficient, and one cannot prove the existence of "accidents" by the use of difference equations for a general prime $p \neq 13$. Thus in order to prove that $p(n)$ is divisibly by 13^α in positive density of n it is necessary to compute α accidents even though the *general* M-result is proved. I have in fact found 13 such accidents, so that $p(n)$ is divisible by 13^{13} in positive density of n. (The second "13" is of course an irrelevant accident)

4. THE CASES $q = 17, 19$ AND 23

Concurrently with the work for $q = 13$ described in the last section, the methods of Atkin [1967] were used to obtain suitable systems of modular functions for the primes $q = 17, 19, 23, 29, 31$, and 37, with a view to obtaining R-results. As soon as the M-results for 13 appeared, it required no additional personal effort (and in fact very little machine time) to test the situation on these primes with regard to M-results. I found that the conjectures (14) and (15) held for $q = 17, 19$ and 23, word for word but replacing 13 by q. This provides a further illustration of the value of a computer: with the necessary subroutines already written one can multiply instances without the loss of momentum which hand calculation would involve. There was in this case no particular reason to expect "the same again"; the type of modular equation for $q = 13$ does not exist for $q > 13$.

However a significant difference arose here as to the proof of these M- and R-results. If we define for any power series

$$A(x) = \sum_{n \geq N} a(n) x^n$$

the operator $U = U_q$ by

$$UA(x) = \sum_{qn \geq N} a(qn)\, x^n \, ,$$

then we have

$$\sum_{n=1}^{\infty} c(q^{\alpha}n)\, x^n = U^{\alpha}j(x) \, .$$

As a specific example we now take the simplest case $q = 19$. We can show by modular theory * that there exist functions $g_n(x)$ for $n \geq 1$ with integral coefficients in their power series expansions and leading terms x^n, such that

$$U_{19}j(x) \; \equiv \; a_1 g_{\bar{1}}(x) + 19 a_{\bar{2}} g_{\bar{2}}(x) + 19 a_{\bar{3}} g_{\bar{3}}(x) \pmod{19^2} \, ,$$

$$U_{\overline{19}} g_1(x) \equiv c_{1\bar{1}} g_{\bar{1}}(x) + 19 c_{\overline{12}} g_{\bar{2}}(x) + 19 c_{\overline{13}} g_{\bar{3}}(x) \pmod{19^2} \, , \qquad (17)$$

$$U_{\overline{19}} g_{\bar{2}}(x) \equiv c_{\overline{21}} g_{\bar{1}}(x) + c_{\overline{22}} g_{\bar{2}}(x) + c_{\overline{23}} g_{\bar{3}}(x) + 19 c_{\overline{24}} g_{\bar{4}}(x) \pmod{19^2} \, ,$$

where the a_i and c_{ij} are integral constants. Now it turns out *by actual computation* that some of these constants contain powers of 19 which were not deducible *a priori*; moreover these full powers of 19 which occur in actual fact are needed to prove the M- and R-results. Thus in these cases ($q = 17$, 19 and 23) we have at present the situation that the M- and R-results can only be established for a limited number of fixed values of α, and that even these limited results depend on computation beyond any reasonable prospect of hand calculation (except for $\alpha = 1$). However in view of the complete test of the M-results the programs can be regarded as self-checking, since the M-results follow theoretically from the independently computed values of c_{ij} in (17).

Since the subgroups $\Gamma_0(13)$, $\Gamma_0(17)$, $\Gamma_0(19)$, and $\Gamma_0(23)$ of the modular group have genera 0, 1, 1, and 2 respectively, it is remarkable that all these primes should exhibit the same behaviour with regard to our multiplicative congruence properties. It thus seems possible that some entirely different method or theory may exist which would give an uniform proof of all these cases.

5. THE CASES $q \geq 29$

As the reader may have anticipated from the non-appearance of 29 in §4, the direct analogy to (14) and (15) breaks down for $q = 29$. Considering first the R-results modulo 29 only, we can prove by the combination of modular theory and computing described in §4 that

---

* Of course the same theory could have been applied to the case $q = 13$. The main difficulty is that this comparatively deep theory gives for our present purposes results which are *weaker* than those obtained from an elementary use of the modular equation for $q = 13$.

$$U_{29}(x) \equiv a_1 g_1(x) + a_2 g_2(x) \pmod{29} ,$$
$$U_{29} g_1(x) \equiv 26 g_1(x) + 14 g_2(x) \pmod{29} ,$$
$$U_{29} g_2(x) \equiv 3 g_1(x) + 21 g_2(x) \pmod{29} .$$

Thus

$$U_{29}\{g_1(x) + \mu g_2(x)\} \equiv (3\mu - 3) g_1(x) + (14 - 8\mu) g_2(x) \pmod{29}$$

and if we attempt to make the RHS a multiple of $\{g_1(x) + \mu g_2(x)\}$, we are led to the congruence

$$\mu^2 - 8\mu + 5 \equiv 0 \pmod{29}$$

which has in fact no roots. However if we now consider our various coefficients not as integers modulo 29, but as elements of the Galois field $GF(29^2)$ we may assert (using "=" rather than "$\equiv$" in a field of characteristic 29):

$$c(29n) = a\lambda(n) + \bar{a}\,\bar{\lambda}(n) ,$$

where a, $\lambda(n)$ *and their conjugates* $\bar{a}$, $\bar{\lambda}(n)$ *lie in* $GF(29^2)$, *and*

$$\lambda(29n) = \lambda(29)\,\lambda(n), \quad \bar{\lambda}(29n) = \bar{\lambda}(29)\,\bar{\lambda}(n) . \tag{18}$$

Of course $c(29n)$ itself lies in $GF(29)$. We may infer from (18) that, for all $n \geqslant 1$,

$$c(29^{29^2}n) \equiv c(29n) \pmod{29} .$$

We have also an M-result for $\lambda(n)$ of the usual kind:

$$\lambda(np) - \lambda(n)\,\lambda(p) + p^{-1}\,\lambda(n/p) = 0 \text{ if } p \neq 29 . \tag{19}$$

It is now quite easy to foresee the natural general conjecture for powers of 29 in the form:
For all $\alpha \geqslant 1$ *we have*

$$c(29^\alpha n) = a\lambda(n) + \bar{a}\,\bar{\lambda}(n) ,$$

where a, $\lambda(n)$ *and their conjugates* $\bar{a}$, $\bar{\lambda}(n)$, *lie in an extension of the residue class ring modulo* 29^α *defined by an irreducible quadratic equation, and for* $n \geqslant 1$ *we have*

$$\lambda(29n) = \lambda(29)\,\lambda(n)$$

and

$$\lambda(np) - \lambda(n)\lambda(p) + p^{-1}\lambda(n/p) = 0 \text{ if } p \neq 29 . \tag{20}$$

This is subject to the same reservations as the cases $q = 17, 19$, and 23; it is only proved for $\alpha \leqslant 5$, and then only by a combination of modular theory and computation.

The case $q = 31$ is precisely analogous to $q = 29$, while for $q = 37$ we find that *three* conjugates are required over an extension of the ring modulo 37^{α} defined by an irreducible *cubic* equation. At this point it seemed unprofitable to compute any further cases in detail, since no essentially new features arose after 29. However brief preliminary investigations for all primes q with $41 \leqslant q \leqslant 67$ suggest that in general $c(q^{\alpha}n)$ will be a linear combination of $[q/12]$ multiplicative coefficients lying in various extensions of the ring modulo q^{α}. In addition the analogy with Hecke theory for modular forms of negative dimension which we now discuss briefly in §6 below indicates that (20) is the right kind of property to generalise for all q.

6. THE ANALOGY WITH HECKE THEORY

We now return to the exact multiplicative properties such as (10). These have been extensively generalised by Hecke, Petersson, and others; for a useful summary we refer to Rankin [1967]. As a particular example of the theory we take the case of

$$\sum_{n=2}^{\infty} t_2(n)\, x^n = x^2 f^{48}(x) \, ,$$

for which Hecke showed that

$$t_2(n) = a\lambda(n) + \bar{a}\,\bar{\lambda}(n) \, ,$$

where a, $\lambda(n)$ and their conjugates $\bar{a}$, $\bar{\lambda}(n)$ lie in the quadratic field $Q(\sqrt{144169})$, and for $n \geqslant 1$ and prime p we have

$$\lambda(np) - \lambda(n)\, \lambda(p) + p^{23}\, \lambda(n/p) = 0 \, . \tag{21}$$

It seems clear that the multiplicative congruence properties we have described in terms of extensions of residue class rings are closely analogous to the exact multiplicative properties of Hecke theory in terms of algebraic number fields. We have not described in this account the underlying common feature of the Hecke operators, but it seems reasonable to conjecture that some kind of "$\mathfrak{P}$-adic" Hecke theory exists for modular forms of positive and (as for $c(n)$) zero dimension, which is a counterpart of the exact theory for forms of negative dimension. The present difficulties in the way of precise formulation and proof seem formidable in so far as the *congruences* we have considered in this paper arise essentially at just one point $(\tau = i\infty)$ of the complex upper half-plane, whereas the *identities* of Hecke theory exist at all points of the upper half-plane, taking the form of multiplicative properties for Fourier coefficients at $\tau = i\infty$.

7. NON-RAMANUJAN CONGRUENCES FOR PRIMES $q \leqslant 11$.

Once the above properties for primes $q \geqslant 13$ has been found it was clear that something similar must exist for the smaller primes as well. As an example with $q = 5$ we find:
   Let $* t(n) = c(5^{\alpha}n)/c(5^{\alpha})$. *Then*

$$t(5n) \equiv t(5)t(n) \pmod{5^{3\alpha}}$$

and (22)

$$t(np) - t(n)t(p) + p^{-1} t(n/p) \equiv 0 \pmod{5^{3\alpha}} \text{ if } p \neq 5 \text{ is prime.}$$

For $q = 2, 3, 5$ and 7 these results can be fully proved as for $q = 13$; for $q = 11$ we have again the same reservations as for $q = 19$. In a sense we may feel that the Ramanujan-type properties (5) which do not generalise to higher primes have previously concealed the existence of the multiplicative properties. Thus (to suppose what is in fact false) had $c(2^{\alpha}n)$ been prime to 2, its multiplicative properties might have been sought and found by hand; as it is, the first non-Ramanujan prime is 13 which is beyond the scope of hand computation. On the other hand had $p(5n+4)$ been prime to 5 the whole possibility of considering congruences for modular forms might never have been noticed.

We may finally try to summarise the distinction between Ramanujan-type and multiplicative properties in this way. The Ramanujan-type property asserts that

$$\sum_{n=1}^{\infty} c(5^{\alpha}n) x^n = 5^{\alpha+1} P(x) ,$$

where $P(x)$ is a power series with integral coefficients. The multiplicative property now asserts that $P(x)$ itself is an interesting series.

8. NOTES ON COMPUTATION

The main requirement for most of this work was the ability to compute the Fourier expansions of various modular forms and functions modulo m. If we have available in store various power series $g_i(x)$ up to the term in x^N, then it is clear that addition and subtraction of constant multiples of these series, testing for "accidents", etc., takes a time approximately proportional to N; we shall abbreviate this to "takes $O(N)$". The test for M-results takes

$$O\left(\sum_{p<N} N/p \right) = O\left(N \log \log N\right)$$

---

* Since $5^{\alpha+1}\big|c(5^{\alpha}n)$ and $5^{\alpha+1}\big|\big|c(5^{\alpha})$ this definition is legitimate in any residue class ring modulo 5^{β}.

= $O(N)$ in practice for computers in this millenium.

Next if we have a given series $g(x)$, and multiply (divide) it by Euler's series *

$$f(x) = \prod_{r=1}^{\infty} (1-x^r) = 1 - x - x^2 + x^5 + x^7 - x^{12} \ldots = 1 + \sum_{n=1}^{\infty} (-1)^n \{x^{\frac{1}{2}n(3n-1)} + x^{\frac{1}{2}n(3n+1)}\},$$

this takes $O(N^{\frac{3}{2}})$. The subroutines for this were expertly coded by Dr. Paul Bryan from my Fortran version. Specifically the time required for $1000N$ terms was about $\frac{1}{4}N^{\frac{3}{2}}$ second, so that (for example) to compute $p(n)$ modulo m for $n \leqslant 40000$ takes about a minute. The reduction modulo m in the operation

$$a(n) = b(n) - b(n-1) - b(n-2) + b(n-5) + b(n-7) - b(n-12) \ldots$$

is performed only at the end (and not after each individual + or -), so that to avoid overflow there is a restriction that $m \cdot (N/6)^{\frac{1}{2}}$ be less than 6.7×10^{10}.

Finally multiplication (division) of two given general series takes $O(N^2)$ and has to be avoided at all costs. In view of this a certain amount of modular (rather than programming) ingenuity was required; in one case a natural definition $g^2(x)$ with $g(x)$ already computed was replaced by $g^2(x)$ = a sum of three terms each involving several ϑ-multiplications and divisions.

The possibility of multiplying (dividing) by Jacobi's series

$$f^3(x) = 1 - 3x + 5x^3 - \ldots = \sum_{n=0}^{\infty} (-1)^n (2n+1) x^{\frac{1}{2}n(n+1)}$$

was considered, but it turned out to be slightly slower than 3 successive uses of Euler's series, and also involved a heavier restriction of the size of m and N.

In the end the limiting factor for most of these programs was store rather than speed. Although the Atlas Supervisor has a "drum learning" program which enables many jobs to use the concept of a one-level store of about $90K$ without serious loss of efficiency, the random access involved in using Euler's series to multiply (divide) $g(x)$ meant that almost all the terms of $g(x)$ had to be stored in core. In practice $N = 43000$ was about the limit.

The main programs for each prime q were written in Fortran calling on the coded subroutines described above. The only additional feature was a Fortran function IJMODK (K, O, I, J) which obtains the residue of $\overline{I.J}$ (mod K) and overwrites its calling sequence in the execution run, which Dr. Don Russell ingeniously devised for me. This allows both I and J to be as large as 6.7×10^{10}, whereas the direct use of Fortran would limit $I. J$ to this size, and also be about three times as slow. It might be appropriate here to express a hope that computer design should allow for the easy extraction of an integer *remainder* after division, as well as the quotient mainly required in floating point work.

* Or other suitable ϑ-series of the form $\Sigma \lambda(n) . x^{an^2+bn}$.

Finally it may be of interest that some of these programs when run in 1964 exposed a low probability timing fault in the machine's hardware. Whereas a convergent process of numerical integration (for example) may not be affected if a fault occurs once in a million times, arithmetic modulo m depending on remainders rather than quotients is totally destroyed.

REFERENCES

Atkin, A.O.L., 1967, Glasgow Math. J.8, 14–31.

Atkin, A.O.L. and J.N.O'Brien, 1967, Trans. Amer. Math. Soc.126, 442–459.

Atkin, A.O.L. and H.P.F.Swinnerton-Dyer, 1954, Proc. London Math. Soc. (3) 4, 84–106.

Chowla, S., 1934, J.London Math. Soc. 9, 247.

Dyson, F.J., 1944, Eureka 8, 10–15.

Glaisher, J.W.L., 1907, Quart. J. Math. 38, 178–236.

Gupta, H., 1935, Proc. London Math. Soc. (2) 39, 142–149.

Lehner, J., 1949a, Amer. J. Math. 71, 136–148.

Lehner, J., 1949b, Amer. J. Math. 71, 373–386.

Lehner, J., 1950, Proc. Amer. Math. Soc. 1, 172–181.

Mordell, L.J., 1919, Proc. Cambridge Phil. Soc. 19, 117–124.

Newman, M., 1958, Proc. Amer. Math. Soc. 9, 609–612.

Ramanujan, S., 1916, Trans. Cambridge Phil. Soc. 22, 159–184.

Ramanujan, S., 1919, Proc. Cambridge Phil. Soc. 19, 207–210.

Rankin, R.A., 1967, Math. Annalen 168, 40–58.

Watson, G.N., 1938, J. Reine Angew. Math. 179, 97–128.

COVERING SETS AND SYSTEMS OF CONGRUENCES

R. F. CHURCHHOUSE
Atlas Computer Laboratory

1. INTRODUCTION

A set of congruences

$$x \equiv a_i \,(\mathrm{mod}\; n_i),\; 1 < n_1 < n_2 \ldots n_k$$

is called a covering set if every integer satisfies at least one of them. Davenport [1952] drew attention to the problem of finding covering sets and gave 0(mod 2), 0(mod 3), 1(mod 4), 1(mod 6) and 11(mod 12) as the simplest such set. Erdös posed two problems:

Problem 1. *Does a covering set exist for every choice of n_1?*

Problem 2. *Does there exist a covering set based only on odd moduli?*

Erdös found a covering set when $n_1 = 3$ based on the divisors of 120 and Davenport says that Swift found a covering set based on the divisors of 2880 for the case $n_1 = 4$. The only general result is quoted by Erdös:

Theorem. *If the set of congruences*

$$x \equiv a_i \,(\mathrm{mod}\; n_i)\,, \quad i = 1, 2, \ldots, k$$

form a covering set then

$$\sum_{i=1}^{k} \frac{1}{n_i} \geq 1\,.$$

The proof is obvious. This theorem is too weak to be of much use in general although one can deduce from it that

Corollary. *No covering set based on the divisors (excluding unity) of any number of the form $3^n 5^m$ exists.*

Proof

$$\sum_{s=0}^{\infty} \sum_{r=0}^{\infty} 3^{-r} 5^{-s} = \frac{15}{8}$$

Hence the $\sum_{i=1}^{k} \frac{1}{n_i}$ of the theorem is at most $\frac{7}{8}$ and the result follows. The problem of finding covering sets for various choices of n_1 is clearly well suited to a computer attack so I wrote a program for the Atlas Computer of the Science Research Council to study the more general problem of the number of distinct solutions to a system of congruences.

Some details of the program, the results achieved and applications of the theorem discovered are given below.

2. STRATEGY OF THE PROGRAM

Let $N = p_1{}^{m_1} p_2{}^{m_2} \ldots p_k{}^{m_k}$ and let $1 < d_1 < d_2 \ldots d_s$ be a complete set of divisors of N. The object of the program is to choose s integers $a_1, a_2, \ldots, a_s$ satisfying

$$1 \le a_i \le d_i$$

so that the number of integers in the interval $\langle 1, N \rangle$ which satisfy at least one of the congruences

$$x \equiv a_i \pmod{d_i} , \qquad i = 1, 2, \ldots, s$$

is as large as possible.

We first make an estimate of the number of trials required in an exhaustive attack. If we tried every possible combination for all permissible values for each a_i the number of trials would be

$$\prod_{i=1}^{s} d_i \simeq N^{\frac{1}{2}s}$$

since the divisors form $\frac{1}{2}s$ complementary pairs (d_i, d'_i) such that $d_i d'_i = N$ (we ignore the special case when N is a perfect square so that one divisor is its own complement). As to the value of s, the number of divisors of N, clearly

$$s = \prod_{i-1}^{k} (m_i + 1)$$

and for the 'highly composite' values of N in which we are interested Ramanujan [1927] showed that

$$s > 2^{\frac{\log N}{\log \log N}}$$

It is therefore clear that the number of trials involved in an exhaustive approach to this problem soon becomes astronomical. For example if $N = 75600 = 2^4.3^3.5^2.7$ (a number which solves Problem 1 when $n_1 = 8$) there are $5 \times 4 \times 3 \times 2 = 120$ divisors in all or 113 if we eliminate those divisors ≤ 7.

Hence the exhaustive number of trials would be about

$$(75600)^{56} \simeq 10^{270}.$$

It is clear that some strategy must be adopted to cut this number by a massive factor!

The strategy adopted in the program is as follows. The divisors $d_1 < d_2 < \ldots < d_s$ of N are taken in ascending order. Each of the d_1 congruences:

$$1(\bmod d_1), \quad 2(\bmod d_1), \quad \ldots, \quad d_1(\bmod d_1)$$

is taken in turn and the congruence which eliminates the largest number of integers in the interval $\langle 1,N \rangle$ is accepted. Of course, this being the first congruence all are equally good so the program chooses the one with smallest residue, i.e. $1(\bmod d_1)$. All integers $\equiv 1(\bmod d_1)$ in $\langle 1,N \rangle$ are now eliminated.

The d_2 possible congruences $1(\bmod d_2), 2(\bmod d_2), \ldots d_2(\bmod d_2)$ are now tried in turn and the congruence which eliminates the largest number of surviving integers in $\langle 1,N \rangle$ is accepted. If several congruences do equally well the congruence with smallest residue is taken. All integers satisfying this congruence are now eliminated and the next divisor is treated similarly and so on.

In this way the total number of trials is kept down to $N.d(N)$. For example in the case $N = 75600$ quoted above the number of trials is cut to about 10^7.

Of course we must pay for this reduction and we pay by not being able to guarantee finding the best possible set of values for $a_1, a_2, \ldots, a_s$. In practice however it seems that the strategy outlined above does lead to a set of values for the a_i which are nearly optimal.

The Atlas Computer has a $48K$ core store, the word size being 48 bits. It also has $96K$ words of drum and the one-level store concept (Kilburn et al. [1962]) allows one to program as if all the core store is $144K$. For this particular problem only the core store was used; this was because the largest N involved was 604,800 and this is less than the number of bits available in the core (2,359,296). The program used storage according to a parameter L. A block of L words was filled with ones and a routine was generated by the program which consisted of

$$\left[\frac{N}{L}\right] + 1$$

sections. The first section dealt with the leading bit in each of the L words in the block, the second section dealt with the 2nd bit etc. The first $[\frac{N}{L}]$ sections each dealt with all L bits in the appropriate column; the last section dealt with only the first $N-L \times [\frac{N}{L}]$ bits. Thus precisely N bits were dealt with in all.

The program then found the divisors of N, ignoring any $< n_1$ (a parameter). These divisors were arranged in ascending order $n_1 \leqslant d_1 < d_2 \ldots$ $< d_s$. As mentioned above the program now considered each congruence

$$x \equiv a_i \;(\mathrm{mod}\; d_i) \qquad i = 1, 2, \ldots, s$$

in turn allowing a_i to take the values $1, 2, \ldots, d_i$ successively.

In any given trial the numbers a_i and d_i were held in two index-registers (B1, B2) another index-register, B3, held a one-bit mask, the bit being the one appropriate to the column being dealt with; another index-register B4 was used to keep a score of numbers satisfying the congruence. B3 was used to copy into B5 under the mask the contents of the word pointed to by B1 and B2 combined (Atlas allows double indexing); if the result of the masking was non-zero B4 was incremented by 1. B1 was then increased by B2 and so on. When the end of the table was reached the mask in B3 was changed (moved one bit right) B1 was replaced by B1-L and the trial continued until all N words had been examined. The score in B4 was noted if it was better than the best achieved so far using modulus, d_i, otherwise it was rejected. The next trial was then initiated with a_i replaced by $(a_i + 1)$. When $a_i = d_i$ the most successful residue α_i to modulus d_i was recorded and the bits in the words corresponding to integers satisfying

$$x \equiv \alpha_i (\mathrm{mod}\; d_i)$$

were replaced by zeros. The next modulus, $d_{(i+1)}$ was then tried.

A number of time-saving tricks were inserted. For example if the program was searching only for covering sets the theorem quoted in the introduction was continually applied to see if the remaining divisors could possibly eliminate the integers still unaccounted for. If not the run was abandoned. This simple device often terminated an unsuccessful run at about the half-way stage. The running time was, as indicated above, proportional to $N. d(N)$ and for the case $N = 604800$ (which solves Problem 1 for $n_1 = 9$) we have $d(N) = 192$ but eight of these are not to be used, hence the number of trials was about 10^8 and the running time was approximately 20 minutes.

3. STATEMENT OF RESULTS

The program had two objectives. The first was to find covering sets for as many values of n_1 as could be done without using excessive amounts of computer time. The second objective was to see if anything in the nature of a general result could be found.

The first objective was achieved for $n_1 \leq 9$. It is possible that a solution could have been found for $n_1 = 10$ but this was debatable and would certainly have required computer runs of the order of 30 minutes or more. The complete sets of congruences which the machine produced for the cases $n_1 = 2, 3, \ldots, 9$ are given in the appendix. The numbers N which gave rise to these solutions were

n_1	N	n_1	N	n_1	N
2	12	5	2520	8	75600
3	120	6	10080	9	604800
4	720	7	30240		

It is not claimed that the covering sets obtained are optimal in the sense that no smaller value of N for given n_1 can be found though this may well be true for $n_1 \leq 5$. In the search for suitable N one is naturally driven to look for highly composite numbers and it is interesting that for $n_1 \leq 6$ the values of N above are included in Ramanujan's table of highly composite numbers (Ramanujan [1927]); on the other hand for $n_1 = 7, 8, 9$ N is not highly composite and a search for covering sets based on smaller, highly composite, values of N for these cases was not successful, although this does not necessarily mean that they do not exist.

The case $n_1 = 5$, $N = 2520$ perhaps deserves special mention. When $N = 2520$ was first tried the program just failed to find a covering set - 2519 numbers were eliminated, but one was not! I therefore changed the strategy of the program so that instead of choosing the *smallest* values for a_i when several values did equally well the program took the *largest* value. However there was an obscure bug in the program which meant that this changed strategy applied only from the second congruence on. Had this bug not been present no covering set would have been found; as it was, the bug produced exactly the right effect and 2520 just worked, though as will be seen from the table every divisor associated with 2520 had to be used.

The second objective was achieved by the discovery of the theorem stated below. This discovery was made not by studying the covering sets but by analysis of the performance of those systems of congruences which had failed to provide covering sets. The theorem is somewhat like the one quoted above but is much more powerful. Without the computer I would not have found this theorem; indeed I at first thought that the evidence from the computer was misleading and only gradually realised that the theorem below was true and found a proof valid for the cases needed below. This theorem which relates to the general problem of the number of distinct solutions to a set of congruences has its main application to Problem 2.

The theorem is:

Theorem A. *Let* $N = p_1{}^{m_1} p_2{}^{m_2} \ldots p_k{}^{m_k}$ *and let* $d_1 < d_2 < \ldots < d_s$ *be divisors of* N. *Then the number of distinct integers which lie in the interval* $1 \leq x \leq N$ *and which satisfy at least one congruence of any system of the type*

$$x \equiv a_i (\mathrm{mod}\ d_i) \qquad i = 1, 2, \ldots, s$$

does not exceed

$$N \left(\sum_{i=1}^{k} \sum_{r=1}^{m_i} p_i{}^{-r} \right).$$

For application to Problem 2 an alternative form is used, this is

Theorem B. *Let* $N = p_1{}^{m_1} p_2{}^{m_2} \ldots p_k{}^{m_k}$ *and let* $d_1 < d_2 \ldots < d_s$ *be a complete set of divisors of* N, *excluding unity. Let* S *be a set of congruences*

$$x \equiv a_i (\mathrm{mod}\ d_i) \qquad i = 0, 1, \ldots s.$$

Let $N' = pN$ and let $S' = S + T$ where T is a set of congruences

$$x \equiv a_i \pmod{pd_i} \qquad i = 0, 1, \ldots, s$$

where $d_0 = 1$. Then the number of integers which lie in the interval $\langle 1, N' \rangle$ which satisfy at least one of the congruences in T but none of the congruences in S is at most:

$$\frac{N'}{p} \text{ if } p \neq p_i \qquad i = 1, 2, \ldots, k$$

$$\frac{N'}{p_i^{(m_i+1)}} \text{ if } p = p_i .$$

I have not yet found a completely general proof of these theorems but I have a proof which covers the case where $N = p^a q^b r^c s^d$.

4. APPLICATIONS OF THE THEOREM

We begin with an application of theorem A to prove a stronger form of the corollary proved in the introduction.

Corollary 1. *No covering set based on the divisors of any number of the form $3^a 5^b 7^c$ exists.*

Proof. Let $N = 3^a 5^b 7^c$. Then the maximum number of distinct solutions in the interval $\langle 1, N \rangle$ of any set of congruences based on the divisors of N is

$$N \left(\sum_{n=1}^{a} 3^{-n} + \sum_{n=1}^{b} 5^{-n} + \sum_{n=1}^{c} 7^{-n} \right)$$

$$< N \left(\sum_{n=1}^{\infty} 3^{-n} + 5^{-n} + 7^{-n} \right) = N \left(\tfrac{1}{2} + \tfrac{1}{4} + \tfrac{1}{6} \right) < N$$

Q. E. D.

Theorem A is not quite strong enough to dispose in a similar way of the possibility of covering sets based on numbers of the type $3^a 5^b 7^c 11^d$ since the sum

$$\sum_{n=1}^{\infty} (3^{-n} + 5^{-n} + 7^{-n} + 11^{-n}) = \tfrac{61}{60} .$$

To dispose of this case we use a preliminary lemma and theorem B. The preliminary lemma is

Lemma. *Let $N = pqrs$ be the product of 4 distinct primes and let $1 < d_1 < d_2 \ldots < d_{15}$ be the 15 divisors of N, excluding unity. Then the number of integers in the interval $\langle 1, N \rangle$ which satisfy at least one of the congruences*

$$x \equiv a_i \pmod{d_i} \qquad i = 1, 2, \ldots, 15$$

is at most

$$N\left(\frac{1}{p} + \frac{1}{q} + \frac{1}{r} + \frac{1}{s}\right) - (p + q + r + s + 1) .$$

The proof is simply a matter of writing down the 15 congruences and choosing the a_i so that no integer can ever satisfy any pair of congruences

$$x \equiv a_i \pmod{d_i}$$

and $x \equiv a_j \pmod{d_j}$

if $(d_i, d_j) > 1$. In practice if $p (< q < r < s)$ is sufficiently small it may not be possible to choose the a_i in this optimal way.

The lemma tells us that theorem A can be improved in the special case $N = pqrs$, the improvement being given by the last term in the expression above. I do not prove here but think it worth stating that theorem A gives the best possible result for any case when N is divisible by only two primes, neither of which is 2, i. e. $N = p^m q^n$ where $2 < p < q$.

By means of the lemma and theorem B we can now prove

Corollary 2. *No covering set based on the divisors of any number of the form $3^a 5^b 7^c 11^d$ exists.*

Proof. By the lemma, taking $N = 1155 = 3.5.7.11$ no set of congruences based on the divisors of N can have more than

$$(385 + 231 + 165 + 105 - 3 - 5 - 7 - 11 - 1) = 859$$

solutions in $\langle 1, 1155 \rangle$.

By theorem B, taking $N = 3.5.7.11$ and $N' = 3^a.5^b.7^c.11^d$ the number of solutions of congruences based on those divisors of N' which are not divisors of N does not exceed

$$N' \left(\sum_{n=2}^{\infty} 3^{-n} + 5^{-n} + 7^{-n} + 11^{-n} \right) = N' \left(\frac{1}{6} + \frac{1}{20} + \frac{1}{42} + \frac{1}{110} \right)$$

and so since

$$\frac{859}{1155} + \frac{1}{6} + \frac{1}{20} + \frac{1}{42} + \frac{1}{110} = \frac{4589}{4620} < 1$$

Q. E. D.

the result follows.

The line of proof used in corollary 2 is certainly capable of being pushed further. A computer run on sets of congruences based on divisors of $N = 225225 = 3^2.5^2.7.11.13$ together with an application of theorem B indicates that it is highly unlikely that a covering set based on the divisors of any number of the form $3^a 5^b 7^c 11^d 13^e$ exists. It appears, in fact, that finding a covering set based on odd moduli, assuming it exists at all, may prove to be beyond the range of existing computers.

APPENDIX. COVERING SETS OF CONGRUENCES

$n = 2$

Modulus	Residue	N	Removed	Remaining
2	1	12	6	6
3	1	12	2	4
4	2	12	2	2
6	2	12	1	1
12	12	12	1	

$n = 3$

Modulus	Residue	N	Removed	Remaining
3	1	120	40	80
4	1	120	20	60
5	1	120	12	48
6	2	120	16	32
8	3	120	8	24
10	2	120	4	20
12	6	120	6	14
15	3	120	3	11
20	4	120	2	9
24	23	120	4	5
30	30	120	2	3
40	7	120	1	2
60	15	120	1	1
120	39	120	1	

$n = 4$

Modulus	Residue	N	Removed	Remaining
4	1	720	180	540
5	1	720	108	432
6	2	720	96	336
8	3	720	72	264
9	1	720	40	224
10	2	720	40	184
12	6	720	36	148
15	4	720	20	128
16	7	720	30	98
18	4	720	16	82
20	8	720	16	66
24	12	720	12	54
30	10	720	8	46
36	3	720	4	42
40	7	720	7	35

$n = 4$ (continued)

Modulus	Residue	N	Removed	Remaining
45	43	720	5	30
48	47	720	9	21
60	24	720	6	15
72	15	720	3	12
80	15	720	3	9
90	30	720	2	7
120	120	720	4	3
144	63	720	2	1
180	103	720	1	

$n = 5$

Modulus	Residue	N	Removed	Remaining
5	5	2520	504	2016
6	1	2520	336	1680
7	1	2520	240	1440
8	2	2520	216	1224
9	2	2520	168	1056
10	2	2520	144	912
12	3	2520	144	768
14	2	2520	72	696
15	3	2520	81	615
18	5	2520	96	519
20	4	2520	80	439
21	3	2520	30	409
24	9	2520	45	364
28	4	2520	26	338
30	16	2520	39	299
35	6	2520	22	277
36	17	2520	46	231
40	14	2520	37	194
42	14	2520	12	182
45	8	2520	22	160
56	5	2520	9	151
60	28	2520	24	127
63	17	2520	9	118
70	26	2520	15	103
72	35	2520	14	89
84	9	2520	9	80
90	68	2520	10	70
105	21	2520	12	58
120	118	2520	15	43
126	35	2520	3	40
140	46	2520	5	35
168	165	2520	9	26
180	107	2520	4	22
210	27	2520	3	19
252	21	2520	2	17
280	69	2520	3	14
315	311	2520	3	11
360	359	2520	4	7
420	189	2520	2	5

$n = 5$ (continued)

Modulus	Residue	N	Removed	Remaining
504	189	2520	1	4
630	341	2520	1	3
840	191	2520	1	2
1260	357	2520	1	1
2520	431	2520	1	

$n = 6$

Modulus	Residue	N	Removed	Remaining
6	1	10080	1680	8400
7	1	10080	1200	7200
8	2	10080	1080	6120
9	2	10080	840	5280
10	2	10080	576	4704
12	3	10080	720	3984
14	2	10080	384	3600
15	3	10080	324	3276
16	4	10080	290	2986
18	5	10080	480	2506
20	4	10080	240	2266
21	3	10080	168	2098
24	9	10080	240	1858
28	4	10080	126	1732
30	10	10080	132	1600
32	6	10080	121	1479
35	6	10080	100	1379
36	17	10080	232	1147
40	14	10080	111	1036
42	10	10080	54	982
45	8	10080	87	895
48	21	10080	114	781
56	40	10080	68	713
60	35	10080	48	665
63	17	10080	42	623
70	56	10080	72	551
72	35	10080	56	495
80	30	10080	42	453
84	9	10080	24	429
90	68	10080	35	394
96	45	10080	45	349
105	13	10080	27	322
112	12	10080	32	290
120	118	10080	27	263
126	122	10080	16	247
140	20	10080	30	217
144	71	10080	28	189
160	150	10080	20	169
168	21	10080	12	157
180	107	10080	10	147
210	28	10080	18	129
224	61	10080	12	117
240	46	10080	12	105

$n = 6$ (continued)

Modulus	Residue	N	Removed	Remaining
252	84	10080	6	99
280	46	10080	18	81
288	143	10080	9	72
315	35	10080	6	66
336	333	10080	12	54
360	359	10080	5	49
420	420	10080	12	37
480	191	10080	4	33
504	392	10080	4	29
560	446	10080	10	19
630	140	10080	2	17
672	573	10080	9	8
720	6	10080	1	7
840	166	10080	3	4
1008	54	10080	1	3
1120	726	10080	3	

$n = 7$

Modulus	Residue	N	Removed	Remaining
7	1	30240	4320	25920
8	1	30240	3240	22680
9	1	30240	2520	20160
10	2	30240	2304	17856
12	3	30240	2160	15696
14	2	30240	1536	14160
15	5	30240	1368	12792
16	5	30240	1332	11460
18	4	30240	960	10500
20	4	30240	840	9660
21	5	30240	720	8940
24	6	30240	720	8220
27	7	30240	580	7640
28	3	30240	488	7152
30	8	30240	576	6576
32	13	30240	600	5976
35	6	30240	419	5557
36	31	30240	576	4981
40	34	30240	364	4617
42	11	30240	324	4293
45	25	30240	252	4041
48	45	30240	261	3780
54	25	30240	175	3605
56	4	30240	160	3445
60	48	30240	324	3121
63	14	30240	168	2953
70	66	30240	284	2669
72	18	30240	156	2513
80	16	30240	96	2417
84	23	30240	288	2129
90	30	30240	168	1961

$n = 7$ (continued)

Modulus	Residue	N	Removed	Remaining
96	29	30240	123	1838
105	56	30240	132	1706
108	43	30240	152	1554
112	18	30240	56	1498
120	14	30240	132	1366
126	42	30240	78	1288
135	43	30240	80	1208
140	46	30240	78	1130
144	13	30240	87	1043
160	56	30240	39	1004
168	83	30240	108	896
180	180	30240	108	788
189	133	30240	33	755
210	96	30240	69	686
216	214	30240	36	650
224	55	30240	27	623
240	138	30240	54	569
252	35	30240	72	497
270	60	30240	42	455
280	196	30240	28	427
288	47	30240	18	409
315	150	30240	24	385
336	335	30240	45	340
360	138	30240	24	316
378	119	30240	21	295
420	180	30240	16	279
432	205	30240	17	262
480	456	30240	15	247
504	371	30240	24	223
540	268	30240	28	195
560	536	30240	11	184
630	510	30240	24	160
672	167	30240	27	133
720	258	30240	18	115
756	70	30240	12	103
840	546	30240	12	91
864	70	30240	5	86
945	691	30240	12	74
1008	119	30240	12	62
1080	538	30240	14	48
1120	63	30240	2	46
1260	60	30240	8	38
1440	214	30240	4	34
1512	474	30240	4	30
1618	1680	30240	4	26
1890	376	30240	9	17
2016	1631	30240	4	13
2160	2014	30240	8	5
2520	2490	30240	4	1
3024	1960	30240	1	

$$n = 8$$

Modulus	Residue	N	Removed	Remaining
8	1	75600	9450	66150
9	1	75600	7350	58800
10	2	75600	6720	52080
12	3	75600	6300	45780
14	2	75600	3840	41940
15	5	75600	4050	37890
16	5	75600	3885	34005
18	4	75600	2880	31125
20	4	75600	2520	28605
21	5	75600	1800	26805
24	6	75600	2160	24645
25	1	75600	1371	23274
27	7	75600	1632	21642
28	3	75600	1164	20478
30	8	75600	1800	18678
35	1	75600	884	17794
36	31	75600	1680	16114
40	34	75600	1110	15004
42	11	75600	855	14149
45	25	75600	790	13359
48	45	75600	1476	11883
50	6	75600	638	11245
54	25	75600	569	10676
56	7	75600	380	10296
60	48	75600	1080	9216
63	20	75600	387	8829
70	46	75600	426	8403
72	13	75600	492	7911
75	15	75600	324	7587
80	18	75600	330	7257
84	23	75600	684	6573
90	30	75600	432	6141
100	16	75600	272	5869
105	29	75600	315	5554
108	43	75600	402	5152
112	45	75600	190	4962
120	14	75600	330	4632
126	41	75600	285	4347
135	43	75600	240	4107
140	66	75600	186	3921
144	125	75600	201	3720
150	30	75600	216	3504
168	35	75600	342	3162
175	21	75600	149	3013
180	60	75600	216	2797
189	62	75600	96	2701
200	36	75600	134	2567
210	113	75600	210	2357
216	214	75600	136	2221
225	45	75600	108	2113
240	138	75600	270	1843
252	251	75600	152	1691
270	**268**	**75600**	**150**	**1541**

$n = 8$ (continued)

Modulus	Residue	N	Removed	Remaining
280	146	75600	96	1445
300	96	75600	108	1337
315	92	75600	75	1262
336	317	75600	114	1148
350	336	75600	100	1048
360	330	75600	108	940
378	124	75600	28	912
400	136	75600	46	866
420	407	75600	120	746
432	205	75600	79	667
450	360	75600	108	559
504	77	75600	54	505
525	266	75600	39	466
540	394	75600	50	416
560	416	75600	31	385
600	66	75600	36	349
630	356	75600	33	316
675	225	75600	36	280
700	696	75600	33	247
720	29	75600	15	232
756	245	75600	12	220
840	306	75600	36	184
900	900	75600	48	136
945	286	75600	11	125
1008	749	75600	24	101
1050	146	75600	12	89
1080	450	75600	12	77
1200	336	75600	18	59
1260	617	75600	15	44
1350	1350	75600	12	32
1400	266	75600	4	28
1512	754	75600	6	22
1575	1511	75600	6	16
1680	496	75600	2	14
1800	196	75600	4	10
1890	376	75600	3	7
2100	566	75600	4	3
2160	286	75600	1	2
2520	2086	75600	1	1
2700	1996	75600	1	

$n = 9$

Modulus	Residue	N	Removed	Remaining
9	9	604800	67200	537600
10	1	604800	53760	483840
12	2	604800	50400	433440
14	2	604800	31200	402240
15	4	604800	37440	364800
16	4	604800	26640	338160
18	3	604800	26880	311280
20	3	604800	23520	287760

$n = 9$ (continued)

Modulus	Residue	N	Removed	Remaining
21	1	604800	17280	270480
24	8	604800	21600	248880
25	2	604800	13800	235080
27	6	604800	15456	219624
28	5	604800	10720	208904
30	5	604800	18720	190184
32	12	604800	11484	178700
35	7	604800	8176	170524
36	30	604800	13440	157084
40	13	604800	8880	148204
42	4	604800	8892	139312
45	10	604800	8400	130912
48	17	604800	5760	125152
50	7	604800	6104	119048
54	24	604800	7280	111768
56	24	604800	4032	107736
60	59	604800	10080	97656
63	13	604800	4740	92916
64	28	604800	4702	88214
70	17	604800	3624	84590
72	48	604800	5568	79022
75	22	604800	2880	76142
80	73	604800	4320	71822
84	10	604800	4704	67118
90	25	604800	5280	61838
96	92	604800	2520	59318
100	67	604800	2816	56502
105	28	604800	2610	53892
108	42	604800	4480	49412
112	40	604800	1368	48044
120	29	604800	4320	43724
126	34	604800	2700	41024
128	60	604800	968	40056
135	15	604800	2470	37586
140	26	604800	1440	36146
144	33	604800	1392	34754
150	47	604800	2304	32450
160	9	604800	1320	31130
168	82	604800	1632	29498
175	137	604800	1212	28286
180	175	604800	2400	25886
189	55	604800	773	25113
192	89	604800	666	24447
200	87	604800	1072	23375
210	196	604800	2205	21170
216	96	604800	1288	19882
224	96	604800	588	19294
225	24	604800	694	18600
240	193	604800	1280	17320
252	118	604800	832	16488
270	105	604800	1840	14648
280	278	604800	720	13928
288	156	604800	417	13511

$n = 9$ (continued)

Modulus	Residue	N	Removed	Remaining
300	17	604800	792	12719
315	175	604800	1215	11504
320	249	604800	636	10868
336	208	604800	588	10280
350	37	604800	854	9426
360	159	604800	896	8530
378	15	604800	256	8274
384	124	604800	335	7939
400	187	604800	368	7571
420	25	604800	480	7091
432	51	604800	288	6803
448	54	604800	114	6689
450	447	604800	416	6273
480	219	604800	208	6065
504	496	604800	416	5649
525	67	604800	288	5361
540	429	604800	432	4929
560	110	604800	240	4689
576	267	604800	104	4585
600	437	604800	288	4297
630	70	604800	720	3577
640	299	604800	52	3525
672	166	604800	228	3297
675	69	604800	150	3147
700	317	604800	336	2811
720	85	604800	240	2571
756	121	604800	120	2451
800	387	604800	172	2279
840	502	604800	270	2009
864	636	604800	97	1912
896	278	604800	30	1882
900	85	604800	120	1762
945	220	604800	96	1666
960	467	604800	54	1612
1008	121	604800	64	1548
1050	937	604800	180	1368
1080	69	604800	240	1128
1120	937	604800	72	1056
1152	1131	604800	46	1010
1200	137	604800	72	938
1260	1165	604800	192	746
1344	1174	604800	30	716
1350	267	604800	68	648
1400	517	604800	96	552
1440	339	604800	72	480
1512	373	604800	32	448
1575	762	604800	44	404
1600	1587	604800	74	330
1680	625	604800	64	266
1728	771	604800	36	230
1800	817	604800	36	194
1890	625	604800	32	162
1920	99	604800	18	144

$n = 9$ (continued)

Modulus	Residue	N	Removed	Remaining
2016	249	604800	10	134
2100	517	604800	24	110
2160	1689	604800	24	86
2240	467	604800	20	66
2400	579	604800	6	60
2520	2157	604800	16	44
2688	291	604800	2	42
2700	717	604800	24	18
2800	1737	604800	8	10
2880	1059	604800	10	

REFERENCES

Davenport, H., 1952, The Higher Arithmetic (Hutchinson, London) p. 57.
Erdös, P., 1965, Some recent advances and current problems in number theory. In: Saaty, T.L., ed., Lectures on modern mathematics, vol. 3 (Wiley, New York) pp.196-244.
Kilburn, T., D.B.G.Edwards, M.J.Lanigan and F.H.Sumner, 1962, IRE Trans. Electronic Computers, EC-11, 223-235.
Ramanujan, S., 1927, Collected Papers (Cambridge Univ. Press) pp. 78-128.

A TABULATION CF SOME INFORMATION CONCERNING FINITE FIELDS

J. H. CONWAY
University of Cambridge

1. INTRODUCTION

Some time ago, M. J. T. Guy and I made some extensive tables of information concerning various finite fields, which we hope to publish in the
near future. This paper gives a brief account of the material tabulated, after a condensed exposition of finite field theory which should suffice to ex-
plain the notation involved.

Finite fields have many applications to widely separated branches of
mathematics, and these applications amply justify the tabulations here described. The field of integers modulo a given prime number p is the most
familiar finite field, and many of its properties extend to properties of finite fields in general (thus the existence of primitive roots). But the simplicity of this particular field has meant that tables concerning its properties
have little value, and perhaps this has influenced the situation for more
general fields, which have been but little tabulated. We might remark that
tables of indices of numbers modulo a given prime are in a sense a specia-
lisation of the tables presented here.

A *field* is a set of elements considered together with two binary operations $X + Y$, XY, and two singulary operations $-X$, X^{-1} defined for all arguments except that X^{-1} is not defined for $X = 0$. These operations are required to satisfy the associative and commutative laws of addition and multiplication, the distributive law, and various units and inverse laws:

1)
$$X + Y = Y + X, \quad XY = YX, \quad X + (Y + Z) = (X + Y) + Z,$$

$$X(YZ) = (XY)Z, \quad X(Y + Z) = XY + XZ$$

ii) there are particular elements 0 and 1 such that

$$0 + X = X, \quad (-X) + X = 0, \quad 0X = 0, \quad 1X = X, \quad (X^{-1})X = 1,$$

the final equation being for $X \neq 0$.

The *order* of a field is the number of elements it contains, and the field
is said to be finite if its order is finite. We find it convenient to require
that the order shall exceed 1. Finite fields are often called Galois fields
after their discoverer, and the finite field of order r is often denoted by
$GF(r)$, but we here prefer F_r.

It is easy to show that the requirement that addition be commutative is redundant. A famous theorem of Wedderburn asserts that for a finite field the same is true of multiplication. Moore proved that the order of every finite field is a prime power, and that there is a single field of each prime power order.

2. THE ADDITIVE STRUCTURE OF A FINITE FIELD

Let F_r be a field of order r. Then the elements $0, 1, 1+1, \ldots$ of F_r cannot all be distinct, and it is easy to deduce from this that we must have $p = 0$ for some positive integer p (regarded as the sum $1 + 1 + \ldots$ to p terms), and that the least such integer p (called the *characteristic* of F_r) must be a prime, for in a field the equation $AB = 0$ implies either $A = 0$ or $B = 0$. Furthermore, the elements $0, 1, \ldots, p-1$ themselves form a field, isomorphic to the field F_p of integers modulo p. (For any fixed $a \neq 0$ of F_p, consider the set of all elements ax for which $x \in F_p$. No two of these can coincide, since $p \mid a(x - x')$ implies $p \mid (x - x')$, and so there must be some x for which $ax = 1$, so that indeed F_p is a field).

We shall therefore analyse the behaviour of F_r over a typical subfield F_q. Since F_r can be regarded as a vector space over F_q, there will be a positive integer n (the *degree* of F_r over F_q), and elements $U_0, U_1, \ldots U_{n-1}$ of F_r such that any element X of F_r is uniquely expressible in the form

$$X = U_0 x_0 + U_1 x_1 + \ldots + U_{n-1} x_{n-1} \, , \tag{1}$$

with all the x_i in F_q. In these circumstances the (U_i) are said to form a *base* for F_r over F_q. Since there are just q choices for each x_i, there will be just q^n possible values for X, and so $r = q^n$. Therefore *the order of any finite field is always a power of the order of any subfield*. Considering in particular the subfield F_p we see that *the order of any finite field is a prime power*. More sophisticated arguments show that for any prime power r there is (to within isomorphism) just one field F_r of order r, and that F_q is a subfield of F_r whenever r is a power of q. From now on we shall suppose therefore that $r = q^n$, $q = p^m$, and will consider the general finite field F_r of characteristic p in connection with its typical subfield F_q and its prime subfield F_p.

3. THE MULTIPLICATIVE STRUCTURE

We can show in a similar way to the above that for any non-zero $X \in F_r$ there is a positive integer t such that $X^t = 1$, the least such t being called the *order* of X. Moreover, t is a divisor of $r - 1$ (which is the order of the multiplicative group of F_r), and so X satisfies $X^{r-1} = 1$. But now if $r - 1 = dd'$ is any factorisation of $r - 1$ into two positive factors, we have

$$X^{r-1} - 1 = (X^d - 1)(X^{(d'-1)d} + \ldots + X^{2d} + X^d + 1) \, . \tag{2}$$

Since the left hand side of this equation has just the $r-1$ non-zero elements of F_r as zeros, and since neither factor of the right-hand side can have more zeros than its degree, we conclude that *the equation $X^d = 1$ has exactly d roots whenever d divides $r-1$*. Letting N_d be the number of elements of order exactly d, this tells us that

$$\sum_{t \mid d} N_t = d \tag{3}$$

for each divisor d of $r-1$. But the equations (3) inductively determine the values of the N_d, and since they are the same as the equations determining the number of elements of order exactly d in a cyclic group of order $r-1$, F_r *must have some elements of order exactly $r-1$*, and indeed just $\phi(r-1)$ of them, where ϕ is Euler's totient function.

Such elements are called *primitive roots* of F_r - if e is any primitive root, we can display the elements of F_r as

$$0, 1, e, e^2, \ldots, e^{r-2} \tag{4}$$

and we have $e^{r-1} = 1$. It is convenient to introduce a formal symbol * defined by the equation $e* = 0$, so that we can express the general element X of F_r in the form e^x, where x is either the symbol * or an integer modulo $r-1$. This representation is especially convenient for computational purposes.

4. ALGEBRAIC EQUATIONS, CONJUGATES, AND AUTOMORPHISMS

For any prime p the binomial coefficients $\binom{p}{i}$ $(0 < i < p)$ are all divisible by p. It follows that $(X+Y)^p = X^p + Y^p$ in any field F_r of characteristic p. Since also $0^p = 0$, $1^p = 1$, and $(XY)^p = X^p Y^p$ it follows that the operation of taking pth powers preserves all the structure of F_r - that is to say, is an *automorphism* or *symmetry* of F_r. Plainly the p^ith power function will also define an automorphism of F_r for each i. Now the equation $X^q = X$ has as roots in F_r just the q elements of the subfield F_q. Hence the qth power function is an automorphism of F_r which leaves fixed precisely the members of F_q.

Now suppose that the element X of F_r satisfies an equation of the form

$$a_0 + a_1 X + \ldots + a_t X^t = 0 \tag{5}$$

whose coefficients a_i lie in F_q. Applying the qth power operation we deduce that $Z = X^q$ also satisfies (5), then that X^{q^2} does also, and so on. Calling the elements $X, X^q, X^{q^2}, \ldots$ the *conjugates* of X (over F_q), we see that any equation satisfied by X is satisfied also by all conjugates of X. On the other hand, the sum of the distinct conjugates of X is left fixed by the qth power operation, and so belongs to F_q. Since the same is true of any other symmetric function of these conjugates, X satisfies a particular equation (its *minimal equation*) over F_q whose roots are just the distinct conjugates of X. The minimal equation is a factor of any other equation satisfied by X over F_q.

Since $X^{q^n} = X^r = X$ for each $X \in F_r$, each conjugate of X appears the same number of times in the sequence $X, X^q, \ldots, X^{q^{n-1}}$. It follows that the equation

$$(\Lambda - X)(\Lambda - X^q) \ldots (\Lambda - X^{q^{n-1}}) \equiv \Lambda^n - x_1 . \Lambda^{n-1} + x_2 . \Lambda^{n-2} - \ldots \pm x_n = 0 \quad (6)$$

is a perfect power of the minimal equation. (6) is called the *characteristic equation* of X over F_q, and the coefficients x_1 and x_n are respectively called the *trace*, $\mathrm{tr}(X)$ and the *determinant*, $\det(X)$ of X over F_q.

Now the trace is a linear function from F_r to F_q, since we have the equations

$$\mathrm{tr}(X + Y) = \mathrm{tr}(X) + \mathrm{tr}(Y), \qquad \mathrm{tr}(aX) = a\,\mathrm{tr}(X)\,(a \in F_q) . \quad (7)$$

Indeed, since any linear function from F_r to F_q is completely determined by its values at a base, there are just $q^n = r$ such functions, and since $\mathrm{tr}(KX)$ is such a function for any $K \in F_r$, we see that *any linear function from F_r to F_q has the form $\mathrm{tr}(KX)$ for some $K \in F_r$*. (The fact that the functions $\mathrm{tr}(KX)$ are distinct is easily proved.) Thus in terms of the trace function we have a very handy form for the general linear function from F_r to F_q.

The trace function gives us also a very useful test for the linear dependence of n elements X_i of F_r over F_q. To see this, we observe that n elements of a vector space of dimension n are linearly dependent if and only if there is a non-trivial linear function f for which $f(X_i) = 0$ for each of the X_i. Hence *n elements X_i of F_r are linearly dependent over F_q if and only if there is a non-zero $K \in F_r$ such that $\mathrm{tr}(KX_i)$ vanishes for each i*.

The properties just found make the trace the most important simple function from F_r to F_q, but the determinant function also has its uses, being plainly a multiplicative function of X (that is $\det(XY) = \det(X)\det(Y)$). It follows immediately from its definition that the determinant of X is simply the power X^t, where t is $1 + q + \ldots + q^{n-1} = (r - 1)/(q - 1)$.

5. PARTICULAR BASES. THE NOTION OF DUAL BASE

The number of distinct bases for F_r over F_q is precisely

$$(q^n - 1)(q^n - q)(q^n - q^2) \ldots (q^n - q^{n-1}) ,$$

which is usually rather large. Accordingly, it is wise to restrict one's attention to certain special types of base. We consider two of these types here.

First, let us observe that there are certain U for which it is possible to express an arbitrary X as a polynomial in U with coefficients in F_q. Since

U satisfies an equation of degree n over F_q (its characteristic equation), we can always choose this polynomial to have degree less than n, and so $(1, U, \ldots, U^{n-1})$ forms a base, which we call the *polynomial base* corresponding to U. The condition that $(1, U, \ldots, U^{n-1})$ should be a base is that U satisfies no equation of degree less than n over F_q, and so that its characteristic equation should coincide with its minimal equation. Our derivation of these equations shows that this happens if and only if the conjugates $U, U^q, \ldots, U^{q^{n-1}}$ are all distinct, that is to say, if and only if no U^{q^i} $(0 < i < n)$ coincides with U, or equivalently, if and only if U belongs to no proper subfield F_{q^i} of F_γ which contains F_q. In these circumstances we call U a *generator* of F_γ over F_q, since F_γ is the smallest extension of F_q which contains U.

Suppose now that U is known to be a generator of F_γ over F_q. How can we find the expression of an arbitrary X as a polynomial in U? Or, more generally, if the base (U_i) of F_γ over F_q is given, how can we find the expression of an arbitrary X in the form (1)? We answer this more general question. Referring to the form (1), let us observe that the coefficients x_i are linear functions of X which lie in F_q. Accordingly there exist constants $V_i \in F_\gamma$, independent of X, for which $x_i = \operatorname{tr}(V_i X)$. Putting $X = U_j$, we see that the V_i are defined by the equations $\operatorname{tr}(V_i U_j) = \delta_{ij}$, and so the relation between the U's and the V's is symmetrical and either defines the other. In these circumstances (V_i) is called the *dual base* of (U_i).

In particular, we see that if we wish to find the expression of an arbitrary X as a polynomial in a given generator U, it suffices if we have available the trace function and the n elements $V_0, \ldots, V_{n-1}$ which form the dual base of the polynomial base (U^i).

Another type of base which is specially interesting for many theoretical purposes is the *normal base* defined by a suitable element U. This is the base formed by the n conjugates $U, U^q, \ldots, U^{q^{n-1}}$, when these are linearly independent over F_q. A rather deep theorem asserts that such elements U always exist, and indeed Davenport [unpublished] has shown that in a finite field U can almost be chosen as a primitive root. It is obvious that the dual base of a normal base is normal, so that to obtain the expression of an arbitrary X as a linear function of the conjugates $U, U^{q^{n-1}}$ of U we need only know the trace function and the particular element V which defines the dual base (V^{q^i}) of (U^{q^i}).

Of course it should be pointed out that it is harder to compute the dual base of a given base (U_i) than to express a particular X in the form (1). But once the dual base is known, we can use it to determine the expression (1) for as many X as we like with no further trouble.

6. TABULATION IN F_γ

We have seen that the typical element of F_γ can be represented either in the additive form (1) (for a suitable base) or the multiplicative form (4) (for a suitable primitive root). For the purposes of tabulation the latter form is by far the most convenient, but, if we adopt this form, we must learn how to add. Let us define the function $Z(x)$ (*the Zech's logarithm of x*) by the equation

$$e^{Z(x)} = e^x + 1 .$$

Then the equation $e^x + e^y = e^z$ has the unique solution $z = y + Z(x-y) = x + Z(y-x)$ for z. (The reader must take for himself the appropriate conventions concerning the formal symbol *.) Accordingly, if we tabulate the one-variable function Z we shall have at our fingertips the entire arithmetic structure of the field, since multiplication is easily performed by adding indices (modulo $r-1$).

If in addition we tabulate the characteristic equation of each X, then we shall have the trace function, and so a handy form for the general linear function from F_r to F_q, and an equally handy test for linear dependence over F_q. We can also tabulate for each generator U the dual base corresponding to U, and so (with the trace function) we can readily express any X as a polynomial in U. This is one of the most frequently used representations of the general X, and it is remarkable that all such representations can be made available with a comparatively small amount of tabulation.

It is fortunate that those cases for which U is not a generator are just the cases for which U's minimal equation differs from its characteristic equation, for in these cases we can use the space not occupied by the dual base of (U^i) to give the minimal equation of U.

Finally, for each U which belongs to a normal base, we can tabulate the element V which defines the dual normal base. Using again the already tabulated trace function, this gives us the expression of an arbitrary X in terms of an arbitrary normal base, all for a single column of extra tabulation!

7. THE FORM AND USE OF THE TABLES

We give as samples our tables for the fields F_4, F_8, F_{16}, F_{32}, F_{64} of characteristic 2. We shall illustrate the form of these tables with a portion of the table for F_{64}.

x	Zx	OVER $F2$			OVER $F4$		OVER $F8$	
$+20 \to 26$	$(100001)26$	6 49 29	9 46:19	$(XYY)29\ 35$	7: $- (BE)16\ 45{:}47$
$21 \to 42$	(101011)	(11)	$(XY1)$	(X)	$(11)42$	$0{:}21$

The column headed 'x' has one entry for each non-zero element $X = e^x$ of F_r. This is preceded by '+' should X be a primitive root. The column headed 'Zx' gives the Zech's logarithm of x. Thus the two lines of the table above tell us that $e^{20} + 1 = e^{26}$ and $e^{21} + 1 = e^{42}$, while e^{20} is a primitive root and e^{21} is not.

The remaining parts of the table all depend on the particular subfield F_q, and are repeated once for each proper subfield. We give in order the characteristic equation of X, then the dual base of the polynomial base (X^i) (if X

is a generator), and finally the defining element of the normal base dual to the normal base (X^{q^i}), if this exists. If X is not a generator neither of these bases can exist, and so we give instead the minimal equation of X over F_q.

The form of the tabulation is as follows. $(x_1 x_2 \dots x_n)$ denotes the characteristic equation in the form (6). It should be noted that in this formula the x's appear with alternating signs. This rather confusing convention was chosen so that the trace and determinant functions should be readily available. The fields which we give here as samples all have characteristic 2, so the sign convention will not affect the reader of this book, but we remark on it in case he consults our more extended tables without reading their introduction.

The minimal equation, when given, is abbreviated in the same fashion. Referring to the illustrated portion, we see that the characteristic equations of e^{20} and e^{21} over F_2 are

$$\Lambda^6 - 1.\Lambda^5 + 0.\Lambda^4 - 0.\Lambda^3 + 0.\Lambda^2 - 0.\Lambda + 1 = 0 ,$$

and

$$\Lambda^6 - 1.\Lambda^5 + 0.\Lambda^4 - 1.\Lambda^3 + 0.\Lambda^2 - 1.\Lambda + 1 = 0 ,$$

while the minimal equation of e^{21} is

$$\Lambda^2 - 1.\Lambda + 1 = 0 .$$

It follows that e^{21} must lie in F_4, and a glance at the corresponding part of the table shows that indeed its minimal equation over F_4 is just

$$\Lambda - X = 0 ,$$

and so it is the element of F_4 which we have called X. (We remark at this point that the elements of the subfields F_q have been given proper names consisting of a single symbol each, so as to condense the table. The elements of the subfields F_p have their usual names as integers reduced modulo p, and the other elements of F_q have been assigned suitable letters.)

The element e^{20} defines the polynomial base

$$1, \quad e^{20}, \quad e^{40}, \quad e^{60}, \quad e^{80}, \quad e^{100},$$

over F_2, whose dual base is read off from the table as

$$e^{26}, \quad e^6, \quad e^{49}, \quad e^{29}, \quad e^9, \quad e^{46} .$$

It follows that the expression of an arbitrary X as a polynomial in e^{20} is

$$X = \text{tr}(e^{26}X) + e^{20}\text{tr}(e^6 X) + e^{40}\text{tr}(e^{49}X) +$$

$$+ e^{60}\text{tr}(e^{29}X) + e^{80}\text{tr}(e^9 X) + e^{100}\text{tr}(e^{46}X) .$$

Thus, from the remainder of the table, we find, for instance

$$e^{21} = e^{60} + e^{80} + e^{100} \, ,$$

remembering that the trace is the first digit of the characteristic polynomial.

We can check this result by use of the Zech's logarithm table. We have

$$e^{60} + e^{80} = e^{60}(e^{20} + 1) = e^{60}e^{26} = e^{86} = e^{23} \, ,$$

(remember that we can reduce indices modulo 63), and then we find
$e^{23} + e^{100} = e^{23} + e^{37} = e^{23}(e^{14} + 1) = e^{23}e^{61} = e^{21}$, as expected.

The portions of these lines which refer to the subfields F_4 and F_8 are interpreted similarly. Note that an element of F_r can have quite different behaviours over differing subfields F_q. Thus e^{21} is not a generator of F_{64} over F_2 or F_4, but over F_8 it is not only a generator, but even defines a normal base. Again, e^{20} defines normal bases for F_{64} over F_2 and F_8, but not over F_4.

8. SOME NOTES ON APPLICATIONS OF THESE TABLES

Finite fields arise in number theory as algebraic extensions of the field of integers modulo p, and so appear naturally, for instance, in the solution of Diophantine equations to given moduli. Groups of matrices over finite fields form a large part of the text of finite group theory - in particular, the most interesting simple groups are all defined in this way. It might reasonably be observed in this direction that the first half of Dickson's [1960] book is an exposition of the theory of finite fields.

These fields have a wealth of combinatorial structure which causes them to arise in the solution of a vast number of combinatorial problems of which we mention only those problems arising in coding theory (see Selmer's [1966] book) and in the theory of perfect difference sets. In all these applications tabulated information about the fields concerned can materially assist in the solution of particular problems. I think it will also be found by many users that reference to such information can often illuminate the mechanism of the structure underlying a particular problem, and so aid us in the discovery of a more general abstract solution.

We close with an amusing example of the application of the theory to finite geometry. The elements of the finite projective plane over the field F_4 may be represented by non-zero vectors $V = (X, Y, Z)$ of elements of F_4, the vectors V and KV denoting the same point for any non-zero $K \in F_4$.

But, as we remarked in 2, F_{64} is a vector space of dimension 3 over F_4, so we can use the non-zero elements of F_{64} as the vectors V and say that two such elements determine the same point if their quotient is a member of F_4. Observe that the test for linear dependence of vectors given in §4 now becomes a test for collinearity of points. Thus the finite geometry under discussion has a peculiarly simple structure.

Indeed, let us name the points P_0, P_1, ..., P_{20}, P_i being the point corresponding to the element e^i of F_{64}, and the subscripts being taken modulo 21. Then P_i, P_j, P_k, P_l, P_m are collinear if and only if there is some x such that

$$\text{tr}(e^{i+x}) = \text{tr}(e^{j+x}) = \text{tr}(e^{k+x}) = \text{tr}(e^{l+x}) = \text{tr}(e^{m+x}) = 0 .$$

Since this depends only on the vanishing or non-vanishing of the trace, and not on its precise value, we can wrap the circle of 63 values of the trace function around on itself to produce the cycle

$$N, N, N, O, N, N, O, O, N, N, N, N, O, N, O, N, N, N, N, N, N ,$$

where 'N' merely means 'non-zero'. Thus the points P_3, P_6, P_7, P_{12}, P_{14} form a line in this geometry, and the other lines are obtained from this one by translating the subscripts modulo 21. Thus another line is P_7, P_{10}, P_{11}, P_{16}, P_{18}. If we call the lines L_0, L_1, ..., L_{20} in the natural order, we see that P_i lies on P_j if and only if $i - j$ is one of 3, 6, 7, 12, 14 modulo 21.

In Beirne's [1965] book, the reader will find a similar treatment of a 'Euclidean' geometry based on the field F_5. O'Beirne's results are explained from the present point of view by embedding his 25 point Euclidean geometry in the 31 point projective geometry whose points are the 124 non-zero elements of F_{125} considered modulo the 4 non-zero elements of F_5.

9. SOME DETAILS OF THE METHOD OF COMPUTATION OF THE TABLES

The tables given, and the more extended tables from which they were selected, were computed on the computer EDSAC 2 by a programme written by M. J. T. Guy. We are grateful to the Director of the Cambridge University Mathematical Laboratory, Dr. M. V. Wilkes, for permission to use the computer for this purpose. We applied the problem to all fields of composite order up to 1024, except that the fields of order p^2 ($p = 23, 29, 31$) were omitted. We also performed some more special calculations outside this range.

The first thing to be computed was the table of Zech's logarithms, since when this was known, the characteristic equation could be calculated from the identity (6), and the dual bases found by a simple search programme using the definition $\text{tr}(U_i V_j) = \delta_{ij}$. (It was this searching process which took most of the time involved.) The minimal equation was found in the same way as the characteristic equation, when the two were distinct.

We observed that if e were a primitive root with characteristic equation (6), then the corresponding difference equation

$$u_n - u_{n-1}x_1 + u_{n-2}x_2 - \cdots \pm u_0 x_n = 0$$

had, if considered modulo p (with $F_q = F_p$) a periodic solution of period $r - 1$.

This entailed that the successive values

$$u_0, u_1, \ldots, u_{r-2}$$

were the values of a linear function from F_r to F_p at the points

$$e^0, e^1, \ldots, e^{r-2}$$

of F_r, and so were the values of $\mathrm{tr}(Ke^i)$ for a suitable K. But now we have $\mathrm{tr}(Ke^{i+x}) + \mathrm{tr}(Ke^{i+y}) = \mathrm{tr}(Ke^{i+z})$ whenever $e^x + e^y = e^z$, no matter what the value of i. This condition sufficed to find the value of z given the values of x and y, and so in particular defined the Zech's logarithm table.

The computation was therefore begun by a search for a recurrence relation modulo p whose period was $r - 1$. This found, the programme searched for z in the above equation, given the value of x and the value of $y = 0$, and n adjacent values of i. This value of z was then noted as the Zech's logarithm of x. As soon as the entire Zech's logarithm table had been computed, the original recurrence relation was discarded, and the calculation proceeded as sketched above.

10. FACTOR TABLES OF POLYNOMIALS OVER PRIME FIELDS

For use in conjunction with the main tables, we have prepared also some factor tables relating to polynomials over the field F_p. In these tables each polynomial is represented by its sequence of coefficients, and the factors are written in the same form. For irreducible (prime) polynomials, we use the space which would otherwise be occupied by the factorisation to indicate an element of the corresponding finite field which has the given polynomial as minimal polynomial. (This element is defined only to within conjugacy.) A sample factor table is included which covers the same range as the sample field tables. This table was computed by the usual sieve method.

APPENDIX

F_4 OVER F_2

```
0 →* [01]  [1]
+1 → 2 [11]2 0:1
+2 → 1 [11]1 0:2
```

F_8 OVER F_2

```
0 →* [111]   [1]
+1 → 5 [101]4 3 5:1
+2 → 3 [101]1 6 3:2
+3 → 2 [011]0 6 3:-
+4 → 6 [101]2 5 6:4
+5 → 1 [011]0 3 5:-
 6 → 4 [011]0 5 6:-
```

F_{16} OVER F_2 OVER F_4

```
  0 → * [0001]   [1]              [01 ]   [1]
+ 1 →  4 [0011]14  2   1 0: -    [1X ] 4  0: 1
+ 2 →  8 [0011]13  4   2 0: -    [1Y ] 8  0: 2
+ 3 →14 [1111]14 10   1 2:11    [Y1 ] 2  5:13
+ 4 →  1 [0011]11  8   4 0: -    [1X ] 1  0: 4
+ 5 →10 [0101]   [11]            [0Y ]   [X]
+ 6 →13 [1111]13  5   2 4: 7    [X1 ] 4 10:11
+ 7 →  9 [1001] 9  2  10 1: 6    [XX ] 8 10:12
+ 8 →  2 [0011] 7  1   8 0: -    [1Y ] 2  0: 8
+ 9 →  7 [1111] 7  5   8 1:13    [X1 ] 1 10:14

+10 →  5 [0101]   [11]            [0X ]   [Y]
+11 →12 [1001]12  1   5 8: 3    [YY ] 4  5: 6
+12 →11 [1111]11 10   4 8:14    [Y1 ] 8  5: 7
+13 →  6 [1001] 6  8  10 4: 9    [XX ] 2 10: 3
+14 →  3 [1001] 3  4   5 2:12    [YY ] 1  5: 9
```

F_{32} OVER F_2

```
  0    * [10011]   [1]
+ 1 →19 [10111]16  3   6  5 17: 1
+ 2 →  7 [10111] 1  6  12 10  3: 2
+ 3 →11 [01001] 0 28  25  6  3: -
+ 4 →14 [10111] 2 12  24 20  6: 4
+ 5 →29 [01111] 4 28   5 14  9: -
+ 6 →22 [01001] 0 25  19 12  6: -
+ 7 →  2 [00101]27 20  17 10  3: -
+ 8 →28 [10111] 4 24  17  9 12: 8
+ 9 →15 [01111] 1  7   9 19 10: -

+10 →27 [01111] 8 25  10 28 18: -
+11 →  3 [11101]23 12   7  6  3:15
+12 →13 [01001] 0 19   7 24 12: -
+13 →12 [11101]30 17  28 24 12:29
+14 →  4 [00101]23  9   3 20  6: -
+15 →  9 [11011]26 20   5 19 10:11
+16 →25 [10111] 8 17   3 18 24:16
+17 →21 [01001] 0 14  28  3 17: -
+18 →30 [01111] 2 14  18  7 20: -
+19 →  1 [00101]29 10  24  5 17: -

+20 →23 [01111]16 19  20 25  5: -
+21 →17 [11101]27  6  19  3 17:23
+22 →  6 [11101]15 24  14 12  6:30
+23 →20 [11011]13 10  18 25  5:21
+24 →26 [01001] 0  7  14 17 24: -
+25 →16 [00101]30  5  12 18 24: -
+26 →24 [11101]29  3  25 17 24:27
+27 →10 [11011]22  5   9 28 18:26
+28 →  8 [00101]15 18   6  9 12: -
+29 →  5 [11011]11 18  20 14  9:13

+30 →18 [11011]21  9  10  7 20:22
```

F_{64} OVER F_2

```
 0 →  *  [010101]                         [1]
+ 1 →  8  [101101]44 43 58 54 53 45: -
+ 2 → 16  [101101]25 23 53 45 43 27: -
+ 3 → 53  [010111]60 47 46 43  3  0: -
+ 4 → 32  [101101]50 46 43 27 23 54: -
+ 5 → 38  [100001]38 33 28 23 18 43:52
  6 → 43  [010111]57 31 29 23  6  0: -
  7 → 62  [001001]42 35 28  0 56 49: -
+ 8 →  1  [101101]37 29 23 54 46 45: -
+ 9 → 45  [010001]                       [101]

+10 → 13  [100001]13  3 56 46 36 36 23:41
+11 → 51  [110011]37 14  3 55 36 48:11
 12 → 23  [010111]51 62 58 46 12  0: -
+13 → 10  [100111]10  7 59 46 33 23:17
 14 → 61  [001001]21  7 56  0 49 35: -
 15 → 44  [110101]51 36 46 31 47  3:15
+16 →  2  [101101]11 58 46 45 29 27: -
+17 → 41  [100001]41 24  7 53 36 58:13
 18 → 27  [010001]                       [101]
+19 → 34  [100111]34 49 62 43 24 53:20

+20 → 26  [100001]26  6 49 29  9 46:19
 21 → 42  [101011]                        [11]
+22 → 39  [110011]11 28  6 47  9 33:22
+23 → 12  [000011]40 29  6 46 23  0: -
 24 → 46  [010111]39 61 53 29 24  0: -
+25 → 30  [110011]44 49 24 62 36  6:25
+26 → 20  [100111]20 14 55 29  3 46:34
 27 → 58  [000101]                       [011]
 28 → 59  [001001]42 14 49  0 35  7: -
+29 → 48  [000011]34 53 24 58 29  0:
```

OVER F_4

```
[111 ]                  [1]
[XXX]47 54 27: 8
[YYY]31 45 54:16
[0Y1] 0  6  3: -
[XXX]62 27 45:32
[XYY]23 56 49: -
[0X1] 0 12  6: -
[00X] 0 56 49: -
[YYY]61 54 27: 1
[101 ]36 27 45: 9

[YXX]46 49 35: -
[X1Y]55 48 24:25
[0Y1] 0 24 12: -
[XYX]43 49 35: -
[00Y] 0 49 35: -
[Y01]18  3 33:57
[XXX]59 45 54: 2
[XYY]53 14 28: -
[101 ] 9 54 27:18
[XYX]58 28 56: -

[XYY]29 35  7: -
[XY1]                  [X]
[Y1X]47 33 48:50
[1XY]31 24 12:58
[0X1] 0 48 24: -
[Y1X]62  6  3:11
[YXY]23 35  7: -
[011 ] 0 54 27: -
[00X] 0 35  7: -
[1XY]61 33 48:43
```

OVER F_8

```
[01 ]        [1]
[1A ] 8  0: 1
[1B ]16  0: 2
[FD ]42 18:39
[1C ]32  0: 4
[CF ] 4 27:59
[DE ]21 36:15
[E1 ] 2  9:25
[1A ] 1  0: 8
[0B ]        [A]

[AD ] 8 54:55
[AC ]16 54:56
[EF ]42  9:30
[AE ]32 54:58
[F1 ] 4 18:50
[CA ]21 27: 6
[1B ] 2  0:16
[AD ] 1 54:62
[0C ]        [B]
[BF ] 8 45:46

[BE ]16 45:47
[11 ]42  0:21
[BA ]32 45:49
[EB ] 4  9:41
[FD ]21 18:60
[AC ] 2 54: 7
[BF ] 1 45:53
[OE ]        [D]
[D1 ] 8 36:37
[DA ]16 36:38
```

30→25	[110101]39 9 29 62 31 6:30	[X01]36 6 3:51	[AB]42 54:12
+31→35	[01101]25 29 61 0 24 56: -	[11X]46 28 56: -	[DD]32 36:40
+32→ 4	[11010]22 53 29 27 58 54: -	[YYY]55 27 45: 4	[1C] 4 0:32
33→58	[01011]30 55 23 53 33 0: -	[0X1] 0 3 33: -	[EF]21 9:51
+34→19	[10000]19 48 14 43 9 53:26	[YXX]43 28 56: -	[BE] 2 45:61
35→31	[00100]21 49 14 0 28 56: -	[00Y] 0 28 56: -	[D1] 1 36:44
36→54	[01000] [101]	[101]18 45 54:36	[OA] [C]
+37→57	[10011]50 7 33 59 18 24:37	[Y1X]59 24 12:44	[CB] 8 27:28
+38→ 5	[10011] 5 35 61 23 48 43:40	[YXY]53 56 49: -	[CD]16 27:29
39→22	[11010]57 18 23 47 55 33:39	[X01] 9 33 48:60	[BC]42 45: 3
+40→52	[100001]52 12 35 58 18 29:38	[YXX]58 7 14: -	[CF]32 27:31
+41→17	[10011]17 56 31 53 12 58:10	[YXY]29 14 28: -	[AE] 4 54:23
42→21	[10101] [11]	[YX1] [ ]	[11]21 0:42
+43→ 6	[00001]20 46 3 23 43 0: -	[1YX]47 12 6:29	[DA] 2 36:52
+44→15	[11011]22 56 12 31 18 3:44	[X1Y]31 3 33:37	[CB] 1 27:35
45→ 9	[00010] [011]	[011] 0 27 45: -	[OD] [F]
+46→24	[00001]17 58 12 29 46 0: -	[1YX]62 48 24:53	[FC] 8 18:19
+47→49	[01101]44 46 62 0 12 28: -	[11Y]23 14 28: -	[FF]16 18:20
48→29	[01011]15 59 43 58 48 0: -	[0Y1] 0 33 48: -	[DE]42 36:57
49→47	[00100]42 56 7 0 14 28: -	[00X] 0 14 28: -	[F1]32 18:22
+50→60	[110101]25 35 48 61 9 12:50	[X1Y]61 12 6:22	[BA] 4 45:14
51→11	[110101]60 9 43 55 59 48:51	[Y01]36 48 24:30	[AB]21 54:33
+52→40	[100111]40 28 27 58 6 29: 5	[XYX]46 7 14: -	[CD] 2 27:43
+53→ 3	[00001]10 23 33 43 53 0: -	[1XY]55 6 3:46	[FC] 1 18:26
54→36	[00010] [011]	[011] 0 45 54: -	[OF] [E]
+55→56	[01101]22 23 31 0 6 14: -	[11X]43 7 14: -	[EE] 8 9:10
56→55	[00100]21 28 35 0 7 14: -	[00Y] 0 7 14: -	[E1]16 9:11
57→37	[110101]30 36 53 59 61 24:/7	[X01]18 24 12:15	[CA]42 27:48
+58→33	[00001] 5 43 48 53 58 0: -	[1YX]59 3 33:23	[EB]32 9:13
+59→28	[01101]11 43 47 0 3 7: -	[11Y]53 35 7: -	[DD] 4 36: 5
60→50	[110101]15 18 58 61 62 12:60	[Y01] 9 12 6:39	[BC]21 45:24
+61→14	[01101]37 53 55 0 33 35: -	[11X]58 49 35: -	[EF] 2 18:34
+62→ 7	[01101]50 58 59 0 48 49: -	[11Y]29 56 49: -	[EE] 1 9:17

The polynomial $x_0 \cdot \Lambda^n + x_1 \cdot \Lambda^{n-1} + \ldots + x_n$ is here denoted by $x_0 x_1 \ldots x_n$. We suppose $x_n \neq 0$ so as to avoid the existence of a trivial factor. When the polynomial is reducible over F_2 its irreducible factors are given. Otherwise the entry is an element of some finite field which has the given polynomial as its minimal and characteristic polynomial, together with the field in question. Thus for instance the polynomial $1011 = \Lambda^3 + \Lambda + 1$ is irreducible, and has the root e^3 in F_8.

		First three digits			
		100	101	110	111
	none	-	11^2	-	$e^1(F_4)$
	1	11.111	$e^3(F_8)$	$e^1(F_8)$	11^3
	01	11^4	111^2	$e^7(F_{16})$	11.1011
	11	$e^1(F_{16})$	11.1101	$11^2.111$	$e^3(F_{16})$
	001	11.11111	$e^3(F_{32})$	111.1011	$11^2.1101$
	011	111.1101	11.11001	11^5	$e^{15}(F_{32})$
Final digits	101	$e^7(\ 32)$	$11^3.111$	11.10011	$e^{11}(F_{32})$
	111	$11^2.1011$	$e^5(F_{32})$	$e^1(F_{32})$	11.111^2
	0001	$11^2.111^2$	1101^2	$e^5(F_{64})$	11.101111
	0011	$e^{23}(\ 64)$	11.111.1011	$11^2.11111$	$e^{11}(F_{64})$
	0101	1011	11^6	11.111.1101	$e^{15}(F_{64})$
	0111	11.111101	$e^3(F_{64})$	$e^{13}(F_{64})$	$11^4.111$
	1001	$e^7(F_{64})$	11.110111	$11^3.1011$	111.10011
	1011	$11^3.1101$	$e^{31}(F_{64})$	111^3	11.101001
	1101	11.111011	111.11111	$e^1(F_{64})$	$11^2.11001$
	1111	111.11001	$11^2.10011$	11.100101	1011.1101

REFERENCES

Davenport, H., Special primitive roots in finite fields (unpublished).

Dickson, L. E., 1960, Linear Groups (Dover, New York).

O'Beirne, T. H., 1965, Puzzles and Paradoxes (O.U.P., London).

Selmer, E. S., 1966, Linear Recurrence Relations over Finite Fields (Dept. of Math., Univ. of Bergen).

ON A SPECIFIC SIMILARITY OF FINITE SEMIGROUPS

P. DEUSSEN
Mathematical Institute of the Technische Hochschule, Munich

1. SUMMARY

The relation of similarity between subsemigroups of a finite transition semigroup is refined in a particular way which was suggested by the theory of finite automata. This refinement is shown to be characterized completely by a double coset partition of a symmetric group. In order to obtain this partition an ALGOL program was written which computes representatives and the orders of the resulting classes.

2.

Let F be a semigroup of mappings f from the finite set S into itself. By the symbol F^p denote the (isomorphic) semigroup $p^{-1}Fp$, where $p \in \mathfrak{S}_S$, the symmetric group on S. Clearly, F and F^p as well as $\mathfrak{S}_S$ are subsemigroups of the semigroup $\mathfrak{T}_S$ of all mappings from S into itself. However, F^p may be the same set as F, i.e. $F^p = F$. A natural question now is to ask how many different sets F^p are in $\mathfrak{T}_S$ as p ranges over $\mathfrak{S}_S$. The answer is given by the group

$$\mathfrak{N}(F) := \{p : p \in \mathfrak{S}_S,\ pF = Fp\}$$

which is the normalizer of F within $\mathfrak{S}_S$; namely, $F^p = F^q$ is equivalent to saying $pq^{-1} \in \mathfrak{N}(F)$, which means that there are exactly $[\mathfrak{S}_S : \mathfrak{N}(F)]$ different subsemigroups F^p in $\mathfrak{T}_S$. Nevertheless, as explained below equality between F^p and F^q is a relation too coarse for our purposes. Define

$$F^p \sim F^q \ :\leftrightarrow \forall f \in F : f^p = f^q$$

and let

$$\mathfrak{Z}(F) := \{p : p \in \mathfrak{S}_S,\ \forall f \in F:\ pf = fp\}$$

be the centralizer of F within $\mathfrak{S}_S$. Then $F^p \sim F^q$ if and only if $pq^{-1} \in \mathfrak{Z}(F)$. Furthermore, for a subgroup $A \subseteq \mathfrak{S}_S$, define

$$F^p \approx F^q \bmod A \ :\leftrightarrow \exists a \in A : F^{pa} \sim F^q \ ,$$

which is an equivalence relation as is the relation $\sim$. Since $F^{pa} \sim F^q$ means $paq^{-1} \in \mathfrak{Z}(F)$, we obtain

$$F^p \approx F^q \bmod A \leftrightarrow p \in \mathfrak{Z}(F)qA \ .$$

Consequently, the number of classes into which the system $\{F^p \colon p \in \mathfrak{S}_S\}$ is decomposed by the relation $\approx \bmod A$ equals the number k of classes of the double coset partition

$$\mathfrak{S}_S = \bigcup_{i=1}^{k} \mathfrak{Z}(F)\, q_i\, A$$

of $\mathfrak{S}_S$. Unfortunately, k cannot be calculated from the orders of $\mathfrak{Z}(F)$ and A, but we will give upper and lower bounds. The numbers

$$l_i = [A \colon q_i^{-1} \cdot \mathfrak{Z}(F) \cdot q_i \cap A]$$
$$r_i = [\mathfrak{Z}(F) \colon q_i A q_i^{-1} \cap \mathfrak{Z}(F)] \qquad i = 1 .. k$$

are the numbers of right cosets $\mathfrak{Z}(F)p$ and left cosets qA, respectively, which are contained in $\mathfrak{Z}(F)q_iA$.

Let

$$l = [\mathfrak{S}_S \colon \mathfrak{Z}(F)]$$

$$r = [\mathfrak{S}_S \colon A] \ .$$

Then (Specht [1956]), r_i, l_i and k fulfil the relations

$$\sum_{i=1}^{k} r_i = r \ , \qquad \sum_{i=1}^{k} l_i = l \ , \qquad \frac{l_i}{r_i} = \frac{l}{r} \ , \qquad i = 1 \ldots k \ , \tag{1}$$

and clearly

$$r_i \neq 0 \ , \qquad l_i \neq 0 \ ,$$

In order to obtain an upper bound for k, regard the system (1) as a diophantine problem for r, l being given; the manifold of solutions then is characterized in the following way. Let h be any common divisor of r and l, and let $\sum_{i=1}^{k} s_i = h$ be a partition of h; then by $hr_i = rs_i$ and $hl_i = ls_i$, r_i and l_i are defined for $i = 1 .. k$ and they fulfil (1) when we assume $s_i \neq 0$. Conversely, each solution of (1) is obtained in this way. But $s_i \neq 0$ for $i = 1 \ldots k$ implies $k \leq h$, and since h is any common divisor of r and l, we get $k \leq \gcd(r, l)$. This bound is sharp since if $\mathfrak{Z}(F) = \{e\}$, $k = r = \gcd(r, l)$. As for the lower bound, note that $|\mathfrak{Z}(F)q_iA| \leqslant |\mathfrak{Z}(F)| \cdot |A|$, whence $|\mathfrak{S}_S| \leqslant k \cdot |\mathfrak{Z}(F)| \cdot |A|$ or $|\mathfrak{S}_S|/(|\mathfrak{Z}(F)| \cdot |A|) \leqslant k$; this bound is also sharp, for let $\mathfrak{Z}(F)$ or A be normal subgroups of $\mathfrak{S}_S$ such that $\mathfrak{Z}(F) \cap A = \{e\}$, then $\mathfrak{Z}(F)q_iA$ equals $q_i\mathfrak{Z}(F)A$ or $\mathfrak{Z}(F)Aq_i$, respectively, and $\mathfrak{Z}(F)A$ is a subgroup of order $|\mathfrak{Z}(F)| \cdot |A|$.

Since $|\mathfrak{S}_S|/(|\mathfrak{Z}(F)| \cdot |A|) = r/|\mathfrak{Z}(F)|$, we finally get

$$\frac{r}{|\mathfrak{Z}(F)|} \leqslant k \leqslant \gcd(r, l) . \tag{2}$$

3.

The reason we are interested specifically in the relation $\approx$ mod A rests on the theory of automata. An abstract automaton can be regarded as a semigroup F acting on the set S of "states"; furthermore, by an index set X (the "input alphabet") and by an index function $\varphi : X \to F$, a subset $\varphi(X) \subseteq F$ is distinguished which generates F (see Deussen [1965]). From the technical point of view, the binary representation of the abstract automaton, i.e. the encoding of the elements $s \in S$ by strings of the binary symbols 0 and 1 influences the complexity of the resulting switching functions. F^p and F^q belong to different encodings of S and $F^p \approx F^q$ mod A means that these encodings and hence the associated switching functions are not essentially different in view of their complexity; "essentially" here means "up to the group A", which is determined by technical considerations. For these reasons we consider the following case. First, we assume $|S| = 2^n$ for some natural n. Second, A shall be the inhomogeneous affine group in n dimensions over GF(2), its order being

$$|A| = 2^n \cdot (2^n-1)(2^n-2)(2^n-2^2)\ldots(2^n-2^{n-1}) .$$

Third, F is transitive on S, which implies that $|\mathfrak{Z}(F)|$ is a divisor of $|S|$ (Fleck [1962], Deussen [1965]).

From this we calculate that r divides l, whence now

$$\frac{r}{|\mathfrak{Z}(F)|} \leqslant k \leqslant r$$

instead of inequality (2).

In order to obtain the exact value of k and representatives q_i of the double coset partition, an ALGOL program was written which actually performs the partition. Aside from organizational data, the input of the program are A and $\mathfrak{Z}(F)$, where $\mathfrak{Z}(F)$ is to be given explicitly. If possible, A should be represented as a product $A = B \cdot V$ (B a subgroup, V any subset of $\mathfrak{S}_S$) in order to minimize the working storage; again, V is to be given explicitly, whereas only the generators of B are to be read in. Each element $p \in \mathfrak{S}_S$ is primarily represented as a one dimensional array $p[1:|S|]$, where $p[i] = j$ if the permutation $p \in \mathfrak{S}_S$ turns s_i into s_j $(s_i, s_j \in S)$.

For storage economy, the elements of the entire group $\mathfrak{S}_S$ and of each class $\mathfrak{Z}(F)q_iA$ are stored as the integers

$$\bar{p} = \sum_{i=1}^{k} p[i] \times 10^{m-i} \text{ where } m = |S| .$$

In the present form the program theoretically works for $|S| \leq 9$. As a practical example we took $\mathfrak{Z}(F)$ to be the cyclic group of order 8 generated by the cycle (12345678), and A as mentioned above for $n = 3$, that is, the double coset partition was computed for the $\mathfrak{S}_8$. A was represented in the form $A = GL(3, 2) \cdot V$, where $V \simeq \mathfrak{S}_2 \times \mathfrak{S}_2 \times \mathfrak{S}_2$.

4. RESULTS

i	q_i	$|\mathfrak{Z}(F)q_iA|$	r_i	l_i
1	e	2688	2	336
2	(78)	2688	2	336
3	(45)(67)	2688	2	336
4	(67)	5376	4	672
5	(68)	5376	4	672
6	(678)	10752	8	1344
7	(45)(678)	10752	8	1344

Total runtime of program: 4.8 h.

It should be mentioned that the main computational problem was neither the generation of the $\mathfrak{S}_S$ nor the generation of the classes $\mathfrak{Z}(F)q_iA$, but the fact that the elements of these classes so far obtained are to be erased from the $\mathfrak{S}_S$ in order to obtain the next representative q_{i+1}. The erasing process was sped up by ordering each of the classes $\mathfrak{Z}(F)q_iA$ and by generating the entire group $\mathfrak{S}_S$ in lexicographically ordered form.

Computing times for the example:
Generation of GL(3,2)   : 7.6 min
Generation of $\mathfrak{S}_8$: 2.5 min
Erasing of $\mathfrak{Z}(F)q_iA$ from $\mathfrak{S}_8$: 1.5 min (mean value)

The generation and the ordering of a class $\mathfrak{Z}(F)q_iA$ are linear and quadratic processes, respectively. Let n_i be the order of this class. Then for our example, we have obtained the following formulas for the computing times t_i.

Generation of $\mathfrak{Z}(F)q_iA$:
$t_i = 5.4 \times 10^{-3} \cdot n_i$ (sec)   ($t_1 = 15$ sec, $t_6 = 59$ sec)
Ordering this class:
$t_i = 7.54 \times 10^{-5} \cdot n_i^2 + 200$ (sec)   ($t_1 = 8.2$ min, $t_6 = 143$ min)

The computation was performed on the TR4 computer of the LEIBNIZ RECHENZENTRUM, Bavarian Academy of Science, Munich.

ACKNOWLEDGEMENT

The author is gratefully indebted to Prof. Dr. F. L. Bauer (Mathematical Institute of the Technische Hochschule Munich) for clarifying discussion on the subject and to Dr. Chr. Reinsch (Mathematical Institute of the Technische Hochschule Munich) for placing the generation program of the symmetric group at the author's disposal.

REFERENCES

Deussen, P., 1965, ICC Bull. 4, 231-264.
Fleck, A., 1962, JACM 9, 469-476.
Specht, W., 1956, Gruppentheorie (Springer-Verlag, Berlin) p. 55.

CALCULS ALGÉBRIQUES DANS L'ANNEAU
DES VECTEURS DE WITT

J.-J. DUBY
Cie IBM-France

1. INTRODUCTION

Le but de cette étude est de montrer une application des ordinateurs à un problème d'algèbre. Ce problème est celui de la manipulation des vecteurs de Witt. Comme nous le verrons dans la seconde partie de cet exposé, les vecteurs de Witt forment un ensemble sur lequel on définit deux lois de composition, somme et produit, qui déterminent une structure d'anneau. L'originalité de cette algèbre est que ces opérations ne sont pas définies directement à partir des composantes des vecteurs, mais sur des composantes "fantômes". Si l'on veut opérer sur les composantes (de chair et d'os), on est conduit très rapidement - dès que le nombre de composantes est supérieur à deux - à des calculs extrêmement longs et complexes. La troisième partie de cet exposé montre comment ces calculs peuvent être très facilement programmés sur un ordinateur. Mais auparavant, il nous a paru utile de rappeler que la théorie des vecteurs de Witt, loin d'être une simple curiosité mathématique, est très fréquemment utilisée dans les recherches actuelles en topologie algébrique et en géométrie algébrique.

2. RAPPEL HISTORIQUE

2.1. *Les vecteurs de Witt dans la recherche mathématique moderne*

En 1936, E. Witt, en étudiant la structure des corps valués discrets parfaits, a été conduit à construire une généralisation des nombres p-adiques. C'est cette généralisation qui est connue depuis sous le nom de vecteurs de Witt. On trouvera cet exposé original dans Witt [1936].

Ses résultats on été repris et utilisés ces dernières années dans des problèmes sensiblement différents. En théorie des groupes analytiques, Dieudonné [1953a, b, c], puis Cartier [1957] et Barsotti [1959] ont utilisé les vecteurs de Witt. En topologie algébrique, Serre [1958] considère des faisceaux d'anneaux de vecteurs de Witt à composantes dans les anneaux locaux d'une variété algébrique. En géométrie algébrique, Barsotti [1964, 1965a, 1965b] a étendu les vecteurs de Witt aux covecteurs et bivecteurs dans l'étude des variétés abéliennes en caractéristique positive.

Très vraisemblablement, les vecteurs de Witt, qui se sont ainsi révélés être un instrument puissant de recherche mathématique, seront encore mis à contribution dans les années qui viennent. Nous allons voir pourtant combien leur manipulation est complexe.

3. L'ANNEAU DES VECTEURS DE WITT

Dans ce qui suit, n désigne un entier positif, fini ou infini, p un nombre premier, Z l'anneau des entiers, Q le corps des rationnels.

Soit A un anneau commutatif, dont nous supposerons pour le moment qu'il contient Q comme sous-anneau.

3.1. *Définitions:*

On appelle *vecteur de Witt* à composantes dans A de longueur $n+1$ un $n+1$-uple $(x_0, x_1, \ldots, x_n)$ où $x_i \in A$.

On appelle $x_0, \ldots, x_n$ les *composantes* du vecteur de Witt.

On définit les *composantes fantômes* $x^{(0)}, \ldots, x^{(n)}$ du vecteur de Witt $(x_0, \ldots, x_n)$ par les équations:

$$x^{(i)} = \sum_{j=0}^{i} p^{i-j} x_{i-j}^{p^j} \qquad i = 0, \ldots, n \tag{1}$$

Remarquons que les relations (1) permettent inversement d'exprimer les composantes x_i sous forme d'un polynôme en $x^{(0)}, \ldots, x^{(i)}$ à coefficients rationnels, pour $i = 0, \ldots, n$.

On note $W_n(A)$ l'ensemble des vecteurs de Witt de longueur $n+1$ à composantes dans A. On introduit maintenant sur $W_n(A)$ une structure d'anneau commutatif en définissant la *somme* (resp. le *produit*) de deux vecteurs de Witt $(x_0, \ldots, x_n)$ et $(y_0, \ldots, y_n)$ comme le vecteur de Witt de composantes fantômes

$$z^{(i)} = x^{(i)} + y^{(i)} \text{ (resp. } z^{(i)} = x^{(i)} y^{(i)}) .$$

Les vecteurs de Witt sont donc définis par leurs composantes, leur somme et leur produit par leurs composantes fantômes. Mais il est facile de voir que les composantes de la somme et du produit de deux vecteurs de Witt s'expriment en fonction polynômiale à coefficients rationnels des composantes des vecteurs. Plus précisément, on peut poser pour $i = 0, \ldots, n$

$$(x+y)_i = \Phi_i (x_0, \ldots, x_i; y_0, \ldots, y_i) \tag{2}$$

$$(xy)_i = \Psi_i (x_0, \ldots, x_i; y_0, \ldots, y_i) \tag{3}$$

$$\text{avec } \Phi_i \in Q[x_0, \ldots, x_i; y_0, \ldots, y_i]$$

$$\text{et } \Psi_i \in Q[x_0, \ldots, x_i; y_0, \ldots, y_i] .$$

Witt [1936] démontre que les coefficients des polynômes Φ_i et Ψ_i sont *entiers*. Autrement dit:

Théorème: avec les notations précédentes:

$$\Phi_i \in Z[x_0, \ldots, x_i; y_0, \ldots y_i] \qquad \Psi_i \in Z[x_0, \ldots, x_i; y_0, \ldots y_i]$$

Nous pouvons maintenant supposer que A est seulement un anneau commutatif à élément unitaire, et définir directement l'anneau des vecteurs de Witt de longueur $n+1$ à composantes dans A, $W_n(A)$, en définissant la somme et le produit de deux éléments de A^{n+1} directement à l'aide des équations (2) et (3), les composantes fantômes disparaissant.

On considère généralement des vecteurs de Witt par rapport à p à composantes dans un anneau ou un corps de caractéristique p. C'est ainsi que si $A = \mathbf{Z}/p\,\mathbf{Z}$, $W_\infty(A)$ est isomorphe à l'anneau des entiers p-adiques.

Dans ces conditions, il est nécessaire pour calculer dans l'anneau $W_n(A)$ de connaître les polynômes Φ_i et Ψ_i.

3.2. *Exemple:*

A titre d'exemple, calculons Φ_0, Φ_1, Ψ_0 et Ψ_1 pour une valeur de p quelconque.

Nous avons: (relations (1))

$$\begin{cases} Z^{(0)} = Z_0 \\ Z^{(1)} = pZ_1 + Z_0^p \quad \text{D'où:} \end{cases}$$

$$\begin{cases} Z_0 = Z^{(0)} \\ Z_1 = \dfrac{1}{p}\, Z^{(1)} - \dfrac{1}{p}\, Z^{(0)p}\,. \end{cases} \tag{1'}$$

Cela étant:

$$(x+y)_0 = (x+y)^{(0)} = x^{(0)} + y^{(0)} = x_0 + y_0$$

$$\begin{aligned}
(x+y)_1 &= \frac{1}{p}\,(x+y)^{(1)} - \frac{1}{p}\,(x+y)^{(0)p} \\
&= \frac{1}{p}\left[x^{(1)} + y^{(1)} - (x_0 + y_0)^p \right] \\
&= \frac{1}{p}\left[x_0^p + px_1 + y_0^p + py_1 - x_0^p - y_0^p - \sum_{j=1}^{p-1} \binom{p}{j} x_0^j\, y_0^{p-j} \right]
\end{aligned}$$

Soit:

$$(x+y)_1 = x_1 + y_1 - \sum_{j=1}^{p-1} \frac{\binom{p}{j}}{p}\, x_0^j\, y_0^{p-j}$$

De même:

$$(xy)_0 = (xy)^{(0)} = x^{(0)}\, y^{(0)} = x_0\, y_0$$

$$(xy)_1 = \frac{1}{p}\left[(xy)^{(1)} - (xy)^{(0)p} \right] = \frac{1}{p}\left[x^{(1)}\, y^{(1)} - (x_0\, y_0)^p \right]$$
$$= \frac{1}{p}\left[(px_1 + x_0^p)\,(py_1 + y_0^p) - x_0^p\, y_0^p \right]$$

Soit:

$$(xy)_1 = px_1y_1 + x_1y_0^p + y_1x_0^p.$$

Le calcul des composantes suivantes, même pour les petites valeurs de p, devient extrêmement complexe. Le lecteur qui n'en serait pas persuadé est invité à calculer Φ_2 et Ψ_2 pour $p = 2$. Mais c'est précisément la tâche de l'ordinateur que de se charger de ces calculs longs et fastidieux à exécuter manuellement, et où la probabilité d'erreur tend vers 1 très rapidement avec le temps nécessaire. Nous allons voir comment il est possible de programmer ce calcul pour un ordinateur.

4. CALCUL DES COORDONNEES DES VECTEURS DE WITT SUR ORDINATEUR

Nous nous proposons de calculer les polynômes Φ_i et Ψ_i pour $i = 0, 1, 2, \ldots$ et $p = 2, 3, 5, \ldots$. De plus, sur la suggestion de I. Barsotti, nous calculerons également les composantes π_i de x^p en fonction des composantes de x.

4.1. *Description du programme:*

Nous ne décrirons que la méthode de calcul des Φ_i, le calcul des Ψ_i et π_i reposant sur le même principe.

Les Φ_i sont calculés par récurrence sur i. Nous avons vu que

$$\Phi_0 = x_0 + y_0.$$

Supposons connus $\Phi_0, \ldots \Phi_{i-1}$. On a:

$$(x+y)^{(i)} = x^{(i)} + y^{(i)} = \sum_{j=0}^{i} p^{i-j} (x+y)_{i-j}^{p^j}.$$

La dernière égalité donne:

$$p^i(x_i+y_i) + \sum_{j=1}^{i} p^{i-j} \left(x_{i-j}^{p^j} + y_{i-j}^{p^j} \right) - \sum_{j=1}^{i} p^{i-j} (x+y)_{i-j}^{p^j} + p^i (x+y)_i$$

D'où:

$$(x+y)_i = x_i + y_i + \sum_{j=1}^{i} p^{-j} \left(x_{i-j}^{p^j} + y_{i-j}^{p^j} - (x+y)_{i-j}^{p^j} \right)$$

Le polynôme cherché est donc:

$$\Phi_i \equiv x_i + y_i + \sum_{j=1}^{i} p^{-j} \left(x_{i-j}^{p^j} + y_{i-j}^{p^j} - \Phi_{i-j}^{p^j} \right) \tag{4}$$

Le programme reposant sur cette méthode a été écrit pour IBM 7094 en FORMAC (Sammet *et al.* [1964]). Rappelons que FORMAC est une extension de FORTRAN qui permet de manipuler des expressions algébriques, ainsi que certaines fonctions transcendantes. La différence essentielle entre FORMAC et le langage mathématique usuel est une différence de notation: le produit se note *, l'exponentiation se note ** et les indices varient de 1 à n+1 et non de 0 à n. C'est ainsi que le calcul d'un polynôme Φ_i à l'aide de la formule (4) s'effectue très simplement par itération: on initialise Φ_i à $x_i + y_i$, puis on ajoute successivement les polynômes $p^{-j}\left(x_{i-j}^{pj} + y_{i-j}^{pj} - \Phi_{i-j}^{pj}\right)$ correspondant aux valeurs successives de j. Le programme s'écrit:

```
LET PHI(I+1) = X(I+1) + Y(I+1)
DO 1 J = 1, I
LET PHI(I+1) = PHI(I+1) + P**(-J)*(X(I-J+1)**(P**J) + Y(I-J+1)**(P**J)
              - PHI(I-J+1)**(P**J))
1 CONTINUE
```

Le calcul des Φ_i, i variant de 0 à n, s'effectue suivant le même principe: on initialise $\Phi_0 = x_0 + y_0$, et on fait varier i de 1 à n:

```
LET PHI(1) = X(1) + Y(1)
DO 1  I = 1, N
LET PHI(I+1) = X(I+1) + Y(I+1)
DO 1  J = 1, I
LET PHI(1+I) = PHI(I+1) + P**(-J)*(X(I-J+1)**(P**J) + Y(I-J+1)**(P**J)
              - PHI(I-J+1)**(P**J))
1 CONTINUE
```

Le programme complet figure en appendice 1. Il ne diffère du programme précédent que par l'introduction de procédures d'entrée/sortie destinées à rendre le résultat plus facile à lire et à interpréter.

4.2. *Résultats obtenus:*

On trouvera en appendices 2, 3 et 4 les résultats obtenus pour Φ, Ψ et π respectivement. On peut voir que, comme le laissaient pressentir les calculs effectués en 3.1, la longueur des polynômes croît très vite avec i et p. Nous ne pouvons donner ici que les polynômes qui ont pu "tenir en mémoire". Nous espérons que ces premiers résultats pourront être utilisés valablement.

Il n'est certes pas impossible d'obtenir les composantes d'ordre supérieur aux composantes trouvées jusqu'à maintenant, que ce soit à l'aide d'une machine de plus grande capacité ou en utilisant des mémoires lentes de la 7094. Mais alors se pose le problème de l'utilisation par le mathématicien des résultats obtenus. En effet, il est difficile, sinon impossible, à l'esprit humain d'appréhender un polynôme de plusieurs pages de long: la simple analyse - et même la simple lecture - par l'homme d'expressions mathématiques de grandes dimensions sont quasi-certainement entachées d'erreurs. Par contre, la machine peut lire et analyser de telles expressions, et d'une manière plus générale, répondre à des questions précises à leur sujet: recherche de coefficients, de facteurs communs, passage au quotient, ou même application d'opérateurs plus compliqués, tel l'opérateur de "dérivation" des vecteurs de Witt défini par Barsotti [1959] - voir Duby [1967]. C'est au mathématicien de poser ces questions à la machine et, en une sorte de dialogue, d'interpréter les réponses pour orienter ses recherches.

RÉFÉRENCES

Barsotti, I., 1959, Ann. Scuola Norm. Sup. Pisa (3) 13, 303-372.

Barsotti, I., 1964, Ann. Scuola Norm. Sup. Pisa (3) 18, 1-25.

Barsotti, I., 1965a, Ann. Scuola Norm. Sup. Pisa (3) 19, 278-330.

Barsotti, I., 1965b, Ann. Scuola Norm. Sup. Pisa (3) 19, 481-512.

Cartier, P., 1957, C.R. Acad. Sci. Paris, 244, 540-542.

Dieudonné, J., 1955a, Math. Z., 63, 53-75.

Dieudonné, J., 1955b, Amer. J. Math., 77, 429-452.

Dieudonné, J., 1955c, Mathematika 2, 21-31.

Duby, J.-J., 1967, Sophisticated Algebra on a Computer. *In*: Proceedings of IFIP International Working Conference on Symbol Manipulating Languages, Pisa, September 5-9, 1966 (North-Holland, Amsterdam).

Sammet, J.E. et E.Bond, 1964, IEEE Trans. Electronic Computers, EC-13, 386-394.

Serre, J.-P., 1958, Sur la topologie des variétes abéliennes en caractéristique p. *In*: Symposium Internacional de Topología Algebraica, Mexico, août 1956 (Université de Mexico et UNESCO) pp. 24-53.

Witt, E., 1936, J.Reine Angew. Math. 176, 126-140.

APPENDICE 1

```
INPUT TO FORMAC PREPROCESSOR
        $IBFMC MAIN
            SYMARG
            INTEGER    SUM(6),PROD(6),X(6),Y(6),PP(6),LIST(11),P,FACX,FACY
            ATOMIC  XO,X1,X2,X3,X4,X5,X6,Y0,Y1,Y2,Y3,Y4,Y5,Y6
            INTEGER XO,X1,X2,X3,X4,X5,X6,YO,Y1,Y2,Y3,Y4,Y5,Y6
            FMCOMP LATER
            LET X(1)=X0
            LET X(2)=X1
            LET X(3)=X2
            LET X(4)=X3
            LET X(5)=X4
            LET X(6)=X5
            LET Y(1)=Y0
            LET Y(2)=Y1
            LET Y(3)=Y2
            LET Y(4)=Y3
            LET Y(5)=Y4
            LET Y(6)=Y5
         99 READ 999,P,IF
        999 FORMAT(2I1)
            LET SUM(1)=X0+Y0
            WRITE(6,7)P
          7 FORMAT(1H1,3X,13HVECTEUR SOMME,5X,3HP =,I2///)
       1000 DO 3 I=2,IF
       3000 LET SUM(I)=0
            IM1=I-1
            DO 1 J=1,IM1
            IMJ=I-J
            LET SUM(I)=EXPAND
          1        SUM(I)+P**(-IMJ)*(X(J)**(P**IMJ)+Y(J)**(P**IMJ)-SUM(J)
          2**(P**IMJ))
          1 CONTINUE
            LET SUM(I)=EXPAND SUM(I)+X(I)+Y(I)
            WRITE(6,9)I
            LET IRES=ORDER SUM(I),INC,FUL
            Q=0.
        100 LET Q=BCDCON IRES,LIST,11
            WRITE(6,10)(LIST(L),L=2,11)
         10 FORMAT(6X,10A6)
          9 FORMAT(1H0,I2,14HEME COMPOSANTE)
            IF(Q.NE.0.0)GO TO 100
          3 CONTINUE
            GO TO 99
            STOP
            END
```

APPENDICE 2

VECTEUR SOMME   P = 2

2EME COMPOSANTE
-X0*Y0+X1+Y1F

3EME COMPOSANTE
XC*X1*Y0+X0*YC*Y1-X0*YC**3-2*X0**2*Y0**2-X0**3*Y0-X1*Y1+X2+
Y2F

4EME COMPOSANTE
-X0*X1*X2*Y0+4*XC*X1*YC*Y1*Y1**2-X0*X1*Y0*Y2-X0*X1*Y0**3*Y1+4*
XC*X1**2*YC*Y1+XC*X1**3*YC-X0*X2*Y0*Y1+X0*X2*Y0**3-X0*Y0*Y1*
Y2+X0*Y0*Y1**3+XC*Y0**3*Y2-X0*Y0**7-6*X0**2*X1*Y0**2*Y1+X0**
2*X1*YC**4-2*X0**2*X1**2*Y0**2+2*X0**2*X2*Y0**2-2*X0**2*Y0**
2*Y1**2+2*XC**2*Y0**2*Y2+X0**2*Y0**4*Y1-4*X0**2*Y0**6-X0**3*
X1*Y0*Y1+3*X0**3*X1*YC**3+X0**3*X2*Y0+X0**3*Y0*Y2+3*X0**3*Y0
3*Y1-9*XC3*YC**5+XC**4*X1*Y0**2+X0**4*Y0**2*Y1-12*X0**4*
YC**4-9*X0**5*Y0**3-4*X0**6*YC**2-X0**7*Y0+X1*X2*Y1+X1*Y1*Y2
-X1*Y1**3-2*X1**2*Y1**2-X1**3*Y1-X2*Y2+X3+Y3F

VECTEUR SOMME   P = 3

2EME COMPOSANTE
-XC*Y0**2-X0**2*Y0+X1+Y1F

3EME COMPOSANTE
2*X0*X1*Y0**2*Y1+X0*X1**2*Y0**2+X0*Y0**2*Y1**2-X0*Y0**8+2*X0
2*X1*YC*Y1-X02*X1*Y0**4+X0**2*X1**2*Y0+X0**2*Y0*Y1**2-X0
2*Y04*Y1-4*XC**2*YC**7-2*XC**3*X1*Y0**3-2*X0**3*Y0**3*Y1
-9*XC**3*YC**6-XC**4*X1*YC**2-X0**4*Y0**2*Y1-13*X0**4*Y0**5-
13*XC**5*YC**4-9*X0**6*YC**3-4*XC**7*Y0**2-X0**8*Y0-X1*Y1**2
-X1**2*Y1+X2+Y2F

VECTEUR SOMME   P = 5

2EME COMPOSANTE
-X0*Y0**4-2*X0**2*Y0**3-2*X0**3*Y0**2-X0**4*Y0+X1+Y1F

3EME COMPOSANTE
4*X0*X1*Y0**4*Y1**3+6*X0*X1**2*Y0**4*Y1**2+4*X0*X1**3*Y0**4*
Y1+X0*X1**4*Y0**4+X0*Y0**4*Y1**4-X0*Y0**24+8*X0**2*X1*Y0**3*
Y1**3-6*X0**2*X1*Y0**8*Y1**2+12*X0**2*X1**2*Y0**3*Y1**2-6*X0
2*X12*Y0**8*Y1+8*X0**2*X1**3*Y0**3*Y1-2*X0**2*X1**3*Y0**
8+2*X0**2*X1**4*Y0**3+2*X0**2*Y0**3*Y1**4-2*X0**2*Y0**8*Y1**
3-12*X0**2*Y0**23+8*X0**3*X1*Y0**2*Y1**3-24*X0**3*X1*Y0**7*
Y1**2+4*X0**3*X1*Y0**12*Y1+12*X0**3*X1**2*Y0**2*Y1**2-24*X0
3*X12*Y0**7*Y1+2*X0**3*X1**2*Y0**12+8*X0**3*X1**3*Y0**2*
Y1-8*X0**3*X1**3*Y0**7+2*X0**3*X1**4*Y0**2+2*X0**3*Y0**2*Y1
4-8*X03*Y0**7*Y1**3+2*X0**3*Y0**12*Y1**2-92*X0**3*Y0**22
+4*X0**4*X1*Y0*Y1**3-48*X0**4*X1*Y0**6*Y1**2+24*X0**4*X1*Y0
11*Y1-X04*X1*Y0**16+6*X0**4*X1**2*Y0*Y1**2-48*X0**4*X1**
2*Y0**6*Y1+12*X0**4*X1**2*Y0**11+4*X0**4*X1**3*Y0*Y1-16*X0**
4*X1**3*Y0**6+X0**4*X1**4*Y0+X0**4*Y0*Y1**4-16*X0**4*Y0**6*
Y1**3+12*X0**4*Y0**11*Y1**2-X0**4*Y0**16*Y1-506*X0**4*Y0**21
-60*X0**5*X1*Y0**5*Y1**2+72*X0**5*X1*Y0**10*Y1-8*X0**5*X1*Y0
15-60*X05*X1**2*Y0**5*Y1+36*X0**5*X1**2*Y0**10-20*X0**5*
X1**3*Y0**5-20*X0**5*Y0**5*Y1**3+36*X0**5*Y0**10*Y1**2-8*X0
5*Y015*Y1-2125*X0**5*Y0**20-48*X0**6*X1*Y0**4*Y1**2+140*
X0**6*X1*Y0**9*Y1-32*X0**6*X1*Y0**14-48*X0**6*X1**2*Y0**4*Y1
+70*X0**6*X1**2*Y0**9-16*X0**6*X1**3*Y0**4-16*X0**6*Y0**4*Y1
3+70*X06*Y0**9*Y1**2-32*X0**6*Y0**14*Y1-7082*X0**6*Y0**
19-24*X0**7*X1*Y0**3*Y1**2+192*X0**7*X1*Y0**8*Y1-84*X0**7*X1
*Y0**13-24*X0**7*X1**2*Y0**3*Y1+96*X0**7*X1**2*Y0**8-8*X0**7
*X1**3*Y0**3-8*X0**7*Y0**3*Y1**2+96*X0**7*Y0**8*Y1**2-84*X0
7*Y013*Y1-19218*X0**7*Y0**18-6*X0**8*X1*Y0**2*Y1**2+192*
X0**8*X1*Y0**7*Y1-16*X0**8*X1*Y0**12-6*X0**8*X1**2*Y0**2*Y1
+96*X0**8*X1**2*Y0**7-2*X0**8*X1**3*Y0**2-2*X0**8*Y0**2*Y1**
3+96*X0**8*Y0**7*Y1**2-16*X0**8*Y0**12*Y1-4323C*X0**8*Y0**
17+140*X0**9*X1*Y0**6*Y1-232*X0**9*X1*Y0**11+70*X0**9*X1**2*
Y0**6+70*X0**9*Y0**6*Y1**2-232*X0**9*Y0**11*Y1-81639*X0**9*
Y0**16+72*X0**10*X1*Y0**5*Y1-262*X0**10*X1*Y0**10+36*X0**10*
X1**2*Y0**5+36*X0**10*Y0**5*Y1**2-262*X0**10*Y0**10*Y1-
1306CC*X0**10*Y0**15+24*X0**11*X1*Y0**4*Y1-232*X0**11*X1*Y0
9+12*X011*X1**2*Y0**4+12*X0**11*Y0**4*Y1**2-232*X0**11*
Y0**9*Y1-178C7C*X0**11*Y0**14+4*X0**12*X1*Y0**3*Y1-160*X0**
12*X1*Y0**8+2*X0**12*X1**2*Y0**3+2*X0**12*Y0**3*Y1**2-160*X0
12*Y08*Y1-2C7736*X0**12*Y0**13-84*X0**13*X1*Y0**7-84*X0
13*Y07*Y1-207736*X0**13*Y0**12-32*X0**14*X1*Y0**6-32*X0
14*Y06*Y1-178070*X0**14*Y0**11-8*X0**15*X1*Y0**5-8*X0**
15*Y0**5*Y1-1306C0*X0**15*Y0**10-X0**16*X1*Y0**4-X0**16*Y0**
4*Y1-81639*X0**16*Y0**9-43230*X0**17*Y0**8-19218*X0**18*Y0**
7-7C82*X0**19*Y0**6-2125*X0**20*Y0**5-5C6*X0**21*Y0**4-92*X0
22*Y03-12*X0**23*Y0**2-X0**24*Y0-X1*Y1**4-2*X1**2*Y1**3-
2*X1**3*Y1**2-X1**4*Y1+X2+Y2F

APPENDICE 3

```
VECTEUR PRODUIT      P = 2


2EME COMPOSANTE
    X0**2*Y1+X1*Y0**2+2*X1*Y1F

3EME COMPOSANTE
    -X0**2*X1*Y0**2*Y1-2*X0**2*X1*Y1**2+X0**4*Y2-2*X1**2*Y0**2*
    Y1-X1**2*Y1**2+2*X1**2*Y2+X2*Y0**4+2*X2*Y1**2+4*X2*Y2F

4EME COMPOSANTE
    4*X0**2*X1*X2*Y0**2*Y1*Y2+2*X0**2*X1*X2*Y0**2*Y1**3+2*X0**2*
    X1*X2*Y0**4*Y1+2+X0**2*X1*X2*Y0**6*Y1+8*X0**2*X1*X2*Y1**2*
    Y2+4*X0**2*X1*X2*Y1**4+2*X0**2*X1**3*Y0**2*Y1*Y2-17*X0**2*X1
    **3*Y0**2*Y1**3-8*X0**2*X1**3*Y0**4*Y1**2-X0**2*X1**3*Y0**6*
    Y1+4*X0**2*X1**3*Y1**2*Y2-10*X0**2*X1**3*Y1**4+2*X0**4*X1**2
    *Y0**2*Y1*Y2-8*X0**4*X1**2*Y0**2*Y1**3-2*X0**4*X1**2*Y0**4*
    Y1**2+X0**4*X1**2*Y1**2*Y2-8*X0**4*X1**2*Y1**4-2*X0**4*X1**2
    *Y2**2-X0**4*X2*Y0**4*Y2-2*X0**4*X2*Y1**2*Y2-4*X0**4*X2*Y2**
    2+X0**6*X1*Y0**2*Y1*Y2-X0**6*X1*Y0**2*Y1**3+2*X0**6*X1*Y1**2
    *Y2-2*X0**6*X1*Y1**4+X0**8*Y3+8*X1**2*X2*Y0**2*Y1*Y2+4*X1**2
    *X2*Y0**2*Y1**3+X1**2*X2*Y0**4*Y1**2-2*X1**2*X2*Y0**4*Y2+2*
    X1**2*X2*Y0**6*Y1+2*X1**2*X2*Y1**4-8*X1**2*X2*Y2**2+4*X1**4*
    Y0**2*Y1*Y2-10*X1**4*Y0**2*Y1**3-8*X1**4*Y0**4*Y1**2-2*X1**4
    *Y0**6*Y1+2*X1**4*Y1**2*Y2-4*X1**4*Y1**4-X1**4*Y2**2+2*X1**4
    *Y3-2*X2**2*Y0**4*Y1**2-4*X2**2*Y0**4*Y2-8*X2**2*Y1**2*Y2-X2
    **2*Y1**4-6*X2**2*Y2**2+4*X2**2*Y3+X3*Y0**8+2*X3*Y1**4+4*X3*
    Y2**2+8*X3*Y3F



VECTEUR PRODUIT      P = 3


2EME COMPOSANTE
    X0**3*Y1+X1*Y0**3+3*X1*Y1F

3EME COMPOSANTE
    -6*X0**3*X1**2*Y0**3*Y1**2-X0**3*X1**2*Y0**6*Y1-9*X0**3*X1**
    2*Y1**3-X0**6*X1*Y0**3*Y1**2-3*X0**6*X1*Y1*Y1**3+X0**9*Y2-9*X1
    **3*Y0**3*Y1**2-3*X1**3*Y0**6*Y1-8*X1**3*Y1**3+3*X1**3*Y2+X2
    *Y0**9+3*X2*Y1**3+9*X2*Y2F



VECTEUR PRODUIT      P = 5


2EME COMPOSANTE
    X0**5*Y1+X1*Y0**5+5*X1*Y1F

3EME COMPOSANTE
    -500*X0**5*X1**4*Y0**5*Y1**4-150*X0**5*X1**4*Y0**10*Y1**3-20
    *X0**5*X1**4*Y0**15*Y1**2-X0**5*X1**4*Y0**20*Y1-625*X0**5*X1
    **4*Y1**5-150*X0**10*X1**3*Y0**5*Y1**4-30*X0**10*X1**3*Y0**
    10*Y1**3-2*X0**10*X1**3*Y0**15*Y1**2-250*X0**10*X1**3*Y1**5-
    20*X0**15*X1**2*Y0**5*Y1**4-2*X0**15*X1**2*Y0**10*Y1**3-50*
    X0**15*X1**2*Y1**5-X0**20*X1*Y0**5*Y1**4-5*X0**20*X1*Y1**5+
    X0**25*Y2-625*X1**5*Y0**5*Y1**4-250*X1**5*Y0**10*Y1**3-50*X1
    **5*Y0**15*Y1**2-5*X1**5*Y0**20*Y1-624*X1**5*Y1**5+5*X1**5*
    Y2+X2*Y0**25+5*X2*Y1**5+25*X2*Y2F
```

VECTEUR PUISSANCE   P = 2

2EME COMPOSANTE
    2*X0**2*X1+2*X1**2F

3EME COMPOSANTE
    -4*X0**2*X1**3-X0**4*X1**2+2*X0**4*X2+4*X1**2*X2-X1**4+4*X2
    **2F

4EME COMPOSANTE
    16*X0**2*X1**3*X2**2+16*X0**2*X1**5*X2-20*X0**2*X1**7-4*X0**
    4*X1**2*X2**2+6*X0**4*X1**4*X2-33*X0**4*X1**6-8*X0**4*X2**3+
    8*X0**6*X1**3*X2-20*X0**6*X1**5+2*X0**8*X1**2*X2-4*X0**8*X1
    4-X08*X2**2+2*X0**8*X3-16*X1**2*X2**3-2*X1**4*X2**2+4*X1
    4*X3+4*X16*X2-4*X1**8+8*X2**2*X3-6*X2**4+8*X3**2F

5EME COMPOSANTE
    -128*X0**2*X1**3*X2**2*X3**2-128*X0**2*X1**3*X2**4*X3+352*X0
    2*X13*X2**6-128*X0**2*X1**5*X2*X3**2-128*X0**2*X1**5*X2
    3*X3+1120*X02*X1**5*X2**5+96*X0**2*X1**7*X2**2*X3+744*X0
    2*X17*X2**4+160*X0**2*X1**9*X2*X3-64*X0**2*X1**9*X2*X3-
    480*X0**2*X1**9*X2**3-184*X0**2*X1**11*X2**2+80*X0**2*X1**11
    *X3+192*X0**2*X1**13*X2-340*X0**2*X1**15+32*X0**4*X1**2*X2**
    2*X3**2+32*X0**4*X1**2*X2**4*X3-472*X0**4*X1**2*X2**6-48*X0
    4*X14*X2*X3**2-16*X0**4*X1**4*X2**3*X3-140*X0**4*X1**4*
    X2**5+280*X0**4*X1**6*X2**2*X3-382*X0**4*X1**6*X2**4+264*X0
    4*X16*X3**2-24*X0**4*X1**8*X2*X3-1516*X0**4*X1**8*X2**3-
    166*X0**4*X1**10*X2**2+132*X0**4*X1**10*X3+682*X0**4*X1**12*
    X2-1253*X0**4*X1**14+64*X0**4*X2**3*X3**2+64*X0**4*X2**5*X3-
    176*X0**4*X2**7-64*X0**6*X1**3*X2*X3**2-64*X0**6*X1**3*X2**3
    *X3+560*X0**6*X1**3*X2**5+160*X0**6*X1**5*X2**2*X3+776*X0**6
    *X1**5*X2**4+160*X0**6*X1**5*X3**2-32*X0**6*X1**7*X2*X3-688*
    X0**6*X1**7*X2**3+248*X0**6*X1**9*X2**2+80*X0**6*X1**9*X3+
    1136*X0**6*X1**11*X2-2608*X0**6*X1**13-16*X0**8*X1**2*X2*X3
    2+16*X08*X1**2*X2**3*X3-132*X0**8*X1**2*X2**5+40*X0**8*
    X1**4*X2**2*X3+166*X0**8*X1**4*X2**4+24*X0**8*X1**4*X3**2-16
    *X0**8*X1**6*X2*X3-760*X0**8*X1**6*X2**3-236*X0**8*X1**8*X2
    2+24*X08*X1**8*X3+1008*X0**8*X1**10*X2-3314*X0**8*X1**12
    -8*X0**8*X2**2*X3**2+20*X0**8*X2**4*X3-134*X0**8*X2**6-16*X0
    8*X33-32*X0**10*X1**3*X2**2*X3+272*X0**10*X1**3*X2**4-32
    *X0**10*X1**5*X2*X3-144*X0**10*X1**5*X2**3-308*X0**10*X1**7*
    X2**2+40*X0**10*X1**7*X3+712*X0**10*X1**9*X2-2608*X0**10*X1
    11+8*X012*X1**2*X2*X3+28*X0**12*X1**2*X2**4-12*X0**12
    *X1**4*X2*X3+14*X0**12*X1**4*X2**3-221*X0**10*X1**6*X2**2+66
    *X0**12*X1**6*X3+356*X0**12*X1**8*X2-1253*X0**12*X1**10+16*
    X0**12*X2**3*X3-40*X0**12*X2**5-16*X0**14*X1**3*X2*X3+40*X0
    14*X13*X2**3-84*X0**14*X1**5*X2**2+40*X0**14*X1**5*X3+96
    *X0**14*X1**7*X2-340*X0**14*X1**9-4*X0**16*X1**2*X2*X3+10*X0
    16*X12*X2**3-12*X0**16*X1**4*X2**2+8*X0**16*X1**4*X3+10*
    X0**16*X1**6*X2-40*X0**16*X1**8+2*X0**16*X2**2*X3-4*X0**16*
    X2**4-X0**16*X3**2+2*X0**16*X4+128*X1**2*X2**3*X3**2+128*X1
    2*X25*X3-352*X1**2*X2**7-16*X1**4*X2**2*X3**2+40*X1**4*
    X2**4*X3-460*X1**4*X2**6-32*X1**4*X3**3-32*X1**6*X2*X3**2+32
    *X1**6*X2**3*X3-72*X1**6*X2**5+40*X1**8*X2**2*X3+143*X1**8*
    X2**4+26*X1**8*X3**2+4*X1**8*X4-16*X1**10*X2*X3-40*X1**10*X2
    3-36*X112*X2**2+16*X1**12*X3+20*X1**14*X2-40*X1**16-64*
    X2**2*X3**3+20*X2**4*X3**2+8*X2**4*X4+48*X2**6*X3-81*X2**8+
    16*X3**2*X4-28*X3**4+16*X4**2F

APPENDICE 4

```
VECTEUR PUISSANCE      P = 3


2EME COMPOSANTE
    9*X0**3*X1**2+3*X0**6*X1+9*X1**3F

3EME COMPOSANTE
    -729*X0**3*X1**8-972*X0**6*X1**7+18*X0**9*X1**3*X2-726*X0**9
    *X1**6+27*X0**9*X2**2-324*X0**12*X1**5-81*X0**15*X1**4-8*X0
    **18*X1**3+3*X0**18*X2+81*X1**3*X2**2+27*X1**6*X2-240*X1**9+
    81*X2**3F
```

AN ALGORITHM THAT INVESTIGATES
THE PLANARITY OF A NETWORK

A. J. W. DUIJVESTIJN
Twente Institute of Technology, The Netherlands

1. INTRODUCTION

This article is a report on investigations of the planarity of networks by means of an electronic computer. The line of attack was suggested through research on the problem of squaring the rectangle. At first we wanted a method for determining the code of a 3-connected planar graph from its list of branches. The method described is however also useful for arbitrary graphs.

A network consists of a set of wires, a wire being a pair of (connected) vertices. To each pair of vertices V_i and V_j of a wire two arrows are associated, the first directed from V_i to V_j and the second from V_j to V_i. The wire with the arrow directed from V_i to V_j will be called branch $V_i V_j$; the other branch $V_j V_i$. A branch is therefore an oriented wire. The number of vertices is denoted by K, the number of wires by B. If only one of the two branches $V_i V_j$ and $V_j V_i$ is used to indicate the associated wire, then the network has B branches. If the network is planar one can introduce the concept of side or mesh. The number of sides or meshes is denoted by M. In case of planar networks Euler's theorem holds:

$$K + M = B + 2 .$$

The degree of a vertex is the number of wires at that vertex.

2. REPRESENTATION OF NETWORKS

A network or graph N can be represented in several ways such that it can be treated by a computer programme. Examples of representations are:

2.1. *List of branches*

A wire of N is represented by its two vertices, that will be denoted by br1$[i]$ and br2$[i]$; br1$[i]$ and br2$[i]$, being elements of an array br1 and br2 respectively. There are B wires in the network N. We therefore assume $i=1(1)B$. Hence N is represented by the two arrays br1$[i]$ and br2$[i]$, $i=1(1)B$.

2.2. *Vertex-vertex incidence matrix*

The network N is represented by the vertex-vertex incidence matrix $INC[i,j]$, $i=1(1)K$, $j=1(1)K$ with K = number of vertices, such that:

$$INC[i,j] = 0, \text{ if vertex } i \text{ and } j \text{ are not connected,}$$

$$INC[i,j] = -1, \text{ if } i \text{ and } j \text{ are connected and}$$

$$INC[i,i] = \text{number of wires at vertex } i.$$

From the list of branches the vertex-vertex incidence matrix can be obtained and conversely (Duijvestijn [1962]).

2.3. *Code of the network*

If the network is planar the following code can be used as a representation of the network. The planar network is drawn on the sphere. The vertices are numbered arbitrarily from 1 to K. The boundary of a mesh contains a set of vertices.

A code of a mesh is obtained as follows: while walking in the positive sense along the boundary of the mesh starting with V_i, we encounter V_j, V_k, V_l, ... until we return to V_i. The sequence V_i, V_j, V_k, V_l, ..., V_i is a code of the mesh.

A code of the network is the sequence of codes of all its meshes separated by zeros. At the end two more zeros are added. The code can be considered as an array $W[t]$, $t=1(1)2(B+M)+1$, B being the number of wires and M the number of meshes.

All properties of the planarity are saved in this representation. From the code of the network it is easy to obtain the list of branches or the vertex-vertex incidence matrix (Duijvestijn [1962]).

Starting from the list of branches or from the vertex-vertex incidence matrix it is much more difficult to test whether the network is planar and if so to obtain a code of the network.

3. CONNECTION WITH SQUARED RECTANGLES

The relation of linear graphs with squared rectangles and electrical networks has been treated by Brooks, Smith, Stone, Tutte [1940] and by Bouwkamp [1946, 1947]. They showed that each element of the squared rectangle corresponds to a wire or branch; while each horizontal line segment corresponds to a vertex, and each vertical line segment to a mesh not containing other parts of the network in its interior. The vertices corresponding to the upper and lower horizontal sides are the poles of the network. The network obtained in this way is called the normal polar network or normal p-net; see the example of fig. 1. If the two poles are connected by a wire, a net is created from which the rectangular dissection can be obtained by placing an electromotive force (EMF) of value C in this wire. (It was shown by Brooks, Smith, Stone and Tutte [1940] that all first cofactors of INC are the same except for the sign; their common absolute value is called the complexity of the net; it is denoted by C.)

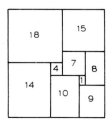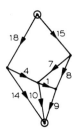

Fig. 1. Example of a squaring and its associated normal p-net; $\odot$ = pole of the net.

The current flow caused in the network is called full flow, while the currents are called the full currents. The full currents are equivalent with the full sides of the squared rectangle.

An adjacent vertex V_2 of a vertex V_1 is a vertex that is connected to V_1. The branch V_1V_2 is called an adjacent branch of V_1. A mesh is said to be left of a branch V_iV_j of its boundary, if the sequence V_iV_j occurs in the code of the mesh.

In that case the branch is said to be right of the mesh. The mesh is said to be right of a branch V_iV_j if the sequence V_jV_i occurs in the code of the mesh; if so the branch is left of the mesh.

Next we consider an arbitrary vertex V_0. To this vertex a set of left-cyclic-ordered adjacent branches is associated in the following way: Take an arbitrary adjacent vertex V_1 of V_0; then search the left mesh L_1 of V_0V_1; then search another adjacent vertex V_2 of V_0 in L_1; then search the left mesh L_2 of V_0V_2, and so on, until V_1 has been reached. If left is replaced by right, then the right-cyclic-ordered adjacent branches of V_0 are obtained.

We now consider the currents through the left ordered adjacent branches of V_0:

$$V_0V_1 \text{ current } V_0V_1$$

$$\vdots \qquad \vdots$$

$$V_0V_k \text{ current } V_0V_k \,.$$

In these currents the first positive current following some negative current is searched (there are at least one positive and one negative current). The corresponding branch V_0V_l, say, is put in class C_{pos}. All successive branches V_0V_{l+1}, $V_0V_{l+2}, \ldots, V_0V_s$ that carry a positive current are put in class C_{pos}. The branch V_0, V_{s+1} carrying a negative current, is put in class C_{neg}, while all successive branches $V_0, V_{s+2}, \ldots, V_0V_t$ that carry a negative current are put in class C_{neg}. All indices of the second vertex are taken mod(k). Then the following theorem (sign theorem) can be formulated (Duijvestijn [1962]).

All branches $V_0V_1, \ldots, V_0V_k$ *are belonging either to* C_{pos} *or* C_{neg} *if the network is planar.* (A branch with a current equal to zero is put either in C_{pos} or C_{neg}.) In other words, the branches carrying positive currents are separating the branches carrying negative currents.

This property can be used to reduce the number of possibilities that has to be tried in order to find out what cyclic sequence of adjacent branches must be used for drawing the network on the sphere in case of planarity.

We focus on a certain vertex V_0 and calculate the currents (a column) in adjacent branches of V_0 by placing an EMF in one of the B branches. This can be done in B different ways. Therefore we deal with B columns, for each of which must hold that the positive and negative currents separate. In fact the adjacent branches of V_0 must be permuted in such a way that in each column the positive and negative currents separate.

I conjectured four years ago that the permutation of adjacent branches is determined by the fact that in each column the positive and negative currents should separate. Since then several three-connected networks have been investigated by means of a computer.

The conjecture appeared to need addition because only recently I found a counter-example. In the underlying example the cyclic sequence could be determined by putting a resistor R in one of the branches and by considering two cases $0 < 1/R < 1$ and $1/R > 1$ respectively. The use of arbitrary resistors has not been investigated further yet. Much more experiments have to be done on the computer in order to find out whether there is an indication of the existence of a certain class of networks for which the conjecture is true.

Two other problems had to be solved namely:
1. How can the current flow be determined by the knowledge of the list of branches only?
2. How can we obtain a code of the network as soon as the cyclic sequence of adjacent branches of all vertices are known?

4. DETERMINATION OF THE CURRENT FLOW

In the network there are K vertices, arbitrary numbered from 1 to K and B branches. We assume a current source $I'[i]$ impressed on vertex i. The branch currents and the current sources are connected by the relation $I' = AI$. Here I is a vector of the branch currents having the elements $I[k]$, $k = 1(1)B$, while I' is the vector of source currents having the elements $I'[j]$, $j = 1(1)K$, and A the well known vertex-branch incidence matrix having K rows and B columns. Furthermore we consider the vector E with elements $E[l]$, $l = 1(1)B$, denoting the voltage difference on branch: $br1[l]$, $br2[l]$ and the vector E' with the elements $E'[j]$, $j = 1(1)K$, denoting the voltage of vertex j (the voltage of one of the vertices is taken equal to zero). The vectors E and E' are connected (Kron [1939], Cauer [1954]) by the relation $E = A^t E'$ where A^t denotes the transpose of A.

Now writing Y for AA^t it can easily be seen that $Y = AA^t$ is equal to the vertex-vertex incidence matrix INC. From the definition it follows $Y = Y^t$. The matrix Y is singular; its first cofactors are equal except for the sign and equal to the complexity (C).

Instead of using the vector I' we define a vector i' with elements $i'[j] = I'[j]$, $j = 1(1)K-1$ and $e'[j] = E'[j]$, $j = 1(1)K-1$. A matrix α is defined by $i' = \alpha I$. Apparently α can be obtained by omitting a suitable row from A. Furthermore it follows that $E = \alpha^t e'$. Next the matrix η is formed by taking $\eta = \alpha \alpha^t$. The matrix η is obtained by omitting a suitable row and column from Y. The matrix η is non-singular. Furthermore it can be shown that

$$E = \alpha^t (\alpha \alpha^t)^{-1} i' .$$

We now focus at one branch with vertices br1$[m]$, br2$[m]$. We choose $i'[\text{br1}[m]] = C$ and $i'[\text{br2}[m]] = -C$. All other elements of i are taken equal to zero.

We have the following situation at branch: br1$[m]$, br2$[m]$ (fig. 2).

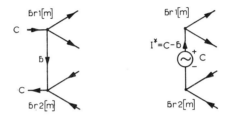

Fig. 2.

According to the theorem of Thévenin this is equivalent to an EMF caus-ing a current $I^* = C - b$ in branch br1$[m]$, br2$[m]$, where b is the original current in br1$[m]$, br2$[m]$ caused by the two current sources: C and $-C$ at its two vertices br1$[m]$ and br2$[m]$ respectively. This means that the matrix

$$S = C \alpha^t (\alpha \alpha^t)^{-1} \alpha - C \epsilon, \text{ with } \epsilon \text{ the unity matrix,}$$

describes the current flow in the network. S is a matrix having B rows and B columns, S is a symmetric matrix, of which an element $S[m, n]$ is denot-ing the current through the branch br1$[m]$, br2$[m]$ caused by an EMF of value $-C$ in br1$[n]$, br2$[n]$. This completes the proof that the current flow can be obtained from the list of branches only.

As input we use an identification number of the network that is obtained as follows: Consider the vertex-vertex matrix INC. The off-diagonal ele-ments of INC are either zero or minus one. We replace the off diagonal ele-ments by their absolute values. The new matrix will be denoted by X, with elements X_{ij}. $(i, j = 1, 2, \ldots, K)$. To X an integer $G(X)$ will be associated (an identification number). The binary notation is obtained by writing the elements of X to the right of the main diagonal in the sequence $X_{12} X_{13} \ldots X_{1K}, X_{23}, X_{24}, \ldots X_{2K}, \ldots X_{K-1,K}$ so that its decimal value is given by

$$G(X) = X_{K-1,K} + X_{K-2,K} \cdot 2 + X_{K-2,K-1} \cdot 2^2 + X_{K-3,K} \cdot 2^3 + X_{K-3,K-1} \cdot 2^4 +$$
$$+ X_{K-3,K-2} \cdot 2^5 + \ldots$$

Starting from this identification number $G(X)$ the incidence matrix INC can be obtained and from this the current flow can be calculated.

The output of "programme 1" is the following: the number of branches: B, the number of vertices: K, the list of branches: $br1[m]$, $br2[m]$, $m = 1(1)B$ and sign $(S[m, n])$, $m = 1(1)B$, $n = m+1(1)B$, where sign(X)

$$= 1 \text{ if } X > 0$$
$$= -1 \text{ if } X < 0$$
$$= 0 \text{ if } X = 0.$$

An example of typical output is given below

```
13   7
21  31  52  54  61  63  64  65  72  73  74  75  76

-1   1  -1   1   1   1  -1  -1  -1   1   1  -1   1
    -1   1  -1   1  -1  -1   1   1  -1   1   1   1
        -1   1   1   1  -1  -1   1   1  -1  -1  -1
            -1  -1  -1   1  -1  -1  -1   1  -1   1
                -1   1   1   1   1   1  -1  -1  -1
                    -1   1   1  -1   1  -1  -1  -1
                        -1   1  -1  -1   1   1  -1
                            -1   1  -1   1   1  -1
                                -1   1   1   1   1
                                    -1   1   1   1
                                        -1   1   1
                                            -1   1
                                                 1
```

A second programme uses the output of programme 1 and generates the following output: vertex, degree of this vertex, left- or right-cyclic-ordered adjacent vertices of this vertex.
Example

```
13   7
6    5   1   3   7   4   5
7    5   2   5   4   6   3
5    4   2   6   4   7
4    3   5   6   7
3    3   1   6   7
1    3   2   3   6
2    3   1   5   7
```

In case a cyclic sequence cannot be found the programme indicates that the network is not planar. In case a cyclic sequence is not determined in that adjacent branches can be interchanged without conflicting the sign theorem, this is also indicated by programme 2. Some typical output is shown below.

$$S[m,n]$$

br1		2	3	5	5	6	6	6	6	7	7	7	7	7
	br2	1	1	2	4	1	3	4	5	2	3	4	5	6
2	1	-1	1	-1	1	1	1	-1	-1	-1	1	1	-1	1
3	1	1	-1	1	-1	1	-1	-1	1	1	-1	1	1	1
5	2	-1	1	-1	1	1	1	-1	-1	1	1	-1	-1	-1
5	4	1	-1	1	-1	-1	-1	1	-1	-1	-1	1	-1	1
6	1	1	1	1	-1	-1	1	1	1	1	1	-1	-1	-1
6	3	1	-1	1	-1	1	-1	1	1	-1	1	-1	-1	-1
6	4	-1	-1	-1	1	1	1	-1	1	-1	-1	1	1	-1
6	5	-1	1	-1	-1	1	1	1	-1	1	-1	1	1	-1
7	2	-1	1	1	-1	1	-1	-1	1	-1	1	1	1	1
7	3	1	-1	1	-1	1	1	-1	-1	1	-1	1	1	1
7	4	1	1	-1	1	-1	-1	1	1	1	1	-1	1	1
7	5	-1	1	-1	-1	-1	-1	1	1	1	1	1	-1	1
7	6	1	1	-1	1	-1	-1	-1	-1	1	1	1	1	-1

vertex	degree
6	5
7	5
5	4
4	3
3	3
1	3
2	3

6	1	1	1	1	-1	-1	1	1	1	1	1	-1	-1	-1
6	3	1	-1	1	-1	1	-1	1	1	-1	1	-1	-1	-1
6	4	-1	-1	-1	1	1	1	-1	1	-1	-1	1	1	-1
6	5	-1	1	-1	-1	1	1	1	-1	1	-1	1	1	-1
6	7	-1	-1	1	-1	1	1	1	1	-1	-1	-1	-1	1

6	1	1	1	1
6	3	1	-1	1
6	7	-1	-1	1
6	4	-1	-1	-1
6	5	-1	1	-1

```
7  2 -1  1  1 -1  1 -1 -1  1 -1  1  1  1  1
7  3  1 -1  1 -1  1  1 -1 -1  1 -1  1  1  1
7  4  1  1 -1  1 -1 -1  1  1  1  1 -1  1  1
7  5 -1  1 -1 -1 -1 -1 -1  1  1  1  1  1 -1  1
7  6  1  1 -1  1 -1 -1 -1 -1 -1  1  1  1  1 -1


7  2  1  1  1  1  1
7  5  1 -1  1 -1  1
7  4 -1 -1 -1 -1  1
7  6 -1 -1 -1  1 -1
7  3 -1  1  1  1 -1


5  2 -1  1 -1  1  1  1 -1 -1  1  1 -1 -1 -1
5  4  1 -1  1 -1 -1 -1  1 -1 -1 -1  1 -1  1
5  6  1 -1  1  1 -1 -1 -1  1 -1  1 -1 -1  1
5  7  1 -1  1  1  1  1 -1 -1 -1 -1 -1  1 -1


5  2  1  1
5  6 -1  1
5  4 -1 -1
5  7  1 -1
```

5. DETERMINATION OF THE CODES

We start with a planar subgraph (the adjacent branches of a certain vertex) and we add branches of the network to the subgraph such that it remains planar and connected. We therefore need a test if a branch can be
layed without crossings. To this end we introduce the concept of left (or
right) keeping road from vertex V_0 to vertex V_t, with respect to branch
$V_0 V_b$.

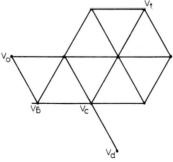

Fig. 3.

We construct a left keeping road as follows: Starting with V_0V_b we take the next left cyclic ordered adjacent branch of V_bV_0, let this be V_bV_c; then we take the next left cyclic ordered adjacent branch of V_cV_b, let this be V_cV_d; then take the next left cyclic ordered adjacent branch of V_dV_c, and so on until we reach V_t (fig. 3). If we return at V_0 the branch V_0V_t cannot be layed. In case V_0V_t can be layed, it will be layed in a right cyclic order with respect to V_0V_b. The details of the branch laying process is best described by an example.

Let the following cyclic ordering be given:

vertex	degree [vertex]	cyclic sequence [vertex]
2	5	1, 3, 8, 9, 10
10	5	2, 9, 11, 7, 1
6	4	8, 3, 5, 7
7	4	6, 11, 10, 5
8	4	2, 6, 11, 9
1	3	2, 4, 10
3	3	2, 4, 6
4	3	3, 1, 5
5	3	6, 4, 7
9	3	2, 8, 10
11	3	8, 10, 7

We choose a vertex of highest possible degree. Let us take vertex 2. Clearly all adjacent branches of vertex 2 can be layed. In that case we use the branches 2, 1; 3, 2; 2, 8; 2, 9; 2, 10 and 1, 2; 2, 3; 8, 2; 9, 2; 10, 2. We have used the vertices (nodepoints) 1, 3, 8, 9, 10. We continue with one of the used vertices with highest possible degree. This is vertex 10. We search the first used adjacent branch of vertex 10. This happens to be 10, 2. We assume the cyclic sequence of vertex 10 to be a left cyclic sequence. The branch we try to lay is then 10, 9. It can be layed because there exists a left keeping road from 10 to 9, with respect to 10, 2. This process continues until the following situation has been reached (fig. 4).

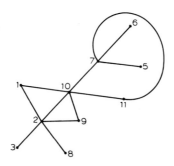

Fig. 4.

We continue with vertex 6. We search for the first used adjacent branch of vertex 6:(6, 7). Because we assume the cyclic sequence of vertex 6 to be the left cyclic sequence we have to try 6, 8. Now there does not exist a left keeping road from 6 to 8 with respect to 6, 7. That means that branch 6, 8 cannot be layed. We remove the layed branches of vertex 6 and try the cyclic sequence as a right cyclic sequence. We search the first used branch: 6, 7. The next branch 6, 5 can be layed but after that we have to try branch 6, 8; this branch can still not be layed. We remove the layed branches of vertex 6 and because two cyclic directions of 6 have been tried we also remove the used branches of vertex 7 and try the right cyclic sequence of 7 and so on. As soon as all branches have been layed the code of the network is calculated. When all vertices are removed the network is not planar. An exact description of the process is given in ALGOL programme 3, which we give in full. Finally we give some typical computer output of programme 3. The programmes were tested on the PASCAL syntactical ALGOL translator constructed by P. Medema (Philips Computer Industries, Apeldoorn, The Netherlands).
Example

Input: 13	7							Output: 1	2	5	6	1	0	
6	5	1	3	7	4	5		1	3	7	2	1	0	
7	5	2	5	4	6	3		1	6	3	1	0		
5	4	2	6	4	7			2	7	5	2	0		
4	3	5	6	7				3	6	7	3	0		
3	3	1	6	7				4	5	7	4	0		
1	3	2	3	6				4	6	5	4	0		
2	3	1	5	7				4	7	6	4	0	0	

Input: 20	11						Output: 1	2	3	4	1	0	
1	3	2	4	10			1	4	5	7	10	1	0
2	5	1	3	8	9	10	1	10	2	1	0		
3	3	2	4	6			2	8	6	3	2	0	
4	3	3	1	5			2	9	8	2	0		
5	3	6	4	7			2	10	9	2	0		
6	4	8	3	5	7		3	6	5	4	3	0	
7	4	6	11	10	5		5	6	7	5	0		
8	4	2	6	11	9		6	8	11	7	6	0	
9	3	2	8	10			7	11	10	7	0		
10	5	2	9	11	7	1	8	9	10	11	8	0	0
11	3	8	10	7									

ACKNOWLEDGEMENT

I am indebted to J. N. S. Calis (Philips Computer Industries) for his assistance in debugging ALGOL programme 3. Furthermore I want to acnowledge D. Severein (Twente Institute of Technology) for his help in preparing ALGOL programmes 1 and 2.

APPENDIX - PROGRAMME 3

```
begin comment laying networks with use of cyclic sequence,Duijvestijn;
      integer b,bb,bm,i,j,k,m,used,not used,left,right,ready,
              aimnode,begin node,nodepoint,other node,
              address,endaddress,last address,refer,
              pointer layorder,number of branches used;
      stop(16);
next network:
      input(b,⟨I2.I2⟩,b,k);
      used:= 1;
      not used:= 0;
      left              := 0;
      right             := 1;
      ready             :=-1;
      number of branches used:= 0;
      bb:= 2*b;
      bm:= 2*(bb-k)+5;

      begin integer array layed nodes,degree,used nodes,direction,
                          beginaddress[1:k],
                          used branches,cyclic sequence,
                          reference[1:bb],
                          code[1:bm];
            procedure search next important node(nodepoint);
            begin integer i,maxdegree;
                  maxdegree:= 0;
                  for i:= 1 step 1 until k do
                  if 0 < used nodes[i] ∧ used nodes[i] < degree[i]
                              ∧ degree[i] > maxdegree
                  then begin nodepoint:= i;
                             maxdegree:= degree[i]
                       end
            end search nxt imp nde pnt;


            procedure next cyclic address (nodepoint,address);
            begin integer wr;
                  if direction[nodepoint]= left
                  then wr:= address+1
                  else wr:= address-1;
                  address:= if wr=beginaddress[nodepoint]+
                                        degree[nodepoint]
                            then beginaddress[nodepoint]
                            else if wr < beginaddress[nodepoint]
                                 then beginaddress[nodepoint]+
                                             degree[nodepoint]-1
                                 else wr
            end next cyclic address;
```

```
procedure search first used branch with this (nodepoint,
                                    nextnode,address);
begin integer i;
      endaddress:= beginaddress[nodepoint]+degree[nodepoint]-1;
      for i:= beginaddress[nodepoint] step 1
                                    until endaddress do
      if used branches[i]=used then goto found;
found:address:= i;
      nextnode:= cyclic sequence[i]
end search first used branch;



boolean procedure can branch be layed(nodepoint,aimnode,
                                    address,lastaddress);
value nodepoint,aimnode,address;
integer nodepoint,aimnode,address;
begin integer i,oldnode,nextnode;
      if used nodes[aimnode]=not used
      then can branch be layed:= true
      else begin oldnode:= nodepoint;
           nxt:  for i:= 1,2 while used branches[address]=notused
                      do next cyclic address(nodepoint,address);
                 nextnode:= cyclic sequence[address];
                 if nextnode=aimnode
                 then can branch be layed:= true
                 else if nextnode=oldnode
                      then can branch be layed:= false
                      else begin nodepoint:= nextnode;
                                 address:= reference[address];
                                 goto nxt
                      end
      end;
      if msw(2) then
      begin output(1,←TO/,T17/↲,←output c.b.b.l. :↲);
            print;
            output(1,←TO//↲,↺)
      end;
      lastaddress:= address
end can branch be layed;

procedure print;
if msw(1) then
begin for i:= 1 step 1 until bb do
      begin if i=1 mod 40 then output(1,←TO/↲,↺);
            output(1,←I2↲,used branches[i]);
      end;
      for i:= 1 step 1 until k do
      begin if i=1 mod 10 then output(1,←TO/↲,↺);
            output(1,←B2I2,I2,I2,B2TO↲,i,
                      used nodes[i],direction[i],↺);
      end;
      for i:= 1 step 1 until pointerlayorder do
      begin if i=1 mod 10 then output(1,←TO/↲,↺);
            output(1,←I2,B4TO↲,layed nodes[i],↺);
      end;
      output(1,←TO///↲,↺);
end print;
```

```
address:= 1;
for i:= 1 step 1 until k do
begin input(h,<I2>,nodepoint);
        beginaddress[nodepoint]:= address;
        input(h,<I2>,m).;
        degree[nodepoint]:= m;
        for j:= 1 step 1 until m do
        begin input(h,<I2>,cyclic sequence[address]);
                address:= address+1
        end
end;
for j:= 1 step 1 until 10 do input(h,<I2>,m);
for nodepoint:= 1 step 1 until k do
begin endaddress:= beginaddress[nodepoint]+degree[nodepoint]-1;
        for address:= beginaddress[nodepoint] step 1 until
                                        endaddress do
        begin othernode:= cyclic sequence[address];
                m:= beginaddress[other node]+degree[other node]-1;
                for j:= beginaddress[other node] step 1 until m do
                if cyclic sequence[j]=nodepoint then
                begin reference[address]:= j;
                        j:= m
                end
        end
end;
nodepoint:= cyclic sequence[reference[1]];
for i:= 1 step 1 until k do
begin direction[i]:= left;
        used nodes[i]:= 0
end;
for i:= 1 step 1 until bb do
used branches[i]:= not used;
pointer layorder:= 1;
layed nodes[pointer layorder]:= nodepoint;
endaddress:=beginaddress[nodepoint]+degree[nodepoint]-1;
for i:= beginaddress[nodepoint] step 1
                                until endaddress do
begin used branches [i]:= used;
        used branches [reference[i]]:= used;
        used nodes[cyclic sequence[i]]:= 1;
end;
number of branches used:=
used nodes[nodepoint]:= degree[nodepoint];
next nodepoint: pointer layorder:= pointer layorder+1;
        search next important node(nodepoint);
        layed nodes[pointer layorder]:= nodepoint;
search first used branch with this nodepoint:
        search first used branch with this(nodepoint,begin node,address);
        print;
next cyclic branch:
        next cyclic address(nodepoint,address);
        aimnode:= cyclic sequence[address];
        if aimnode=begin node
        then goto next nodepoint
        else  if used branches[address]=used
        then goto next cyclic branch;
        if can branch be layed
                                (nodepoint,aimnode,address,lastaddress) then
```

```
        begin i:= reference[lastaddress];
              refer:= reference[address];
              if used nodes[aimnode] ≥ 2 then
              begin
              again: next cyclic address(aimnode,i);
                         goto if i=refer
                              then correct
                         else if used branches[i] = not used
                              then again
                         else if used nodes[aimnode]=2
                              then rightoriented
                         else break off;
              rightoriented: direction[aimnode]:= right;
                         correct:

              end;
              used branches[address]:= used;
              used branches[reference[address]]:= used;
              used nodes[aimnode]:= used nodes[aimnode]+1;
              used nodes[nodepoint]:= usednodes[nodepoint]+1;
              number of branches used:= number of branches used+1;
              print;
              goto if number of branches used=b
                       then all ready
                       else next cyclic branch
        end;
break off:
        nodepoint:= layed nodes[pointer layorder];
        endaddress:= beginaddress[nodepoint]+degree[nodepoint]-1;
        for i:= beginaddress[nodepoint] step 1
                                  until endaddress do
        begin other node:= cyclic sequence[i];
              if used nodes[other node] ≠ degree[other node]
                       ∧ used branches [i]=used
              then begin
                         used branches[i]:= not used;
                         used branches[reference[i]]:= not used;
                         used nodes[nodepoint]:= used nodes[nodepoint]-1;
                         used nodes[othernode]:= used nodes[othernode]-1;
                         if used nodes[othernode]=2
                         then direction[othernode]:= left;
                         number of branches used:= number of branches used -1
                  end
        end;
        if used nodes[nodepoint] > 2 then goto decrease p 1 ;
        if direction[nodepoint]= left
        then begin
                         direction[nodepoint]:= right;
                         goto search first used branch with this nodepoint
              end
        else begin
                         if pointer layorder=1
                         then goto network not planar;
                         direction[nodepoint]:= left;
        decrease p 1:pointer layorder:= pointer layorder-1;
                         goto break off
              end;
```

```
    network not planar:
        output(1,◄T18*►,◄network not planar►);
        goto next network;
    all ready:
        output(1,◄T9*►,◄all ready►);
                            comment evaluation of the codes;

        output(1,◄T37///,T4,B4T6,B5T25//►,◄the following network has been
layed :►, ◄node ►, ◄degree►,◄connected with the nodes:►);
        for i:= 1 step 1 until k do
        begin output(1,◄I2,B6I2,B6T0►,i,degree[i],◄►);
              endaddress:= beginaddress[i]+degree[i]-1;
              for j:= beginaddress[i] step 1 until endaddress do
              output(1,◄B1I2►,cyclic sequence[j]);
              output(1,◄T0/►,◄►)
        end;
        output(1,◄T0////,T11//►,◄►,◄its code is:►);
        m:= 1;
        for i:= 1 step 1 until bb do
                            used branches[i]:= not used;
        for i:= 1 step 1 until k do
        begin endaddress:= beginaddress[i]+degree[i]-1;
              for j:= beginaddress[i] step 1 until endaddress do
              if used branches[j]= not used then
              begin address:= j;
                    code[m]:= i;
                    m:= m+1;
                    output(1,◄I2►,i);
        continue:   nodepoint:= cyclic sequence[address];
                    code[m]:= nodepoint;
                    m:= m+1;
                    output(1,◄I2►,nodepoint);
                    used branches[address]:= used;
                    address:= reference[address];
                    if nodepoint=i then
                    begin code[m]:= 0;
                          m:= m+1;
                          output(1,◄I2/►,0);
                          goto nxtj
                    end;
                    next cyclic address(nodepoint,address);
                    goto continue;
              nxtj:
              end;
        end;
        code [m]:= 0;
        output(1,◄I2*►,0);
        goto next network;
    end
end
end;
```

REFERENCES

Bouwkamp, C.J. , 1946, Proc. Acad. Sci. Amst. , 49, 1176-1188 (=1946, Indag. math. , 8, 724-736).

Bouwkamp, C.J. , 1947, Proc. Acad. Sci. Amst. , 50, 58-78, 1296-1299 (=1947, Indag. math. , 9, 43-63, 622-625).

Brooks, R.L. , C.A.B.Smith, A.H.Stone and W.T.Tutte, 1941, Duke math. J. , 7, 312-340.

Cauer, W. , 1954, Theorie der linearen Wechselstromschaltungen, 2nd ed. (Akademie-Verlag Berlin) pp. 56-91.

Duijvestijn, A.J.W. , 1962, Electronic Computation of squared rectangles, Thesis Eindhoven, the Netherlands. In: Philips Res. Repts 17, 523-613.

Kron, G. , 1939, Tensor analysis of electrical networks (John Wiley and Sons, Inc. , New York).

ON SOME NUMBER-THEORETICAL PROBLEMS
TREATED WITH COMPUTERS

C. E. FRÖBERG
University of Lund

1. INTRODUCTION

The use of computers for research within different fields of pure mathematics has developed much more slowly than is the case in other similar disciplines. However, there is one exception for which the application of computers has been very natural, namely number theory. Such problems as finding integer solutions of diophantine equations or testing conjectures of different kinds have been treated on computers already in the early fifties. While the problems in this area in their general form are often of a very deep nature, many of them can quite easily be formulated in such a way as to be understandable even for the lay-man. The famous Goldbach problem is an outstanding example in this respect.

2. WILSON REMAINDERS

The well-known theorem by Wilson states that if p is a prime, then

$$(p-1)! \equiv -1 \pmod{p} \tag{1}$$

Putting $q = ((p-1)! + 1)/p$ we define W_p as the remainder when q is divided by p:

$$W_p = q - (q \div p)p \tag{2}$$

where $\div$ stands for integer division. Of special interest are values of p such that $W_p = 0$. Only three such values are known: $p = 5, 13$ and 563. All W_p were computed for $3 \leqslant p < 50,000$ (Fröberg [1962]) but no additional zeros were found. Some heuristic arguments were presented with respect to the chance of finding new zeros in a certain interval.

3. FERMAT REMAINDERS

According to a theorem by Fermat, if p is a prime and a an integer not divisible by p, then

$$a^{p-1} \equiv 1 \ (\text{mod } p) \tag{3}$$

The remainders F_p are defined by

$$F_p \equiv (a^{p-1} - 1)/p \ (\text{mod } p) \tag{4}$$

with the additional condition $0 \leqslant F_p < p$. Computations were performed in the special case $a = 2$ for $p < 50,000$ (Fröberg [1958]). The only zeros found were obtained for $p = 1093$ and $p = 3511$; both were known before.

4. INVERSES OF TWIN PRIMES

In 1919 Viggo Brun was able to prove that the sum of the inverses of the twin primes is convergent. His proof, depending on an ingenious generalization of Erathostenes' sieve, does not give an answer to the old question whether the number of twin primes is finite or infinite. However, Hardy and Littlewood gave very good reasons in favor of an infinite number, and even more, they gave an asymptotic formula for the number of twin primes below a given limit N.

Our problem is now to compute the sum

$$S = \frac{1}{3} + \frac{1}{5} + \frac{1}{7} + \frac{1}{11} + \frac{1}{13} + \frac{1}{17} + \frac{1}{19} + \frac{1}{29} + \frac{1}{31} + \frac{1}{41} + \frac{1}{43} + \ldots + \frac{1}{p} + \frac{1}{p+2} + \ldots$$

Riemann's formula states that the number of primes below a certain limit x is approximately

$$P(x) = 1 + \frac{\log x}{S_2} + \frac{(\log x)^2}{2 \cdot 2! \ S_3} + \frac{(\log x)^3}{3 \cdot 3! \ S_4} + \ldots \tag{5}$$

with $S_k = \sum_{r=1}^{\infty} r^{-k}$. A refined form of the conjecture by Hardy and Littlewood for the approximate number of prime pairs below a given limit n is then

$$P_2(n) = 2C_2 \int_2^n P'(x)^2 \ dx \ . \tag{6}$$

Here $C_2 = \prod_{p=3}^{\infty} [1 - 1/(p-1)^2]$ where the product is taken over all odd primes. An approximate numerical value is $C_2 = 0.6601618$.

We now compute the direct sum S_N up to some rather high values (actually $N = 2^\nu$, $\nu = 16(1)20$) and also construct approximate values of the remainder term R_N by use of the conjecture of Hardy and Littlewood. In this way we obtain the final value

$$S = 1.70195$$

with an error estimated at not more than **3** units in the last place. When $N = 2^{20} = 1048576 \simeq 10^6$, R_N is approximately 0.2; in order to decrease this value to 0.1 we need about $N^2 \simeq 10^{12}$ terms. An error of the order 10^{-5} demands a value of N greater than $10^{1\,00,000}$. A more detailed description is given in Fröberg [1961].

5. THE MÖBIUS POWER SERIES

The Möbius power series are defined by

$$f(z) = \sum_{n=1}^{\infty} \mu(n) z^n$$

(7)

$$g(z) = \sum_{n=1}^{\infty} \mu(n) z^n / n$$

Here $\mu(n)$ is the usual Möbius function:

$$\mu(n) = \begin{cases} 1 & n = 1 \\ 0 & \text{if } n \text{ contains a square factor} \\ (-1)^q & \text{if } n \text{ is the product of } q \text{ different prime factors}. \end{cases}$$

For real values x, $0 < x < 1$, of z we can put $x = e^{-t}$ and by use of Mellin transformation we find

$$\varphi_1(t) = \sum_{n=1}^{\infty} \mu(n) e^{-nt} = \frac{1}{2\pi i} \int_S \frac{2^s + 1}{2^s + 1} \frac{\Gamma(s)}{\xi(s)} t^{-s} ds$$

(8)

where S is composed of a vertical line to the right of $\mathrm{Re}(s) = \frac{1}{2}$ and an infinitely large semi-circle in the left half-plane. Similarly, if $-1 < x < 0$ we obtain

$$\varphi_2(t) = \sum_{n=1}^{\infty} (-1)^n \mu(n) e^{-nt} = -\frac{1}{2\pi i} \int_S \frac{2^s + 1}{2^s - 1} \frac{\Gamma(s)}{\zeta(s)} t^{-s} ds$$

(9)

Evaluating the residues we get representations in terms of elementary functions.

An interesting problem is furnished by the function $g(e^{i\varphi})$ or in parametrical form:

$$x = \sum_{n=1}^{\infty} \mu(n) \cos n\varphi / n \qquad y = \sum_{n=1}^{\infty} \mu(n) \sin n\varphi / n$$

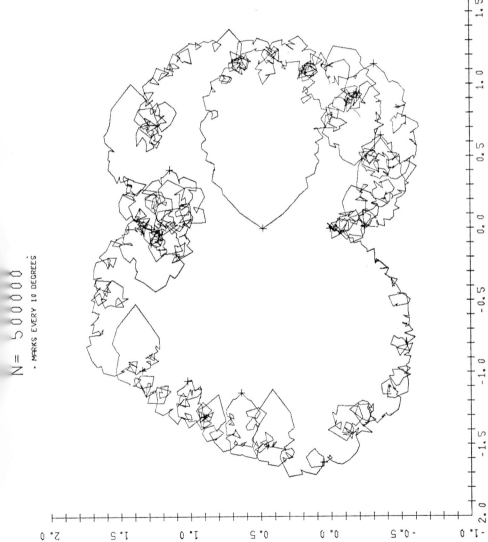

N= 5000000
· MARKS EVERY 10 DEGREES

The function was evaluated numerically by direct summation up to $N =$ 500,000 and the corresponding graph was drawn by a plotter at intervals $0°.1$ (see fig. 1). The "big bend" in the center of the figure corresponds to $\varphi = \pi/3$. The curve is known to be continuous but certainly not differentiable. As a matter of fact the irregular form prevails even if the function is tabulated at shorter intervals, say $0°.01$ and enlarged by a convenient factor.

REFERENCES

Fröberg, C.E., 1958, MTAC 12, 281.
Fröberg, C.E., 1961, BIT 1, 15.
Fröberg, C.E., 1963, Ark. Mat. 4, 479-499.
Fröberg, C.E., 1966, BIT 6, 191.

L'USAGE HEURISTIQUE DES ORDINATEURS EN MATHÉMATIQUES PURES

G. GLAESER

Faculté des Sciences de Rennes

1. PRÉAMBULE

L'objectif du mathématicien est la démonstration de nouveaux théorèmes; il ne peut se contenter de collectionner des propositions plausibles: il sait trop, d'expérience, que l' "evidence" est fragile et l'intuition trompeuse.

La vérification de certaines conjectures sur un nombre limité d'exemples particuliers ne saurait, en général, tenir lieu de démonstration. Cela limite l'emploi des ordinateurs comme outil de déduction aux deux cas suivants:

a) Lorsque la conjecture porte sur un ensemble fini, un examen exhaustif de tous les cas particuliers permet de conclure: c'est l'induction aristotélicienne.

b) La construction d'un seul contre-exemple permet d'affirmer qu'une conjecture est fausse.

A ces deux cas on peut toutefois ajouter quelques variantes. Ainsi, on peut démontrer une proposition par l'absurde. On construit, pour cela, un contre-exemple à la proposition contraire.

L'usage des ordinateurs comme outil de *démonstration* est néanmoins très restreint. Par contre, ce sont des outils *heuristiques* d'un grand avenir.

Tout mathématicien créateur utilise constamment des procédés auxiliaires susceptibles de stimuler l'imagination. Même s'il répugne à tracer des figures géométriques, il emploie des schémas, il s'exprime à l'aide de symboles et d'un langage propre à lui suggérer la solution des problèmes. Employé comme "instrument à faire des figures", l'ordinateur électronique se révèle autrement plus souple et efficace que la craie et le tableau, que la règle et le compas!

L'objet de cet article est de tirer les leçons des tentatives que nous faisons, depuis trois ans, à la Faculté des Sciences de Rennes, pour utiliser un ordinateur IBM 1620, à propos de recherches d'analyse mathématique.

2. LA MÉTHODE

2.1. *Choix des problèmes*

En face d'une nouvelle question, le réflexe du chercheur expérimenté est

d'essayer de "bricoler". Il cherche à entreprendre de "petits calculs" sur
quelques cas particuliers de façon à se familiariser avec les difficultés. Il
espère ainsi formuler quelques conjectures plausibles qu'il essaiera de préciser, puis de démontrer.

Malheureusement, il arrive fréquemment que le calcul, simple et élémentaire dans son principe, que l'on désirerait effectuer pour prendre cons-
cience de "ce qui se passe", soit impraticable à la main; la figure que l'on
aimerait dessiner utilise un espace à n dimensions ($n > 2$).

C'est précisément dans les cas où l'on recule devant le "bricolage" à la
main, qu'il faut onvisager le "bricolage" à la machine!

De nos jours Evariste Galois ne pourrait plus affirmer:

"Étant donnée une équation algébrique à coefficients quelconques, numériques ou littéraux, reconnaître si ses racines ne peuvent s'exprimer en
radicaux, telle est la question dont nous offrons une solution complète.

"Si maintenant vous me donnez une équation que vous aurez choisie à
votre gré et que vous désiriez connaître si elle est ou non résoluble par radicaux, je n'aurai rien à y faire que de vous indiquer le moyen de répondre
à votre question, san vouloir charger ni moi ni personne de le faire. En un
mot, les calculs sont impracticables" (Galois [1962]).

2.2. *Changement de point de vue*

Il convient alors de repenser le problème posé, en fonction des nouvelles
possibilités: c'est là une grosse difficulté psychologique pour le débutant,
qui doit se défaire d'un certain nombre d'habitudes artisanales.

Le mathématicien a appris à déployer des trésors d'ingéniosité pour éviter un calcul fastidieux. Il faut maintenant modifier l'échelle des valeurs:
telle méthode qui était insensée devient très raisonnable lorsqu'on dispose
de nouveaux moyens. Inversement il faut acquérir l'expérience de ce que la
machine ne fait pas, ou ne fait pas encore d'une façon satisfaisante.

Chaque fois que nous avons envisagé d'attaquer un problème sur ordinateur, nous avons préalablement consacré plusieurs mois à le repenser dans
notre nouvelle optique.

Ainsi, dans l'exemple 3.2. ci-dessous, nous avons accepté de manipuler
des systèmes comprenant un grand nombre d'inégalités du premier degré:
cette tâche, qui semblait ingrate et inextricable, est devenue une affaire de
routine dès que nous avons fait appel à des techniciens de la "Programmation linéaire".

2.3. *Choix du collaborateur*

Il n'est pas souhaitable que le mathématicien soit aussi le programmeur:
cela le conduirait constamment à interrompre ses recherches théoriques
pour effectuer des tâches techniques qui requièrent de tout autres qualités.

Le mathématicien n'a même pas besoin de savoir programmer couram-
ment: il lui suffit d'avoir compris les principes de l'utilisation des ordinateurs et d'être en mesure de se faire expliquer les difficultés rencontrées.

La collaborateur chargé d'exécuter les expériences doit comprendre parfaitement la nature du problème posé et être en mesure de dialoguer avec le
mathématicien. Il faut qu'il possède une certaine maîtrise de l'ordinateur;

ses qualités d'imagination doivent le conduire à suggérer de meilleures fa-
çons d'utiliser l'outil. Chaque fois que nous nous sommes adressé à un programmeur expérimenté qui, faute de culture mathématique suffisante, ne
comprenait que superficiellement les problèmes traités, nous avons eu de
gros déboires ....

Par exemple, lorsqu'on a besoin de quelques calculs sur la fonction
$\exp(-1/x^2)$ au voisinage de l'origine, il est agaçant d'apprendre, une se-
maine plus tard, que cette fonction est constante (aux erreurs d'arrondis
près)!!

Le programmeur doit avoir assez d'initiative pour multiplier une telle
fonction par 10^5 avant de la calculer.

2.4. *La construction de l'algorithme fondamental*

On établit un programme susceptible d'effectuer les opérations sur lesquelles va porter l'expérimentation. Comme on envisage de répéter les calculs un grand nombre de fois, on veillera à choisir un algorithme dont le
temps de passage soit raisonnable.

Le programme sera rédigé avec une grande souplesse de façon à per-
mettre des modifications aisées: on se réserve, par l'emploi judicieux des
clés, la possibilité de sortir ou de garder en mémoire des résultats intermédiaires (cf l'exemple 3.4.).

2.5. *Choix d'un objectif et conjecture*

L'essentiel est d'apprendre "à jouer avec la machine". On lui propose
une certaine tâche. En examinant les réponses, on est en mesure de lui
proposer des tâches plus précises, ou plus intéressantes et l'on continue
ainsi jusqu'à ce que l'idée de la démonstration du théorème projeté appa-
raisse clairement.

Insistons sur le fait qu'il n'est ni nécessaire ni même souhaitable de tra-
vailler avec des conjectures très vraisemblables.

Lorsqu'on travaille à la main, on écarte délibérément certaines idées
que l'on soupçonne d'être peu prometteuses, sans savoir précisément pour
quelles raisons. Mais l'emploi du robot permet de satisfaire sa curiosité
même sur ces hypothèses hasardeuses, et c'est en fait à propos de telles
réfutations que l'on obtient les résultats les plus suggestifs (cf particilière-
ment l'exemple 3.2. et le travail de R. Louboutin qui y est cité). L'important est d'acquérir, grâce à des essais nombreux, une bonne familiarité
avec le problème.

2.6. *Rythme de travail*

Il est clair que la collaboration que nous préconisons ne peut s'effectuer
par correspondance! Un mathématicien pur ne doit pas se contenter d'écrire
à un laboratoire de calcul pour lui commander un certain travail: il s'ex-
pose à recevoir une feuille couverte de chiffres dont il ne pourra guère faire
usage. Ce n'est que par des visites quotidiennes au laboratoire de calcul
que l'on peut prendre connaissance, dans les meilleurs délais, des résultats; on peut ainsi exploiter des idées suggérées par les derniers documents
et discuter des modifications qu'il convient d'apporter aux essais ultérieurs.

Inversement, les longs délais entre la conception d'une expérience et la lecture des résultats ont un effet très démoralisant sur l'équipe de recherche.

Il ne faut pas se hâter de classer un problème dès qu'on l'a résolu (ou "plus ou moins résolu"). Au contraire, chaque question doit en amener une autre. Et, en particulier si la réponse est négative, il est bon d'essayer de reformuler une autre question "raisonnable". Il semble que l'utilisation d'un ordinateur favorise la "poursuite des problèmes".

2.7. *Valeur pédagogique de la méthode*

La participation à une équipe est particulièrement formatrice pour le chercheur débutant. Aux prises avec un problème précis, il ne reste cependant pas livré à lui-même. Il peut parfaire sa culture tout en "observant" les associations d'idées de chercheurs plus expérimentés. Un des aspects les plus spectaculaires de la méthode décrite est l'obligation pour les collaborateurs de raconter et de discuter les tentatives auxquelles ils aimeraient se livrer, de décrire les idées fructueuses et les fausses pistes au fur et à mesure de leur gestation. On obtient ainsi une image vivante de la Science, si différente de l'édifice achevé que constituent les traités et les mémoires.

3. QUELQUES EXEMPLES

Pour illustrer les considérations précédentes, nous relatons maintenant quelques aventures mathématiques auxquelles nous avons participé.

Les résultats de ces investigations sont rédigés dans "Le prolongateur de Whitney" *.

L'aspect mathématique est développé dans ce recueil. Ici, nous ne présentons cet aspect que dans la mesure où il est indispensable à l'intelligence de l'aspect heuristique.

3.1. *Étude de la perturbation des différences divisées* (*Lebaud* [1966])

Soit $\Delta(a_1, a_2, \ldots, a_m; f)$ la différence divisée calculée pour une fonction f sur l'ensemble: $\mathcal{A} = (a_1, a_2, \ldots, a_m)$ de m nombres réels. On se propose d'étudier l'erreur que l'on commet lorsqu'on substitue à $\mathcal{A}$ un ensemble "voisin" $\mathcal{B} = (b_1, b_2, \ldots b_m)$.

On est conduit à définir diverses distances entre $\mathcal{A}$ et $\mathcal{B}$. En particulier:

1. Une distance géométrique $d(\mathcal{A}, \mathcal{B})$ qui s'évalue simplement à l'aide des abscisses a_i et b_j.

2. Une distance fonctionnelle $\Phi(\mathcal{A}, \mathcal{B})$ qui est la norme de la fonctionnelle linéaire

$$f \to \Delta(a_1, a_2, \ldots, a_m; f) - \Delta(b_1, b_2, \ldots, b_m; f)$$

définie sur un certain espace de Banach.

* Ces recherches ont bénéficié d'un contrat D.G.R.S.T. no. 65-FR-209.

Il s'agissait d'examiner si ces deux distances sont équivalentes (ce qui se démontre pour $m = 2$). On cherchait s'il existe une constante (ne dépendant que de m) $k(m)$ telle que

$$k(m)\, d(\mathcal{A}, \mathcal{B}) \leqslant \Phi(\mathcal{A}, \mathcal{B}) \leqslant (1/m!)\, d(\mathcal{A}, \mathcal{B})\ .$$

L'algorithme fondamental est un procédé de calcul de $\Phi(\mathcal{A}, \mathcal{B})$: cette distance apparaît comme l'intégrale de la valeur absolue d'une certaine fonction-spine qui se calcule à partir des abscisses a_i et b_j. Pour $m = 3$ et $m = 4$, le temps de passage sur ordinateur IBM 1620 était au plus de l'ordre de la minute.

Le jeu consistait à trouver les configurations $(\mathcal{A}, \mathcal{B})$ pour lesquelles le rapport: $\Phi(\mathcal{A}, \mathcal{B})/d(\mathcal{A}, \mathcal{B})$ est le plus petit possible.

L'expérience et le raisonnement nous ont conduit à essayer des configurations telles que les b_i ne soient pas constamment à droite (ou à gauche) des a_i correspondants, par example

$$a_1 < b_1 < b_2 < a_2 < b_3 < a_3\ .$$

A chaque séance, M. Lebaud traitait une dizaine d'examples numériques.

Notre attention s'est vite portée vers les configurations symétriques par rapport à $a_2 = b_2$ $(a_1 < b_1 < b_2 = a_2 < b_3 < a_3)$, pour lesquels le raisonnement est venu confirmer certaines observations. Puis, M. Lebaud a songé à examiner les configurations où $a_1 = b_1$. Les résultats obtenus lui ont permis de réfuter notre conjecture, en fournissant l'idée d'un contre-example.

Cependant la question ne semble pas épuisée pour autant et l'on peut conjecturer l'existence de constantes $h(m)$ et $s(m)$ telles que:

$$h(m)\, [d(\mathcal{A}, \mathcal{B})^{s(m)} \leqslant \Phi(\mathcal{A}, \mathcal{B})\ .$$

3.2. *Interpolation osculatrice extrêmale entre deux points* *

On se donne au point a (resp. b) de R un polynôme P_a (resp. P_b) de degré m, et l'on étudie les fonctions f qui admettent en a (resp. b) un contact d'ordre m avec P_a (resp. P_b). P_a est le candidat polynôme de Taylor de f en a. On s'intéresse à celles de ces fonctions qui sont de classe C^m et qui admettent en outre une dérivée $(m+1)$ième appartenant à $L^\infty[a, b]$. On cherche à minimiser la norme $\|f^{m+1}\|^\infty_{[a, b]}$ (borne supérieure essentielle de $f^{(m+1)}$ sur $[a, b]$).

La conjecture, bien naïve, sur laquelle nous avons d'abord opéré consistait à prendre un point c $(a < c < b)$, à construire un polynôme P_c (candidat polynôme de Taylor en c), de façon à minimiser le λ qui figure dans des inégalités analogues à

$$\left[P_a^{(i)}(a) - P_c^{(i)}(a) \right] \leqslant \frac{\lambda\, |a - c|^{m-i+1}}{(m-i+1)!}$$

* La partie expérimentale de ces recherches fait l'objet d'une thèse de 3ème cycle (Louboutin [1966]). Les expériences nous ont permis de developper la théorie (cf Glaeser [1966]).

et à espérer qu'en travaillant ainsi en divers points c on obtiendrait le
champ des polynômes de Taylor de la fonction extrêmale cherchée.

L'algorithme fondamental (étude d'un système d'inégalités du premier
degré, où les inconnues sont les coefficients de P_c et de λ) relève de la
programmation linéaire.

Sans nous faire grande illusion sur le succès de la méthode, nous étions
curieux de nous rendre compte dans quelle mesure et pourquoi cela ne mar-
cherait pas.

Il nous est apparu que le système des $2m+1$ inégalités que nous utilisions
n'était pas assez grand.

Nous avons cherché à adjoindre de nouvelles inégalités "convenables" au
système initial et en cherchant à préciser le choix de ces nouvelles conditions, la solution de problème théorique (qui exige une infinité d'inégalités
convenablement "normées") s'est présentée tout naturellement. En fait, la
conjecture "naïve" précédente se trouve verifiée lorsqu'on utilise ce système infini d'inégalités.

Dans la conjecture correcte, on trouve un λ qui ne dépend pas du choix
du point c, alors que dans les essais initiaux la fonction $c \rightarrow \lambda(c)$ avait un
graphe "en cloche".

Le jeu a consisté à trouver les inégalités supplémentaires qui aplatis-
saient le graphe, jusqu'à l'obtention du λ constant.

Il est clair que ce genre de "bricolage" ne peut même pas être envisagé
raisonnablement à mains nues.

3.3. *Comparison de deux normes sur un espace de polynômes* *
Pour tout polynôme P de degré $\leq m$ on a (pour $b > a$)

$$\underset{t \in [a,\,b]}{\text{Max}} \quad P(t) \quad \leq \quad \frac{4m^2}{|a-b|} \int_a^b |P(t)|\,dt\,.$$

Nous ne serions pas étonné si cette inégalité (éventuellement avec une
meilleure constante) se trouvait depuis longtemps dans la littérature.

L'étude de cette inégalité se prête bien à des investigations expérimen-
tales, car il est facile pour les petites valeurs de m de trouver, parmi tous
les polynômes satisfaisant à

$$\text{Max } |P(t)| = 1 \text{ pour tout } t \in [0,1]\,,$$

les polynômes P_m qui réalisent la plus petite norme $L_1 [0,1]$.

Actuellement, nous sommes parvenu aux conjectures suivantes:

*Il y a deux polynômes P_m qui se déduisent l'un de l'autre par le change-
ment de variable $t \rightarrow 1-t$. L'un d'entre eux prend la valeur 1 pour $t = 0$,
décroit jusqu'à la valeur 0 sur un intervalle $[0, \alpha_m]$, où α_m est très voisin*

---

* Dans Glaeser [1966], nous utilisons cette inegalite (lemme 1). M. Louboutin, per-
fectionnant notre démonstration, a montré que la constante 8 peut être remplacée
par 4. Les recherches dont il est question ici se poursuivent actuellement.

de 0, et sa valeur absolue reste bien plus faible que 1 sur $[\alpha_m, 1]$. *Il est plausible que toutes ses racines soient réelles et situées dans l'intervalle* $[\alpha_m, 1]$.

3.4 *Emploi du langage FORMAC*

Les calculs que l'on désire effectuer sont rarement numériques; heureusement, il est actuellement possible d'effectuer sur machine des manipulations de symboles (opérations algébriques et dérivations partielles de polynômes, de fonctions trigonométriques, exponentielles etc.) grâce au langage FORMAC (à condition de renoncer aux petits ordinateurs).

Depuis un an nous explorons ces nouvelles possibilités. Nous ne signalons ici qu'un exemple de nos balbutiements dans cette voie.

Dans Glaeser [1963], nous avons été amené à considérer la fonction

$$f(x) = \exp(-1/x^2) \left\{ \sin^2 1/x + \exp(-1/x^2) \right\} .$$

Elle est de classe C^∞, mais sa racine carrée n'est que de classe C^1! Le calcul de la dérivée seconde (et à plus forte raison des dérivées suivantes) pour $x \neq 0$ de cette racine carrée est effroyable. Pour ne pas publier une telle horreur nous avions imaginé un moyen artificiel d'éviter ce calcul, en remplaçant f par une fonction analogue (cf loc. cit. p. 206). Cette dérivée seconde ne reste pas bornée au voisinage de 0.

Si l'on veut poursuivre ces investigations en étudiant le comportement des dérivées suivantes et en examinant des racines ièmes, on ne peut accepter de renoncer constamment à effectuer des vérifications sous le prétexte que les calculs "ne sont pas drôles".

La machine fait le travail à notre place. Mais lorsque nous avons commandé, par correspondance, ces calculs à un laboratoire mieux outillé, nous avons reçu une liasse de chiffres (obtenue en moins d'une minute). Il a fallu plus de trois heures pour traduire ces résultats en clair et pour réduire les termes semblables (ce que la machine pouvait fair instantanément, si l'on avait songé à lui donner les instructions nécessaires).

En fait, l'expression complète des dérivées $n$ièmes ne nous intéressait guère: mais la machine pouvait aussi bien les garder en mémoire et nous fournir uniquement certains termes "dominants".

Nous désirerons certainement par la suite manipuler algébriquement ces dérivées et examiner les termes "dominants" des combinaisons obtenues.

De telles exigences paraîtront déraisonnables à ceux qui gardent des habitudes artisanales; de nos jours elles sont parfaitement légitimes, puisqu'on peut les satisfaires à bon compte.

4. L'AVENIR

Le domaine où la mathématique expérimentale peut se donner libre cours est vaste: il n'y a pas lieu de se cantonner à la théorie des nombres et à l'analyse mathématique.

L'examen superficiel des travaux de certains mathématiciens pourraient donner à croire qu'ils exercent leur activité sur des sujets où l'ordinateur ne pourrait leur être d'aucun secours.

Nous sommes persuadé qu'il s'agit d'une illusion due au fait que les problèmes n'ont pas été repensés dans ces nouvelles perspectives.

Lorsque des expériences analogues à celles que nous relatons auront été tentées dans toutes les spécialités des mathématiques pures, la productivité de la recherche s'en trouvera considérablement renforcée. La prétendue opposition entre mathématiques pures et appliquées, entre zélateurs de théorèmes d'existence et de constructeurs d'algorithmes, se dissipera; tandis que se développera le goût des études menées jusqu'au bout, commençant par un examen général et conceptuel, pour aboutir à une explicatation précise des résultats.

RÉFÉRENCES

Galois, E., 1962, Écrits et mémoires mathématiques (Gauthier-Villars, Paris) p. 39.

Glaeser, G., 1963, Ann. Inst. Fourier (Grenoble) 13, 203-210.

Glaeser, G., 1966, Prolongement extrêmal de fonctions différentiables. *In*: Le prolongateur de Whitney (Faculté des sciences de Rennes).

Lebaud, G., 1966, Sur la perturbation des différences divisées. *In*: Le prolongateur de Whitney (Faculté des sciences de Rennes).

Louboutin, R., 1966, Étude expérimentale du théorème de prolongement de Whitney. *In*: Le prolongateur de Whitney (Faculté des sciences de Rennes).

SUR LA CYCLABILITÉ DES GRAPHES

J.-C. HERZ
Cie IBM-France

1. INTRODUCTION

Le plaisir du mathématicien et l'admiration de ses pairs croissent en proportion de l'altitude des pics qu'il explore. Sa technique ascensionnelle consiste à élaguer les hypothèses de ses théorèmes dans l'espoir suprême de transformer leurs conclusions en conditions nécessaires et suffisantes.

Il arrive parfois qu'une brume impénétrable s'obstine à masquer le sommet et que l'alpiniste ne puisse se rendre compte de la distance qui l'en sépare. Il sera alors tout heureux d'avoir visé juste un peu trop haut, c'est-à-dire d'obtenir un théorème vrai sauf sur un sous-ensemble infime. Ce qui revient, dualement, à accorder sa prédilection aux propriétés extrêment rares dans l'ensemble considéré. Celle, pour l'entier positif n, d'être exposant d'une relation de la forme $x^n + y^n = z^n$ entre des entiers positifs, x, y, z est sans doute la plus célèbre de l'histoire des mathématiques. Depuis que Bose, Shrikhande et Parker ont réduit à néant la vieille conjecture d'Euler, l'impossibilité de construire deux carrés latins orthogonaux d'ordre $4n-2$ est devenue à son tour une propriété des plus rares de l'entier n. L'égalité à un carré parfait de la somme des n premiers carrés parfaits ne se rencontre que pour une valeur unique de n, chère aux horlogers. Même unicité dans le joli problème de la multiplication de deux nombres de trois chiffres dont l'exécution fait apparaître chacun des chiffres 0 à 9 exactement deux fois (fig. 1). Il sera question ici de l'unicité du graphe d'ordre $n < 13$ dont tous les sous-graphes d'ordre n-1 sont hamiltoniens sans qu'il le soit lui-même (graphe que nous avons appelé "*hypohamiltonien*"). Le lecteur à qui la borne 13 paraîtrait modeste à première vue est invité à réaliser que l'exploration des graphes d'ordre inférieur à 13 à la recherche de

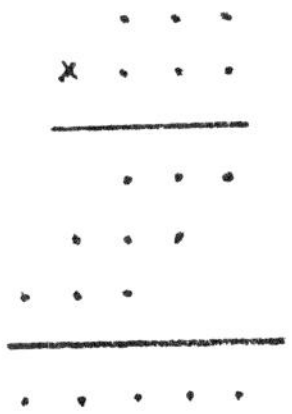

Fig. 1.

l'unique exemplaire qui possède la propriété en question est une tâche des plus ardues dans l'état de nos connaissances, et certainement comparable au travail de Tarry sur le problème des 36 officiers d'Euler.

Une des particularités de ce résultat est d'être resté inédit pendant plus de trente ans. C'est en effet vers 1930 que les frères Sousselier, deux jeunes polytechniciens (l'un civil et l'autre militaire), élaborèrent une *Théorie générale des réseaux* avec le seul secours du mémoire de Sainte-Laguë [1926]. Leurs occupations professionnelles et l'indifférence polie des mathématiciens en place auxquels ils présentèrent leurs recherches firent que leurs manuscrits, progressivement complétés et remaniés, restèrent à l'état de papiers de famille, jusqu'au jour où René Sousselier, le militaire, eut l'idée - habituelle chez Fermat et ses correspondants - de communiquer une de leurs découvertes sous forme d'énigme. Berge [1963,1964] lui ouvrit les colonnes de ses *Problèmes plaisans et délectables* et publia une solution de l'auteur de ces lignes. L'énigme, exprimée en termes de banquet réunissant des personnes irascibles, équivalait à la recherche du graphe hypohamiltonien d'ordre minimum. Celui-ci, un graphe d'ordre 10, portait déjà le nom du mathématicien Petersen [1898] qui l'avait proposé comme exemple de graphe cubique de classe chromatique 4.

En 1965, toujours dans l'ignorance des travaux des Sousselier, je proposai comme sujet d'étude à F. Vigué, élève à l'École des Mines de Nancy, la rédaction d'un programme en langage FORTRAN pour la recherche systématique des graphes hypohamiltoniens. Ce programme, qui utilise un sous-programme très efficace de recherche des circuits hamiltoniens d'un graphe dû à mon collègue J.-J. Duby, fit la preuve qu'il n'existait point de graphe hypohamiltonien d'ordre 11 ou 12. Le 21 avril 1965, après de longs efforts, l'ordinateur accoucha d'un graphe hypohamiltonien d'ordre 13 parfaitement constitué. Les performances positives du programme se bornèrent là en raison du temps de calcul élevé qui empêcha d'explorer exhaustivement les graphes des ordres suivants. Les calculs conduisirent à formuler la conjecture (encore non démontrée) qu'un graphe hypohamiltonien ne possède pas de circuit de longueur inférieure à 5, et par conséquent l'idée que la restriction de l'exploration aux graphes sans circuit de longueur inférieure à 5 devait conduire plus rapidement à la découverte de nouveaux graphes hypohamiltoniens. Modifié en conséquence, le programme livra effectivement le 15 octobre 1965 un graphe d'ordre 15.

Ce n'est qu'en 1966 que j'eus connaissance des manuscrits des Sousselier. Les graphes d'ordre 13 et 15 trouvés par l'ordinateur n'y sont pas mentionnés, mais l'unicité de la solution pour les ordres inférieurs à 13 y est démontrée, ainsi que l'existence d'un graphe cubique hypohamiltonien d'ordre 18 et celle d'une famille infinie de graphes hypohamiltoniens d'ordre $6k+4$ (k entier positif quelconque), généralisant le graphe de Petersen. La conjecture ci-dessus est prouvée dans certains cas particuliers. Et surtout, toutes ces propriétés sont placées dans un cadre beaucoup plus général, qui est l'étude de la *cyclabilité* des graphes.

2. DÉFINITION DE LA CYCLABILITÉ

Rappelons qu'un graphe fini non orienté sans boucle ni arête multiple (nous dirons simplement *graphe* dans la suite de cet article) est un couple $G = (S, A)$ d'ensembles finis; S est l'ensemble des *sommets* de G, A l'ensemble des *arêtes* de G et chaque arête de G est une paire de sommets de G. *L'ordre* n_G de G est le nombre de ses sommets. Le nombre de ses arêtes est au plus égal à $\frac{1}{2}n_G(n_G - 1)$. Un *cycle* de longueur $l \geqslant 3$ de G est une suite de sommets s_i de G, tous distincts, telle que $\{s_i, s_{i+1}\}$ soit une arête de G quel que soit i ($i = 0, 1, \ldots, l-1$; $s_l = s_0$).

Les Sousselier définissent la *cyclabilité* Y_G d'un graphe G comme le plus grand des entiers k tels que k sommets quelconques de G appartiennent à un même cycle de G. La cyclabilité est nulle s'il n'existe aucun tel nombre k. La fig. 2 donne des exemples de graphes de cyclabilité 0, 1 et 2.

$Y = 0$ $Y = 1$ $Y = 2$

Fig. 2.

La cyclabilité d'un graphe est au plus égale à son ordre. Appelons *défaut de cyclabilité* la quantité $n_G - Y_G$; si elle est nulle, G est dit *hamiltonien*; si elle est égale à 1, G est dit *hypohamiltonien*.

3. PROBLÈMES CONCERNANT LA CYCLABILITÉ

La théorie des graphes était déjà riche en *nombres* destinés à la description de leurs particularités: ordre, nombre d'arêtes, nombre de composantes connexes, nombre cyclomatique, nombre cocyclomatique, nombre chromatique, classe chromatique, capacité, nombre de stabilité interne, nombre de stabilité externe, rayon, diamètre, nombre de connexité, degré maximum... Voici donc un nouveau venu, la cyclabilité.

Le problème qui se présente naturellement à l'esprit est la recherche d'un *algorithme* efficace pour calculer la cyclabilité d'un graphe donné. Réciproquement, on peut se proposer de déterminer tous les graphes ayant une cyclabilité donnée; notre travail a porté plus exactement sur les graphes de défaut de cyclabilité donné (dans le cas particulier où il est égal à 1). Il est clair que la solution de ces problèmes nécessite une connaissance des *propriétés* de la cyclabilité.

Parmi les propriétés étudiées par les Sousselier figurent:

a) *conservation* ou *modification* de la cyclabilité par addition ou suppression d'arêtes et de sommets

b) relation entre la cyclabilité et le nombre de *cycles* d'une longueur donnée (particulièrement les cycles de longueur maximale ou minimale)

c) relation entre la cyclabilité et la *scission* minimum (nombre minimum de sommets dont la suppression détruise la connexité)

d) relation entre la cyclabilité et les *degrés* (le degré d'un sommet est le nombre d'arêtes auxquelles il appartient).

Tableau 1

Problème de l'existence d'un graphe d'ordre n et de cyclabilité Y pour $Y \geqslant \frac{1}{2}n$

$n \rightarrow$ / $Y \rightarrow$	2	3	4	5	6	7	8	9	10	11	12	13	14	15	16	17	18
3	0	+															
4	0	0	+														
5		0	0	+													
6		0	0	0	+												
7			0	0	0	+											
8			0	0	0	0	+										
9						0	0	+									
10				+			0	+	+								
11							+	0	0	+							
12						+	+	+	0	0	+						
13						+	+	+	0		.	+					
14						+	+	+	x				+				
15							+	+	x	x	x		.	+			
16							+	+	x	+	x	+		+	+		
17								+	+	+	+	+	+			+	
18								+	+	+	+	+	+	+		+	+
19									+	+	+	+	+	+	+		
20									+	+	+	+	+	+	+	+	
21										+	+	+	+	+	+	+	
22										+	+	+	+	+	+	+	
23											+	+	+	+	+	+	+
24											+	+	+	+	+	+	+
25												+	+	+	+	+	+
26												+	+	+	+	+	+

0 Réponse négative

+ Réponse affirmative   (d'après R. Sousselier)

☐ Problème non résolu

. Existence prouvée par l'ordinateur

x Conséquences de cette existence (d'après R. Sousselier)

Les Sousselier se sont spécialement intéressés aux graphes de *faible cyclabilité* et à ceux de *forte cyclabilité* (à l'exception des graphes hamiltoniens, plus connus). Ils ont *compté* les graphes connexes d'ordre n et de cyclabilité Y pour $Y \leqslant n \leqslant 7$ (ils en ont trouvé au total 989). Ils ont résumé dans le tableau 1 leurs résultats concernant l'*existence* de graphes d'ordre n et de cyclabilité Y donnés pour $n \leqslant 26$, $\frac{1}{2}n \leqslant Y \leqslant 18$.

De nombreuses questions restent encore sans réponse, et en premier lieu celle de l'existence de graphes de défaut de cyclabilité 2 (à part le

graphe trivial d'ordre 2). D'autre part, on peut introduire des notions nouvelles en modifiant la définition de la cyclabilité:

a) en supprimant le mot "quelconque", on remplace la cyclabilité par la
longueur maximum des cycles;

b) en ajoutant après "cycle" la restriction "de longueur k", on définit une
quantité Y'_G inférieure ou égale à Y_G (qui lui est égale dans le cas des
graphes hamiltoniens et hypohamiltoniens);

c) en orientant les graphes, on obtient des propriétés assez différentes.

4. UTILITÉ DU CALCUL AUTOMATIQUE

C'est un truisme que le calcul peut en principe répondre à toute question
portant sur une famille finie de graphes (existence, construction, énuméra-
tion); qu'il peut éventuellement conclure à l'existence d'un graphe ayant certaines propriétés à l'intérieur d'une famille infinie, mais certainement pas
à l'inexistence d'un tel graphe; enfin, qu'il ne peut en aucun cas établir à lui
seul qu'une propriété appartient à une famille infinie de graphes.

Il n'est pas moins banal de constater que, dans la pratique, la première
de ces affirmations doit être fortement tempérée, le temps de calcul crois-
sant généralement en fonction exponentielle de l'ordre des graphes, et qu'en
définitive l'ordinateur échoue souvent là où le mathématicien réussit (c'est
bien ce qui s'est passé pour les carrés latins orthogonaux d'ordre 10).

Pour que le calcul soit efficace, il est nécessaire que s'établisse une
collaboration intelligente entre le mathématicien et sa machine. Celui-là
évitera à celle-ci, grâce à des remarques simplificatrices, de s'enliser
dans les marais combinatoires; la machine, en retour, lui suggèrera, par
ses recherches infatigables, de nouvelles conjectures qu'il essaiera de démontrer. L'étude du problème posé progressera ainsi par des échanges
successifs entre les deux partenaires. Nous illustrerons cette démarche
dans le paragraphe suivant.

5. ÉTUDE DES GRAPHES HYPOHAMILTONIENS

5.1. *But*

Nous avons cherché à construire à l'aide d'un ordinateur le plus grand
nombre possible de graphes hypohamiltoniens; à énumérer, dans les cas
les plus simples, tous les graphes hypohamiltoniens d'ordre donné (ou à
constater qu'il n'en existe pas); à faire une exploration partielle pour les
valeurs plus élevées de l'ordre, dans l'espoir de trouver au moins un graphe
hypohamiltonien, et par là de résoudre la question de l'existence d'un tel
graphe. Nous avons essayé dans tous les cas de tirer le maximum de ren-
seignements du déroulement des calculs. Ce but ne constitue qu'un point de
départ pour une étude minutieuse des propriétés de ces graphes, mais il
fournit des éléments essentiels pour cette étude.

5.2. *Méthode*

Il ne peut être question de construire tous les graphes d'un ordre donné et d'examiner, pour chacun d'entre eux, s'il est hypohamiltonien: d'une part, le nombre des graphes d'ordre n est énorme, même pour des valeurs relativement faibles de n; d'autre part, on aurait à étudier pour chacun l'existence de n cycles de longueur n-1 et celle d'un cycle de longueur n, ce qui nécessiterait de gros calculs. Il faut donc utiliser dans toute la mesure du possible les propriétés connues des graphes hypohamiltoniens pour limiter *a priori* le nombre de graphes à examiner. La plus commode est l'existence d'un *cycle* de longueur n-1; nous nous sommes donc limité aux graphes possédant un tel cycle; ils sont entièrement définis quand on se donne les arêtes auxquelles appartient le sommet restant s_0, que nous appellerons des *rayons*, et celles, $\{s_i, s_j\}$, formées de deux sommets non consécutifs du cycle, que nous appellerons des *cordes*; pour engendrer tous ces graphes, nous fixons les rayons et nous faisons varier les cordes (fig. 3).

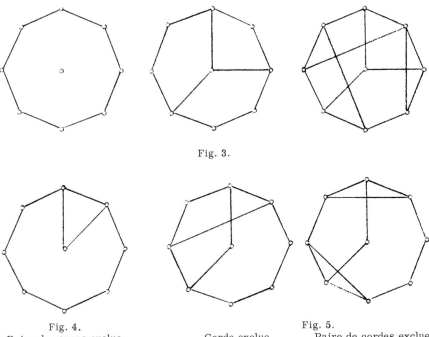

Fig. 3.

Fig. 4.
Paire de rayons exclue

Fig. 5.

Corde exclue   Paire de cordes exclue

Nous utilisons également, et aussitôt que possible, *l'absence* d'un cycle de longueur n. La première conséquence est que deux rayons ne peuvent contenir respectivement deux sommets consécutifs du cycle de base (fig. 4), ce qui restreint considérablement le choix des rayons; de plus, les rayons étant fixés, certaines cordes et certains systèmes de cordes sont exclus (fig. 5). Enfin, si un graphe possède un cycle de longueur n, tous les graphes qui s'en déduisent par addition de cordes possèdent évidemment ce cycle, et il est donc inutile de les construire.

La théorie des graphes hypohamiltoniens montre que le degré d de tout sommet vérifie la condition

$$3 \leqslant d \leqslant \frac{n-4}{2} \, , \tag{1}$$

qui introduit une nouvelle et importante restriction dans le choix des rayons et des cordes.

Deux autres considérations permettent de réduire les calculs. En premier lieu, nous n'examinons pas pour en trouver les cycles de longueur $n-1$ tous les graphes ainsi construits, mais seulement ceux que nous qualifions de *maximaux*: ils n'ont pas de cycle de longueur n, mais toute addition d'une corde respectant (1) en crée un; en effet, tout graphe non maximal G est inclus dans (au moins)un graphe maximal G'; si G' ne contient pas les n cycles de longueur $n-1$ qui le rendent hypohamiltonien, il en est de même *a fortiori* de G; si G' est hypohamiltonien (ce qui est rare) on aura à examiner les graphes obtenus à partir de G' par suppression d'une corde; s'il s'en trouve d'hypohamiltoniens (ce qui ne s'est encore jamais rencontré), on supprimera de nouveau des cordes, etc..

En second lieu, deux graphes d'apparence différente peuvent être en réalité identiques, et il est inutile de les construire et de les examiner séparément. Malheureusement, la reconnaissance de cette *isomorphie* est difficile (fig. 6), et on ne peut éviter qu'une partie de ces répétitions. D'abord, on impose au sommet extérieur au cycle de base d'être un sommet de degré maximum; la condition (1) se trouve ainsi remplacée par la condition plus restrictive

$$3 \leqslant d \leqslant d_0 \, . \tag{2}$$

Ensuite, une isomorphie conservant le cycle de base est facile à reconnaître (elle correspond à une rotation ou à une symétrie sur la figure), de sorte qu'on peut réduire au strict minimum le choix des systèmes de rayons. Mais au-delà, on ne peut pas grand'chose; même une isomorphie conservant le système de rayons est difficilement décelable; on peut en éviter

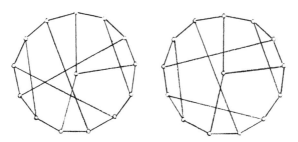

Fig. 6.
Deux graphes isomorphes

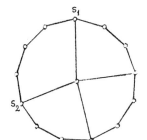

Sans décomposition: $3 \leqslant d_i \leqslant 4$ (tout i)

Avec décomposition:

   1) $d_1 = d_2 = 3$

      $3 \leqslant d_i \leqslant 4 \ (i \neq 1,2)$

   2) $d_1 = 4$

      $3 \leqslant d_i \leqslant 4 \ (i \neq 1)$

Fig. 7.

Élimination de certaines isomorphies par décomposition
d'un cas en deux sous-cas.

quelques-unes en imposant des restrictions sur les degrés des sommets,
mais cela oblige à traiter plusieurs fois le même système de rayons avec
des restrictions différentes (fig. 7).

La méthode que nous venons d'exposer n'est pas forcément la meilleure,
mais on la retrouve, à quelques détails près, dans le manuscrit des Sousselier. Les améliorations qu'on peut espérer viendront de l'utilisation de
propriétés encore inconnues des graphes hypohamiltoniens, que ces calculs
sont précisément destinés à suggérer; on en parlera au §5.3.

Le programme, écrit par F. Vigué pour l'ordinateur IBM 7094 en
FORTRAN IV (à l'exception de la recherche des cycles, adaptée d'un programme précédemment écrit en FAP par J. -J. Duby) accepte comme don-
nées l'ordre n des graphes, le système de rayons et les limites inférieures
et supérieures imposées aux degrés des différents sommets. Il donne tous
les graphes maximaux; pour ceux qui sont hypohamiltoniens, il donne n-1
cycles de longueur n-1 complétant le cycle de base; pour ceux qui ne sont
pas hypohamiltoniens, il indique le premier sommet rencontré dans le cycle de base qui soit tel que les autres sommets du graphe ne sont pas sur
un même cycle. L'ordre n est limité à 18.

Tableau 2

$n \rightarrow$	10	11	12	13	14	15	16	17	18
$d_0 \rightarrow 3$	3 (3, 0)		5 (5, 0)		8 (8, 0)		12 (7, 0)		16
4			4 (4,0)	8 (4, 4)	10 (0, 2)	16	20	29 (0, 1)	35
5					5	10	16	26	38
6							7	16	26
7									8

5.3. *Résultats*

Le tableau 2 donne le nombre de systèmes de rayons pour les diverses valeurs de l'ordre n (jusqu'à 18) et du degré maximum d_0 (soumis à la condition (1)). Lorsque d_0 vaut 3, tous les degrés sont égaux à 3, ce qui ne peut se faire que si l'ordre est pair, d'où les cases blanches en haut du tableau. Chaque système de rayons donne lieu à un calcul (quelquefois à plusieurs si on joue sur le degrés limites pour éviter des isomorphies). Comme on pouvait le prévoir, le temps de calcul croît très fortement avec l'ordre des graphes. On a traité seulement un nombre modeste de cas; pour certains, le calcul n'a pu être terminé dans le temps imparti (de l'ordre d'une heure); le tableau 2 comporte deux chiffres entre parenthèses: le premier est le nombre de cas traités entièrement, le second celui des abandons. Remarquons que le programme, par le jeu des limites sur les degrés, permet de se limiter volontairement à une exploration partielle de certains cas, selon l'intuition du moment. Au total, on a consacré une dizaine d'heures de calcul à cette étude.

Le résultat positif en a été l'apparition d'un graphe hypohamiltonien d'ordre 13 (fig. 8). Mais les résultats négatifs ont probablement beaucoup plus

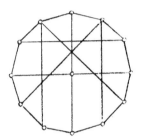

Fig. 8.
Un graphe hypohamiltonien
d'ordre 13.

d'intérêt. On a en effet constaté dans les graphes maximaux que, chaque fois que le premier et le troisième sommets du cycle de base, s_1 et s_3, appartenaient à des rayons, il n'existait pas de cycle passant par tous les sommets sauf s_1 (cela s'est produit environ 1200 fois au cours des calculs). On peut donc conjecturer que si un graphe d'ordre n possède un cycle $(s_1, s_2, \ldots s_{n-1})$ de longueur n-1, un cycle de longueur n-1 ne passant pas par s_1 et les arêtes $\{s_0, s_1\}$ et $\{s_0, s_3\}$, alors il possède un cycle de longueur n. Cette conjecture n'a encore été ni démontrée ni infirmée par un contre-exemple. Il s'ensuivrait que dans un graphe hypohamiltonien un système de rayons ne peut avoir deux sommets séparés par un seul sur le cycle de base, et par conséquent que

$$d_0 \leq \frac{n-1}{3} \, . \tag{3}$$

Nous avons fait une conjecture plus forte: *dans un graphe hypohamiltonien, il n'existe pas de cycle de longueur 4*. Nous y avons joint la conjecture qu'il n'existe pas de cycle de longueur 3, également plus forte que la propriété connue des rayons donnée au début du §5.2, mais que nous n'avons pu démontrer. Mais même en supposant que ces conjectures soient peut-être fausses pour des valeurs élevées de l'ordre, il semblait intéressant de les admettre, et nous avons modifié en conséquence le programme. Le tableau 3 donne le nombre de systèmes de rayons dans cette hypothèse.

Tableau 3

$d_O \rightarrow$ / $n \rightarrow$	10	11	12	13	14	15	16	17	18
3	1 (1)		2 (2)		4 (4)		7 (7)		10
4				1 (1)	1 (1)	3 (3)	4 (2)	8	10
5							1	1	3

Tous les calculs entrepris avec le programme modifié ont été menés à bien. Le nombre de cas traités est indiqué entre parenthèses. Le temps de calcul a été relativement faible. Il est remarquable que dans l'ensemble de ces calculs on ait trouvé seulement six graphes maximaux, dont les trois premiers étaient hypohamiltoniens: le graphe de Petersen, le graphe d'ordre 13 découvert par le premier programme, et un graphe d'ordre 15 (fig. 9).

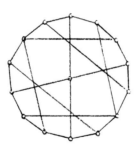

Fig. 9.
Un graphe hypohamiltonien
d'ordre 15.

6. CONCLUSION

Je ne veux point dissimuler ce qu'a d'inachevé cette étude sur la cyclabilité, qui a été par nécessité intercalée entre des activités réputées plus "sérieuses" et n'aurait certainement pas vu le jour sans le concours d'un programmeur de bonne volonté. Elle laisse ouvertes de nombreuses voies de recherche, tant expérimentale que théorique, où je souhaite voir s'engager quelques mathématiciens oisifs.

Que ces futurs explorateurs n'hésitent surtout pas à recourir aux ordinateurs. L'ère des longs calculs à la main et des brouillons innombrables est définitivement révolue. J'entends bien que l'usage des machines n'est point encore entré dans les mœurs du mathématicien moyen (sans quoi cet ouvrage n'eût pas eu à être écrit), et que l'une des raisons en est la distance entre le langage traditionnel du mathématicien et celui de la machine, si habillée soit-elle. Mais l'effort d'adaptation du mathématicien aux servitudes provisoires de son instrument est dès maintenant des plus rentables, en attendant le jour sans doute relativement proche où, grâce à l'incorporation de quelques notions essentielles de logique et d'algorithmique dans la culture mathématique de base et à la satisfaction par les constructeurs de machines et de langages des exigences les plus naturelles de leurs clients, la communication entre l'homme et la machine sera vraiment immédiate.

Cela ne signifie pas, répétons-le, que tout le travail puisse être laissé à l'ordinateur. Il ne s'agit pas de le cravacher à tort et à travers, mais de le guider d'une main ferme vers les obstacles à franchir. C'est cette seule attitude qui fera de l'ordinateur la plus noble conquête du mathématicien.

RÉFÉRENCES

Berge, C., 1958, Théorie des graphes et ses applications (Dunod, Paris).

Berge, C., 1963, Revue Française de Recherche Opérationnelle, 29, 405-406.

Berge, C., 1964, Revue Francaise de Recherche Opérationnelle, 31, 214-218.

Petersen, J., 1898, L'Intermédiaire des Mathématiciens, 5, 225-227.

Sainte-Laguë, A., 1926, Mémorial des Sciences Mathématiques, 18.

A PROBLEM IN STABLE HOMOTOPY THEORY
AND THE DIGITAL COMPUTER

A. LIULEVICIUS *
University of Chicago

1. INTRODUCTION

One of the outstanding problems in algebraic topology is to compute the structure of the homotopy groups of spheres. It is known that the groups $\pi_{n+i}(S^n)$ are independent of n if $i < n-1$ (and will be denoted by G_i), and are finite abelian groups if $i \neq 0$, so in order to study the groups G_i $(i > 0)$ it is sufficient to study their p-primary components. Currently the best method of doing this is due to Adams [1958]: in this method one approximates the p-primary component of G_i by a spectral sequence which starts with a family of vector spaces over Z_p which are defined by a construction in homological algebra. This construction is very tedious to carry out by hand, because the matrices involved in the computation soon become very big. It was natural to use a digital computer to speed up the computation. The first such attempt is described in Liulevicius [1964]. An improved program (much faster and more versatile) was used by Liulevicius [1966] to compute the first term in the Adams spectral sequence for stunted projective spaces over the real, complex, and quaternionic division rings. For stunted real projective spaces Mahowald [1966] used a different (and very clever) method. In this paper we will only describe the homological algebra construction and indicate how the program was constructed.

2. COALGEBRAS AND COMODULES

Let K be a field. A graded coalgebra C over K is a graded vector space $C = \{C_n\}_{n \in Z}$, together with two K-linear maps of degree zero:

$$\psi : C \to C \otimes_K C ,$$

$$\epsilon : C \to K ,$$

where $K_n = 0$ unless $n = 0$, and then $K_0 = K$, and $(C \otimes_K C)_n = \sum_i C_i \otimes_K C_{n-i}$. The maps ψ and ϵ obey the identities:

* The author was partially supported by NSF grant GP-3936 during the preparation of this paper.

$$(1 \otimes \psi) \circ \psi = (\psi \otimes 1) \circ \psi \ , \tag{1}$$

$$(1 \otimes \epsilon) \circ \psi = 1 \ , \tag{2}$$

$$(\epsilon \otimes 1) \circ \psi = 1 \ .$$

A left comodule M over the coalgebra C is a graded vector space over K with a K-linear map

$$\mu : M \to C \otimes_K M$$

of degree zero, such that

$$(\psi \dot{\otimes} 1) \circ \mu = (1 \otimes \mu) \circ \mu \ , \tag{3}$$

$$(\epsilon \otimes 1) \circ \mu = 1 \ . \tag{4}$$

If V is a graded vector space over K, we make $C \otimes_K V$ into a comodule over C by letting $\mu = \psi \otimes 1$. The identities $(1), (2)$ imply the identities $(3), (4)$.

If (M, μ) and (N, ν) are two comodules over C, and $f : M \to N$ is a K-linear map of degree q (that is, $f = \{f_n\}$ where $f_n : M_n \to N_{n+q}$), we say that f is a map of comodules over C if

$$(1 \otimes f) \circ \mu = \nu \circ f \ . \tag{5}$$

The comodules $C \otimes_K V$ above have the following interesting property: a C-comodule map $f : M \to C \otimes_K V$ is completely described by the K-linear map $\bar{f} = (\epsilon \otimes 1) \circ f$. This is easy to prove - suppose we are given such a K-linear map   : we then define $f : M \to C \otimes V$ by

$$f = (1 \otimes g) \circ \mu \ . \tag{6}$$

We claim that f satisfies (5):

$$(1 \otimes f) \circ \mu = (1 \otimes 1 \otimes g) \circ (1 \otimes \mu) \circ \mu \text{ by } (6) \ ,$$

$$= (1 \otimes 1 \otimes g) \circ (\psi \otimes 1) \circ \mu \text{ by } (3) \ ,$$

$$= (\psi \otimes 1) \circ (1 \otimes g) \circ \mu, \text{ since deg } \psi = 0 \ ,$$

$$= (\psi \otimes 1) \circ f \qquad \text{ by } (6) \ .$$

Conversely, given $f : M \to C \otimes V$, if we define

$$\bar{f} = (\epsilon \otimes 1) \circ f \ , \tag{7}$$

we note that

$$(1 \otimes \bar{f}) \circ \mu \; = (1 \otimes \epsilon \otimes 1) \circ (1 \otimes f) \circ \mu \text{ by (7)} ,$$

$$= (1 \otimes \epsilon \otimes 1) \circ (\psi \otimes 1) \circ f \text{ by (5)} ,$$

$$= f \qquad\qquad\qquad \text{by (2)} .$$

And if we start with g, then

$$\bar{f} = (\epsilon \otimes 1) \circ (1 \otimes g) \circ \mu$$

$$= (1 \otimes g) \circ (\epsilon \otimes 1) \circ \mu$$

$$= g \qquad\qquad \text{by (4)} .$$

If M is a C comodule, then by an injective resolution $\mathcal{I}$ is meant a sequence of C comodule maps:

$$0 \to M \overset{\eta}{\to} C \otimes V_0 \overset{d_0}{\to} C \otimes V_1 \to \dots \; C \otimes V_s \overset{d_s}{\to} C \otimes V_{s+1} \dots \tag{8}$$

such that η is a monomorphism, kernel $d_0 =$ image η, and for all q kernel $d_{q+1} =$ image d_q.

If N is any C comodule, then $\mathrm{Hom}_C (N, \mathcal{I})$ is a bigraded cochain complex with the vector space in bigrading (s, t) being all maps of degree t in $\mathrm{Hom}_C(N, C \otimes V_s)$. We define $\mathrm{Ext}_C^{s,t} (N, M) = H_s (\mathrm{Hom}_C(N, \mathcal{I})_t)$.

For the topological applications we will be interested in comodules over the coalgebra C, called the dual of the Steenrod algebra (see Milnor [1958], Epstein and Steenrod [1962]) over $K = \mathbf{Z}_2$, which can be described as follows:

$$C = \mathbf{Z}_2[\gamma_1, \gamma_2, \dots, \gamma_n, \dots] \text{ as algebra} , \tag{9}$$

$$\text{grade } \gamma_n = 2^n - 1 ,$$

ψ is an algebra homomorphism and

$$\psi(\gamma_n) = \sum_{i=0}^{n} \gamma_{n-i}^{2^i} \otimes \gamma_i .$$

We notice that C is finite dimensional over $\mathbf{Z}_2$ in each grading, although the dimension increases rapidly. Indeed, if $p(C) = \sum_n a_n t^n$ is the Poincaré power series of C, where $a_n = \dim_{\mathbf{Z}_2} C_n$, then

$$p(C) = \prod_{i=1}^{\infty} (1 - t^{2^i - 1})^{-1} . \tag{10}$$

3. THE COMPUTATIONAL ALGORITHM

We want to construct an injective resolution $\mathcal{I}$ of a special type: it will be minimal in the sense that dim $(V_{q,n})$ will be the smallest possible.

Let $p:C \to \bar{C}$ be a K-linear retraction onto the elements of strictly positive grading. If M is a C comodule, we let $P(M) = $ kernel $(p \otimes 1) \circ \mu$, and call elements $x \in P(M)$ primitive elements of M.

Proposition 1. *If A, B are C comodules and $f:A \to B$ is a C comodule map, then there is a C comodule $C \otimes W$ and a C comodule map $g:B \to C \otimes W$ such that*

$$\text{kernel } g = \text{image } f, \quad \text{image } g \supset 1 \otimes W. \tag{11}$$

We prove Proposition 1 by letting $D = B/\text{image } f$ with the comodule action inherited from B. We let $W = P(D)$, and let $r:D \to W$ be a K-linear retraction onto the subspace W. We let $j:B \to D$ be the quotient map. To define a C comodule map $g:B \to C \otimes W$ we only have to define a K-linear map $\bar{g}:B \to W$. We let $\bar{g} = r \circ j$.

We first claim that $g \circ f$ is zero. But this is easy, since

$$g \circ f = (1 \otimes \bar{g}) \circ \mu' \circ f$$

$$= (1 \otimes r \circ j) \circ (1 \otimes f) \circ \mu$$

$$= 0, \text{ for } j \circ f = 0.$$

Thus g induces a map $k:D \to C \otimes W$. Suppose kernel $k \neq 0$. We look at the lowest positive degree m in which kernel $k \neq 0$ and pick a $y \in$ kernel k_m. Then $y \in P(D)$, and hence $k(y) = 1 \otimes \bar{k}(y) = 1 \otimes r(y) = 1 \otimes y = 0$, a contradiction. Since $k(P(D)) = 1 \otimes W$, the second assertion of (11) also holds.

4. CONSTRUCTION OF THE PROGRAM

The program was constructed using IBM FAP language. FORTRAN was not useful, since memory space was at a premium and most of the subroutines had to be tailored to the combinatorial nature of the problem.

The first part of the program concerns itself with computing the mapping $\psi:C \to C \otimes C$ in (9). In each grading of C a lexicographic order on the monomials in γ_i is introduced, and a subroutine to generate the next monomial in the sequence is constructed. This allows the computer to write down on demand the ordered monomial basis for C_n for every natural number n.

The machine algorithm is based on Proposition 1. All the maps in (8) have zero degree. The algorithm assumes that (8) has been constructed in grades $<n$ and checks if new generators have to be added in grade n. More precisely: suppose

$$C \otimes V_{s-1} \xrightarrow{\ d_{s-1}\ } C \otimes V_s \xrightarrow{\ d_s\ } C \otimes V_{s+1} \tag{12}$$

is such that $V_{s+1,k} = 0$ for all $k > n-1$, and image d_{s-1} = kernel d_s in grades less than or equal to n. The machine writes down the matrix of d_{s-1} with respect to the standard basis in $(C \otimes V_{s-1})_n$ and $(C \otimes V_s)_n$. The matrix is then row-reduced by elementary row operations, and the columns containing the leading entries are tagged (say by 1-tags). The rows of the matrix for $(d_s)_n$ corresponding to the untagged basis elements in $(C \otimes V_s)_n$ constitute a matrix of the transformation k induced by $(d_s)_n$ on the quotient space of $(C \otimes V_s)_n$ by the image of $(d_{s-1})_n$. Elementary column operations on this matrix are now performed to find out the kernel of k. New tags (say 2-tags) are given to rows which contain leading entries in the column-reduced matrix. If a basis element of $(C \otimes V_s)$ modulo image d_s does not have a 2-tag, it means that it plus a suitable linear combination of the tagged elements is a basis element of kernel k. For every such basis element α we introduce a basis element $\tilde{\alpha}$ in $V_{s+1,n}$, and define

$$(\bar{d}_s)_n : (C \otimes V_s)_n \rightarrow V_{s+1,n}$$

as follows: if β is a basis element in $(C \otimes V_s)_n$ and has no 1-tag and no 2-tag, we send β into $\tilde{\beta}$; if β has no 1-tag and a 2-tag, we send β into zero; if β has a 1-tag, then the coefficient of $\tilde{\gamma}$ in $\bar{d}_s(\beta)$ is obtained as follows: the 1-tag indicates that β heads a column with a leading entry - look up the row A which contains the leading entry, go to the column headed by γ, and let the entry in row A in this column be the scalar c; then the coefficient of $\tilde{\gamma}$ in $\bar{d}_s(\beta)$ is $-c$.

5. COMPUTATION

The machine used for the computation was the IBM 7094. The 1964 program ran rather slowly, since the program stored the results of the computations of ψ on magnetic tape. The 1966 program did not store ψ, but recomputed it whether it was needed. The current version does in a minute of computation time what takes about two weeks of hard work to do by hand.

REFERENCES

Adams, J. F., 1958, Comment. Math. Helv. 32, 180-214.
Epstein, D. B. A. and N. E. Steenrod, 1962, Cohomology operations (Princeton University).
Liulevicius, A., 1964, Coalgebras, resolutions and the computer (The University of Chicago).
Liulevicius, A., 1966, Stable homotopy of stunted projective spaces (to appear).
Mahowald, M., 1966, Metastable homotopy of S^n (to appear).
Milnor, J., 1958, Annals of Math. 67, 150-171.

OBTENTION AUTOMATIQUE
DES ÉQUATIONS DE RUNGE ET KUTTA

J. MARTINET et Y. SIRET
Faculté des Sciences de Grenoble

1. INTRODUCTION

Soit

$$dx/dt = h(x) \qquad (1)$$

une équation différentielle du premier ordre, où h est une fonction numérique indéfiniment dérivable.

On sait que la condition initiale $x(0) = 0$ détermine une solution et une seule x de (1), indéfiniment dérivable également.

Il est clair que :

$$x'(0) = h(0)$$

$$x''(0) = h(0)h'(0) .$$

Plus généralement, l'ensemble des nombres $x'(0)$, $x''(0), \ldots, x^{(k)}(0)$ est déterminé par les valeurs en zéro de h et de ses dérivées d'ordre $\leqslant k\text{-}1$.

Posons :

$$\overline{x}(t) = th\left[t\,\frac{h(0)}{2} \right]$$

on vérifie aisément que :

$$x(0) = \overline{x}(0) ; \quad x'(0) = \overline{x}'(0) ; \quad x''(0) = \overline{x}''(0) .$$

On définit ainsi un procédé pour obtenir des valeurs numériques de la solution x, au voisinage de zéro, avec une erreur du troisième ordre, et ce procédé évite le calcul de $h'(0)$.

Plus généralement, soit :

$$y' = dy/dt = f(y) \qquad (2)$$

un système différentiel canonique du premier ordre dans R^n (espace vectoriel à n dimensions sur R), où f est une application de R^n dans R^n, indéfiniment différentiable.

(On rappelle qu'il est toujours possible de transformer un système $y' = f(y,t)$ en un système canonique: il suffit d'ajouter l'équation $t' = 1$.)

Comme pour (1), la condition $y(0) = 0 \in \mathbf{R}^n$ détermine une et une seule solution de (2), et nous désirons trouver un procédé numérique pour calculer $y(t)$ au voisinage de zéro.

Dorénavant, si g est une application indéfiniment différentiable de $\mathbf{R}^p$ dans $\mathbf{R}^q$, nous appellerons jet d'ordre k en 0 de g (ou k-jet en 0 de g) l'ensemble des valeurs en $0 \in \mathbf{R}^p$ de g et de ses dérivées partielles d'ordre $\leqslant k$.

Il est clair, à partir de l'exemple (1), que le k-jet en 0 de y est une fonction du $(k-1)$-jet en 0 ($\in \mathbf{R}^n$) de f.

La théorie des jets permettra, dans la première partie, de formaliser les calculs correspondants.

Soit A_r (r: entier $\geqslant 1$) un tableau triangulaire de coefficients numériques $A_{i,j}$ ($0 \leqslant i \leqslant j \leqslant r-1$); considérons la fonction $A_r f(t)$ ($t \in \mathbf{R}$), à valeurs dans $\mathbf{R}^n$, définie par:

$$A_r f(t) = \sum_{i=0}^{r-1} A_{i,r-1}\, y^i(t)$$

où:

$$y^0(t) = tf(0)$$

$$y^1(t) = tf[A_{0,0}\, y^0(t)]$$

. . . .

$$y^p(t) = tf\left[\sum_{i=0}^{p-1} A_{i,p-1}\, y^i(t)\right]$$

. . . .

L'application $f \to A_r f$ est appelée un algorithme de Runge-Kutta de rang r (Ceschino et Kuntzmann [1963]).

Il est clair que $A_r f(0) = 0$ et que le k-jet en 0 de $A_r f$ est une fonction du $(k-1)$-jet en 0 de f.

Remarquons que $\bar{x}$, dans l'example (1), est $A_2 h$, avec

$$A_2 = \begin{array}{|c|c|} \hline A_{00} & \\ \hline A_{01} & A_{11} \\ \hline \end{array} = \begin{array}{|c|c|} \hline \frac{1}{2} & \\ \hline 0 & 1 \\ \hline \end{array}$$

et l'on voit que pour tout n et pour tout système (2) de dimension n, $A_2 f(t)$ est, au troisième ordre près, la valeur de la solution vérifiant $y(0) = 0$.

A_2 est appelé un procédé de Runge-Kutta de rang 2 et d'ordre 2 (abréviation RK 2-2).

Maintenant, nous pouvons poser la question suivante: Étant donné deux entiers positifs, r et k, est-il possible de trouver un algorithme de rang r (soit A_r) tel que pour toute application f, indéfiniment différentiable de R^n dans R^n, $A_r f$ et y (solution de (2), avec $y(0) = 0$) aient le même k-jet au point zéro ?

Pour résoudre ce problème, il faut d'abord calculer en fonction du $(k-1)$-jet en 0 de f les k-jets en 0 de y et de $A_r f$, puis les identifier en f: on obtiendra alors un système d'équations en $A_{i,j}$; ce sont les équations de Runge-Kutta pour le rang r et l'ordre k.

La première partie (§§2-5) développe la formalisation des calculs en terme de jets et fournit une méthode systématique pour écrire les équations de Runge-Kutta de rang et d'ordre quelconques.

La deuxième partie (§§6-9) donne, sans entrer dans les détails du programme, les grandes lignes des procédés utilisés pour réaliser ces calculs en machine.

Des exemples de résultats sont donnés en annexe. Il faut insister sur le fait que ces résultats sont déjà connus, depuis assez longtemps. L'aspect nouveau réside dans la formalisation des calculs et leur réalisation en machine.

2. JETS (EHRESMANN [1953])

Tous les espaces vectoriels mentionnés ici sont des espaces vectoriels sur R.

2.1. *Définition*

Soit $E_{n,p}$ l'espace vectoriel des applications indéfiniment différentiables de R^n dans R^p.

Soit ω_k (k entier $\geqslant 0$) la relation d'équivalence sur $E_{n,p}$: $f \equiv g \bmod \omega_k \Leftrightarrow f$ et g ont même valeur en 0, ainsi que toutes leurs dérivées partielles d'ordre $\leqslant k$.

L'espace quotient de $E_{n,p}$ par ω_k est appelé espace vectoriel des *jets* *d'ordre k* (ou k-jets) *en* 0 de *source* R^n *et de but* R^p; on le notera $J_{n,p}^k$.

2.2. *Structure de $J_{n,p}^k$*

2.2.1. Si E et F sont deux espaces vectoriels, on notera $\mathrm{Hom}(E,F)$ l'espace des applications linéaires de E dans F.

On notera $\mathrm{Hom}_S(E^k, F)$ l'espace vectoriel des applications k-*linéaires* et *symétriques* de $E \times \ldots \times E$ (k fois) dans F, c'est-à-dire telles que:

$$h(x_1, \ldots, x_k) = h(x_{\sigma(1)}, \ldots, x_{\sigma(k)})$$

où σ désigne une permutation quelconque de l'ensemble $\{1, 2, \ldots, k\}$.

2.2.2. On sait qu'il existe, pour tout entier $k > 0$ et tout espace vectoriel E, un espace vectoriel appelé puissance symétrique k-ème de E, noté $\overset{k}{\vee}E$, et une application k-linéaire et symétrique i_k de E^k dans $\overset{k}{\vee}E$, tels que $\mathrm{Hom}_S(E^k, F)$ soit isomorphe à $\mathrm{Hom}(\overset{k}{\vee}E, F)$ par l'application qui à $h \in \mathrm{Hom}(\overset{k}{\vee}E, F)$ fait correspondre $h \circ i_k \in \mathrm{Hom}_S(E^k, F)$ (Bourbaki (à paraître)).
    $\overset{k}{\vee}E$ est engendré par les éléments $i_k(x_1, \ldots, x_k)$ avec $x_1, x_2, \ldots, x_k \in E$.
    Evidemment, $\overset{1}{\vee}E = E$.
    L'espace vectoriel

$$\vee E = E \oplus \overset{2}{\vee}E \oplus \ldots \oplus \overset{k}{\vee}E \oplus \ldots$$

est de plus muni de façon naturelle d'une multiplication (notée $\vee$) et appelée produit symétrique, qui en fait une algèbre commutative et qui vérifie la formule:

$$i_k(x_1, \ldots, x_k) = x_1 \vee x_2 \vee \ldots \vee x_k$$

$\vee E$ est *l'algèbre symétrique* de l'espace vectoriel E.
    Enfin, si E et F sont deux espaces vectoriels et si

$$f : \overset{h}{\vee}E \to \overset{l}{\vee}F$$

$$g : \overset{k}{\vee}E \to \overset{m}{\vee}F$$

sont deux applications linéaires, on peut définir une application linéaire

$$f \vee g : \overset{h+k}{\vee}E \to \overset{l+m}{\vee}F$$

par la formule:

$$f \vee g(x_1 \vee \ldots \vee x_{h+k})$$

$$= \frac{1}{(h+k)!} \sum_{\sigma} f(x_{\sigma(1)} \vee \ldots \vee x_{\sigma(h)}) \vee g(x_{\sigma(h+1)} \vee \ldots \vee x_{\sigma(h+k)})$$

où σ parcourt l'ensemble des permutations de l'intervalle $[1, h+k]$.
    L'opération $f \vee g$, ou produit symétrique de f et g, est bilinéaire et commutative.

2.2.3. L'espace $\boldsymbol{J}^k_{n,p}$ de 2.1. s'identifie alors de façon naturelle à la somme directe:

$$\boldsymbol{R}^p \oplus \mathrm{Hom}(\boldsymbol{R}^n, \boldsymbol{R}^p) \oplus \mathrm{Hom}(\overset{2}{\vee}\boldsymbol{R}^n, \boldsymbol{R}^p) \oplus \ldots \oplus \mathrm{Hom}(\overset{k}{\vee}\boldsymbol{R}^n, \boldsymbol{R}^p) . \qquad (3)$$

En effet, si f est une application différentiable de $\boldsymbol{R}^n$ dans $\boldsymbol{R}^p$, le k-jet de en 0 peut s'écrire:

$$(F_0, F_1, \ldots, F_k)$$

où

$$F_0 = f(0) \in \boldsymbol{R}^p$$

F_1 = matrice des dérivées partielles premières de f en 0; celle-ci s'interprète comme élément de $\mathrm{Hom}(\boldsymbol{R}^n, \boldsymbol{R}^p)$ par la règle:

$$F_1(e_i) = \frac{\partial f}{\partial x_i}$$

où $e_i = (0, 0, \ldots, 0, 1 \ldots, 0) \in \boldsymbol{R}^n$, 1 occupant la $i$ème place.

F_k = "tableau" des dérivées partielles d'ordre k de f en 0; il s'interprète comme une application k-linéaire symétrique de $\boldsymbol{R}^n$ dans $\boldsymbol{R}^p$, par la règle:

$$F_k(e_{i_1}, \ldots, e_{i_k}) = \frac{\partial^k f}{\partial x_{i_1} \cdots \partial x_{i_k}}$$

D'autre part, si $F = (F_0, F_1, \ldots, F_k)$ est un élément de la somme directe (3), il est clair que l'application f définie par:

$$f(x) = F_0 + F_1 \cdot x + \frac{1}{2!} F_2 \cdot x^2 + \ldots + \frac{1}{k!} F_k \cdot x^k$$

(où x^k est la k-ème puissance symétrique de $x \in \boldsymbol{R}^n$) a précisément F pour k-jet en 0.

Remarque : Ceci montre, en passant, que le développement de Taylor à l'ordre k, pour une application différentiable de $\boldsymbol{R}^n$ dans $\boldsymbol{R}^p$, s'écrit, en utilisant l'algèbre symétrique, de la même façon que dans le cas d'une seule fonction numérique.

2.2.4. Dans l'expression ainsi précisée de $J_{n,p}^k$, on a les règles évidentes:

$$(F_0, \ldots, F_k) + (G_0, \ldots, G_k) = (F_0 + G_0, \ldots, F_k + G_k)$$

$$\lambda(F_0, \ldots, F_k) = (\lambda F_0, \ldots, \lambda F_k) \quad \lambda \in \boldsymbol{R}$$

2.3. *Cas particulier important: structure de $J_{1,n}^k$*

La structure de cet espace est très simple: il est isomorphe à la somme directe de $(k+1)$ exemplaires de $\boldsymbol{R}^n$, les dérivées successives en un point d'une application différentiable de $\boldsymbol{R}$ dans $\boldsymbol{R}^n$ s'interprétant de façon naturelle comme des éléments de $\boldsymbol{R}^n$ (vecteurs vitesse, accélération, etc. ...).

Deux types d'homomorphismes seront particulièrement utiles dans la suite (il est bon de remarquer qu'ils n'ont de sens que dans ce cas).

a) $$D : J_{1,n}^k \to J_{1,n}^{k-1}$$

défini par:

$$D(F_0, F_1, \ldots, F_k) = (F_1, F_2, \ldots, F_k) \ .$$

Il correspond à l'opération de dérivation des fonctions d'une variable réelle.

b) $$T : \boldsymbol{J}_{1,n}^k \to \boldsymbol{J}_{1,n}^{k+1}$$

défini par:

$$T(F_0, F_1, \ldots, F_k) = (0, F_0, 2F_1, \ldots, (k+1)F_k) \ .$$

Il correspond à l'opération de multiplication d'une fonction $f(t)$ par t.

2.4. *Produit de jets*

    On considère $\boldsymbol{J}_{n,p}^k$ et $\boldsymbol{J}_{p,q}^k$; soient

$$F = (F_0, F_1, \ldots, F_k) \in \boldsymbol{J}_{n,p}^k \text{ et } G = (G_0, G_1, \ldots, G_k) \in \boldsymbol{J}_{p,q}^k \ .$$

Si $F_0 = 0 \in \boldsymbol{R}^p$, on peut définir de façon naturelle un produit $G \circ F$, élément de $\boldsymbol{J}_{n,q}^k$; en effet, si f est une application différentiable de $\boldsymbol{R}^n$ dans $\boldsymbol{R}^p$ dont le k-jet en 0 soit F, et si g est une application différentiable de $\boldsymbol{R}^p$ dans $\boldsymbol{R}^q$ dont le k-jet en 0 soit G, alors comme $f(0) = 0$ $(= F_0)$, le k-jet en 0 de la fontion composée $h = g \circ f$, application de $\boldsymbol{R}^n$ dans $\boldsymbol{R}^p$, est déterminé par les k-jets en 0 de f et g; $G \circ F$ sera par définition le k-jet de h.

    Un calcul facile (la notion de produit symétrique permettant de travailler avec les jets comme avec des polynômes d'une variable réelle, le produit des nombres étant remplacé par le produit symétrique des vecteurs et des fonctions) montre que, si l'on pose

$$H = (H_0, H_1, \ldots, H_h) = G \circ F$$

on a:

$$H_0 = G_0$$

$$H_1 = G_1 \cdot F_1$$

$$\cdots\cdots\cdots\cdots$$

$$H_l = \sum_{m=1}^{l} \sum_{(\alpha, i) \in \theta(m, l)} \binom{m}{\alpha_1} \binom{m - \alpha_1}{\alpha_2} \ldots 1 \cdot G_m \cdot F_{i_1}^{\alpha_1} \vee F_{i_2}^{\alpha_2} \ldots \vee F_{i_s}^{\alpha_s}$$

$$\cdots\cdots\cdots\cdots$$

où

1. $\theta(m, l)$ représente l'ensemble des couples

$$(\alpha, i) = [(\alpha_1, \dots, \alpha_S), (i_1, \dots, i_S)]$$

tels que:

$$\begin{cases} \text{les } \alpha_j \text{ et les } i_j \text{ sont entiers} \\ \alpha_j \geqslant 1 \text{ pour tout } j \\ 1 \leqslant i_1 < i_2 < \dots < i_S \\ \alpha_1 + \alpha_2 + \dots + \alpha_S = m \\ \alpha_1 i_1 + \dots + \alpha_S i_S = l \end{cases}$$

2. Un symbole tel que $F_{i_1}^{\alpha_1}$ représente la α_1-ème puissance symétrique de F_{i_1} ; $\vee$ représente le produit symétrique.

3. Le point $(\cdot)$ dans $G_m \cdot F_{i_1}^{\alpha_1} \vee \dots \vee F_{i_s}^{\alpha_s}$ traduit la composition des applications linéaires $F_{i_1}^{\alpha_1} \vee \dots \vee F_{i_s}^{\alpha_s}$ (à valeur dans $\overset{m}{\vee} R^p$ par définition) et G_m (dont la variable est précisément, par définition, dans $\overset{m}{\vee} R^p$).

En fait, dans la suite, il n'y aura pas à craindre de confusion entre les opérations de composition et de produit symétrique; on écrira le produit de deux jets et ne retenant que les concaténations de symboles tels que $G_3 F_2 F_1 F_1$.

Par exemple, on aura ainsi:

$$H_0 = G_0$$
$$H_1 = G_1 F_1$$
$$H_2 = G_1 F_2 + G_2 F_1 F_1$$
$$H_3 = G_1 F_3 + 2 G_2 F_1 F_2 + G_3 F_1 F_1 F_1$$

etc. ...

Le produit des jets obéit aux règles suivantes:

$$(G + G') \circ F = G \circ F + G' \circ F$$

$$(\lambda G) \circ F = (G \circ F)$$

mais il n'est pas linéaire en F.

3. JETS ET SYSTÈMES DIFFÉRENTIELS

Soit f une application indéfiniment différentiable de R^n dans R^n. Nous avons vu, dans l'introduction, que son $(k-1)$-jet en 0 (élément de $J_{n,n}^{k-1}$)

déterminait le k-jet en 0 de la solution du système différentiel $y' = f(y)$ vérifiant $y(0) = 0$ (ce k-jet étant un élément de $J_{1,n}^k$).

On définit donc ainsi une application de $J_{n,n}^{k-1}$ dans $J_{1,n}^k$, soit S^k.

Il est clair, en passant du langage des fonctions à celui des jets que, pour tout $F \in J_{n,n}^{k-1}$

$$Y = (0, Y_1, \ldots, Y_k) = S^k(F) \in J_{1,n}^k$$

vérifie l'équation suivante:

$$DY = F \circ Y_*$$

où

$$Y_* = (0, Y_1, \ldots, Y_{k-1}) \in J_{1,n}^{k-1}.$$

Cette équation détermine, en revenant aux définitions du produit des jets et de l'opération D, le jet Y.

Exemple: Calculer $Y = (0, Y_1, Y_2) = S^2(F)$

Posons $F = (F_0, F_1)$

$$DY = (Y_1, Y_2) \text{ d'une part },$$

$$F \circ Y_* = (F_0, F_1 Y_1) \text{ d'autre part }.$$

D'où

$$Y_1 = F_0 \text{ et } Y_2 = F_1 F_0$$

c'est-à-dire

$$Y = (0, F_0, F_1 F_0).$$

On trouvera, en Annexe 1, l'expression, calculée en machine, de $S^8 F$ en fonction de F, jet d'ordre 7.

4. JETS ET ALGORITHMES DE RUNGE-KUTTA

Soit A_r un algorithme de Runge-Kutta de rang r.

Si f est une application différentiable de R^n dans R^n, nous avons vu dans l'Introduction que le k-jet en 0 de $A_r f$ est déterminé par le $(k-1)$-jet en 0 de f. A_r définit donc une application A_r^k de $J_{n,n}^{k-1}$ dans $J_{1,n}^k$, quel que soit l'entier $k > 0$.

Il est clair, comme précédemment, que si $F \in J_{n,n}^{k-1}$, alors

$$A_r^k(F) = \sum_{i=0}^{r-1} A_{i,r-1} Y^i$$

où

$$Y^O = T(F \circ 0) \quad (0 \text{ est le jet nul de } \boldsymbol{J}_{1,n}^{k-1})$$

$$Y^1 = T(F \circ A_{0,0} \, Y_*^O)$$

$$\dots\dots\dots\dots\dots\dots$$

$$Y^p = T\left(F \circ \sum_{i=0}^{p-1} A_{i,p-1} \, Y_*^i\right)$$

Exemple: Calculer $A_2^2 F$, où

$$F = (F_0, F_1)$$

et $A_2 =$

$A_{0,0}$	
$A_{0,1}$	$A_{1,1}$

$$Y^O = (0, \, F_0, \, 0)$$

$$Y^1 = T(F_0, \, A_{0,0}F_1 F_0) = (0, \, F_0, \, 2A_{0,0}F_1 F_0)$$

$$A_2^2 F = A_{0,1}Y^O + A_{1,1}Y^1 = [0, \, (A_{0,1}+A_{1,1})F_0, \, 2A_{0,0}A_{1,1}F_1 F_0] \, .$$

On trouvera, en Annexe 2, l'expression, calculée en machine, de $A_4^4 F$.

5. ÉQUATIONS DE RUNGE-KUTTA

D'après l'Introduction, trouver une méthode de Runge-Kutta de rang r et d'ordre k, c'est trouver un algorithme de Runge-Kutta A_r de rang r tel que:

$$S^k(F) = A_r^k(F)$$

pour tout $F \in \boldsymbol{J}_{n,n}^{k-1}$ (et, en fait, quel que soit n).

L'identification des deux jets se fera en égalant les coefficients des divers monômes $F_{i_1} \dots\dots F_{i_p}$, qui sont évidemment indépendants.

Exemple: Equations de Runge-Kutta pour $r = k = 2$.

$$S^2 F = (0, \, F_0, \, F_1 F_0)$$

$$A_2^2 F = (0, \, (A_{0,1}+A_{1,1})F_0, \, 2A_{0,0}A_{1,1}F_1 F_0) \, ;$$

les équations sont donc:

$$A_{0,1} + A_{1,1} = 1$$

$$A_{0,0}A_{1,1} = \tfrac{1}{2}$$

On trouvera, en Annexe 3, les équations pour $r = k = 4$; $r = 6$, $k = 4$.

6. INTRODUCTION À LA DEUXIÈME PARTIE

L'exposé théorique de la première partie montre que toutes les opérations à faire sont des opérations formelles sur des symboles. Nous n'avons
plus à nous soucier de la signification des opérations. Il nous suffit d'écrire
des procédures qui réalisent les concaténations, les substitutions, les combinaisons linéaires et les identifications.

7. REPRÉSENTATION DES SYMBOLES DANS LA MÉMOIRE

7.1. *Note sur les listes*

Nous rappelons ici certaines notions que le lecteur trouvera exposées en
détail dans Cohen et Nguyen-Huu [1965], McCarthy *et al.* [1962], Abrahams
et al. [1964]. (Le lecteur familier des langages de listes, par ex. LISP,
peut sauter au § 8).

On appellera zone de mémoire organisée en liste un ensemble de dou-
blets (un doublet étant constitué par deux mémoires ou deux moitiés de mémoire) tels que le second élément de chaque doublet contienne l'adresse
d'un autre doublet (i.e. l'adresse de son premier élément); le premier élément contient soit une adresse, soit une information (code, chiffre).
Exemple:

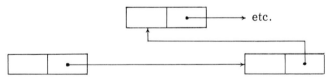

Si nous programmons en Algol (Cohen et Nguyen-Huu [1965]), il nous
suffira de prendre 2 tableaux (appelés TCAR et TCDR), que nous initiali-
serons de la façon suivante:

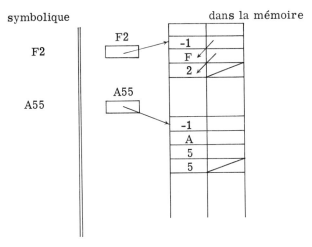

Les adresses sont ici les indices. Une mémoire fixe (IPD) pointe toujours vers la première mémoire libre de la zone (initialement TCAR [1]). Une telle zone est un "réservoir" qui sert à contenir des informations de deux sortes:

- les atomes (i.e. identificateurs ou nombres)
- les listes.

Représentation d'un atome

Les mémoires dont les noms sont F2 et A55 (ou tout autre nom) repèrent dans la zone en liste l'adresse d'un doublet dont la partie TCAR contient -1 (code de début d'un atome) et dont les parties TCAR des suivants contiennent les codes des caractères qui composent l'atome.

Remarques.
    1. La partie TCDR du dernier doublet (notée ) contient un code spécial qui sert de test de fin d'atome.
    2. Il est pratique d'écrire:

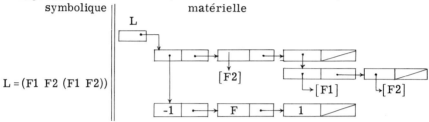

C'est ce que nous ferons dans la suite

Représentation d'une liste (ensemble structuré d'atomes)
                symbolique ‖   matérielle

L = (F1 F2 (F1 F2))

7.2. *Sélection d'éléments dans une liste ou de caractères dans un atome*
    On opère avec deux fonctions:
1. CAR: son argument est l'adresse d'un doublet
            sa valeur est le contenu de la partie TCAR de ce doublet
2. CDR: son argument est l'adresse d'un doublet
            sa valeur est le contenu de la partie TCDR du doublet.
On a: CAR(L) $\underset{\text{def}}{=}$ TCAR [L]

     CDR(L) $\underset{\text{def}}{=}$ TCDR [L] .

Exemple:

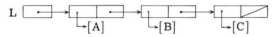

X: CAR(L)   X repère A
Y: CDR(L)   Y repère le 2ème doublet de la liste L, i.e. la liste (B C)
symboliquement:

$$L = (A\ B\ C)$$
$$CAR\,(L) = A$$
$$CDR\,(L) = (B\ C)$$

Par composition de ces deux fonctions, on peut atteindre n'importe quel élément d'une liste ou n'importe quel constituant d'un atome.

exemple 1: si L = (A B C D) alors CAR(CDR(CDR(L))) = C

exemple 2: si L = (A (B C) D) alors CAR(CAR(CDR(L))) = B

7.3. *Construction de listes*

Étant donnés une liste L2 et un élément de liste (atome ou liste) L1, on peut construire une nouvelle liste repérée par exemple par L3 et dont le "CAR" soit L1 et le "CDR", L2. Pour ce, on utilisera la fonction CONS (construire) dont l'essentiel de la définition est:

	commentaires
CONS:=IPD ;	. on prend le premier doublet libre,
M:=IPD;	repéré par IPD
IPD:=TCDR[IPD] ;	. on affecte à IPD l'adresse du doublet libre suivant
TCAR[M]:=L1 ;	. la partie TCAR du doublet pris sera L1,
TCDR[M]:=L2 ;	. sa partie TCDR, L2.

Ainsi, si l'on fait:

L3:=CONS (L1, L2) on aura:

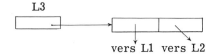

L3

vers L1 vers L2

7.4.

L'utilisation de ces fonctions auxquelles on ajoute des prédicats d'égalité entre atomes ou listes, par exemple, permet de construire un certain nombre de procédures qui réaliseront les opérations définies dans la première partie.

8. PROGRAMMATION DES OPÉRATIONS DÉFINIES DANS LA PREMIÈRE PARTIE

8.1. *Produit*

Rappelons que si l'on a:

$$F = (F_0, F_1, \ldots, F_n)$$

$$\text{et } G = (G_0, G_1, \ldots, G_n)$$

alors $H = F \circ G$ a pour composantes

$$H_0 = F_0$$

$$H_l = \sum_{m=1}^{l} (\text{coeff. numérique}) \times F_m \cdot G_{i_1}^{a_1} G_{i_2}^{a_2} \ldots G_{i_p}^{a_p}$$

$$\begin{cases} a_1 + a_2 + \ldots a_p = m \\ a_1 i_1 + a_2 i_2 + \ldots a_p i_p = 1 \\ a_i \geqslant 1, \quad 1 \leqslant i_1 < i_2 < \ldots < i_p \end{cases}$$

Les puissances du type G_m^p seront en fait écrites

$$\underleftrightarrow{G_m \ G_m \ G_m \cdots G_m}_{p \text{ fois}}$$

On voit que $H_1 = F_1 G_1$ et dans le cas général H_l sera une somme de produits.

8.1.1. *Représentation des jets*
Les jets seront représentés par la liste de leurs éléments. Comme cas particulier, les jets initiaux seront des listes d'atomes:
exemple: F = (F0 F1 F2 F3).

8.1.2. *Représentation des composantes d'un jet*
Comme en général les composantes sont des sommes de produits, il nous faut donner une représentation à ces structures.
    Un produit de la forme $F_2 G_1 G_2$ sera représenté par:
(* F2 G1 G2).
    Une somme de produits $F_2 G_1 G_2 + F_1 G_1$ sera représentée par:
(+(* F2 G1 G2) (* F1 G1)).
    Les opérateurs +, * portent sur la liste des éléments qui suivent. La procédure réalisant le produit aura comme paramètres les deux pointeurs des listes représentant les jets à composer et le nombre d'éléments de la liste résultat.
exemple: F = (F0 F1 F2 ....)
         G = (G0 G1 G2 ....)
Si l'on fait
         X:= Produit (G, F, 2) on aura
         X = (F0 (* F1 G1)).
A partir du rang 3, les éléments de la liste résultat se compliquent. Si l'on revient à la formule générale, on voit qu'il y a deux sortes de sommations:
    a) une sommation sur m: m allant de 1 à l
    b) pour un m donné, une sommation sur tous les termes $F_m G_{i_1} G_{i_2} \ldots G_{i_m}$ fabriqués avec toutes les suites ordonnées (au sens large) de m indices strictement positifs $(i_1, i_2, \ldots, i_m)$ et dont la somme est l.
Exemple, pour $l = 4$, aux coefficients numériques près, le terme H_4 est:

$$F_1 G_4 + \underbrace{F_2 G_1 G_3 + F_2 G_2 G_2}_{m=2} + F_3 G_1 G_1 G_2 + F_4 G_1 G_1 G_1 G_1$$

$$\underset{m=1}{} \qquad\qquad\qquad\qquad \underset{m=3}{} \qquad\qquad \underset{m=4}{}$$

Les termes étant de la forme $F_i G_k G_l \ldots$ on voit que

a) la valeur de m permet de calculer l'indice i de F_i ($i = m+1$). On peut donc prélever le terme F_i dans le jet F.

b) pour un m donné, il faut concaténer certains éléments du jet G dans un ordre bien déterminé. Il est pratique de connaître à priori la suite d'indices qui permet de prélever les éléments de G en vue de cette concaténation.

Cette suite d'indices, ou "trésor", calculée à priori par un programme à part, est entrée sous forme d'une liste, dont le début est le suivant:

$$(1(2\ 11) \quad (3\ 12\ 111) \quad (4(13\ 22)112\ 1111)\ldots)$$

$$l=1 \quad l=2 \qquad l=3 \qquad\qquad l=4$$

On peut voir que

a) chaque sous-liste correspond à une valeur de l

b) chaque sous-liste a comme éléments des nombres ou des sous-listes de nombres, ces sous-listes correspondant à plusieurs décompositions d'indices pour un m donné.

Si l'on se reporte à la façon dont les atomes sont représentés en mémoire

exemple: 112 représenté par

l'on voit que la suite des chiffres qui forme les nombres donne l'ordre dans lequel il faut concaténer les éléments de G.

Exemple: pour $l = 2$, i.e. pour construire le 3ème élément du produit $F \circ G$ nous choisissons dans ce "trésor" d'indices la sous-liste (2 11)

- L'élément du jet F à considérer est F2

- Nous fabriquons les assemblages:

$$(* \ F2\ G2)\ \text{et}\ (* \ F2\ G1\ G2)$$

grâce à une procédure utilisant CONS et nous réunissons ces deux assemblages dans:

$$(+ \ (* \ F2\ G2)\ (* \ F2\ G1\ G1))\ .$$

Dans le cas général, on devra concaténer, dans l'ordre donné par la liste des indices, des produits ou des sommes de produits. Grâce à une procédure de concaténation on se ramènera toujours à une somme de produits.

Exemple:

$$(+ \ a\ b) \cdot (+(* \ c\ d)e) \rightarrow (+(* \ a\ c\ d)(* \ a\ e)(* \ b\ c\ d)(* \ b\ e))\ .$$

Il est clair que le "trésor" des coefficients va de pair avec le "trésor" des indices; on le calculera à partir de ce dernier. Son début est:

$$(1(1\ 1)(1\ 2\ 1)(1\ 3(2\ 1)1)\ldots\ldots\ldots)$$

Ces coefficients (sauf les 1), seront introduits au moment de la sommation sur la suite des indices.

Exemple complet:

$$F = (F0\ F1\ F2)$$

$$Y = (Y0\ Y1\ Y2)$$

$$\text{produit } (F,\ Y,\ 3) = (F0(*\ F1\ Y1)(+(*\ F1\ Y2)(*\ F2\ Y1\ Y1)))$$

8.2. *Détermination des y^k*

Cela correspond à une substitution.

Étant donnée la liste résultat obtenue après avoir effectué le produit (Produit $(F,\ Y,\ n)$), cette opération consiste à substituer successivement dans toute la liste le premier élément (i.e. F0) à Y1, puis le deuxième élément (qui ne contient plus de Y1) à Y2, et de façon générale le $n$ième élément de la liste à Y_n. La procédure de substitution donne comme résultat une liste dont les éléments sont en général des sommes de produits.

Pour notre exemple cela donne:

$$(F0(*\ F1\ F0)(+(*\ F1\ F1\ F0)(*\ F2\ F0\ F0)))$$

8.3. *Opération T*

Partant d'une liste $(G0\ G1\ G2\ldots)$, cette opération se traduit par la création de la liste $(0\ G0(*\ 2\ G1)(*\ 3\ G2)\ldots)$ en distribuant l'entier n, si l'élément de G est une somme de produits.

8.4. *Combinaison linéaire*

On se donne à priori un tableau triangulaire de coefficients A_{ij} entré en mémoire sous forme de liste

$$(A00(A01\ A11)(A02\ A12\ A22)(\ldots))$$

Si l'on a gardé, par exemple dans un tableau, les adresses des n jets déjà construits, il est aisé de prélever le $n$ième élément de cette liste de coefficients et de construire un jet dont les éléments soient une combinaison linéaire des éléments des jets donnés.

Par exemple, si l'on a déjà construit

$$(x_1\ x_2\ x_3)$$

$$(y_1\ y_2\ y_3)$$

$$(z_1\ z_2\ z_3)$$

la procédure donnera pour résultat:

$$((+(*\ A02\ x_1)(*\ A12\ y_1)(*\ A22\ z_1))(+(*\ldots \text{ etc. }\ldots$$

En fait, dans notre cas, tous les jets à combiner linéairement ont pour premier élément l'atome F0. Il est pratique de créer une variable intermédiaire dont la valeur est la somme des coefficients $\sum_i A_{ij}$.

Exemple:

$$B1 = A01 + A11$$

$$B2 = A02 + A12 + A22 \text{ etc. } \dots$$

B0 étant identique à A00 .

Remarque

Il se trouve d'ailleurs que ces variables sont appelées θ_j dans Ceschino et Kuntzmann [1963], et leurs valeurs numériques donnent les subdivisions du pas de la variable indépendante.

Le premier élément de la liste donnée par la procédure qui réalise les combinaisons linéaires sera toujours de la forme $(*[B_i]$ F0).

Exemple complet: si l'on applique l'algorithme de Runge-Kutta, défini dans la première partie, la dernière combinaison linéaire, pour le rang 3 est:

((* B2 F0)

(+(* A12 2 F1 A00 F0)(* A22 2 F1 B1 F0))

(+(* A12 3 F2 A00 F0 A00 F0)(* A22 3 F1 A11 2 F1 A00 F0)

(* A22 3 F2 B1 F0 B1 F0)))

8.5. *Identification*

A ce point de programme, nous avons deux listes obtenues respectivement en 8.2 et 8.4.

L'identification, élément par élément, de ces listes fournit les équations cherchées

élément de la liste 8.2	éléments de la liste 8.4
F0	(* B2 F0)
(* F1 F0)	(+(* A12 2 F1 A00 F0)
	(* A22 2 F1 B1 F0))

On voit que les deux premières équations seront:

$$B2 = 1$$

$$2 \ A12 \ A00 + 2 \ A22 \ B1 = 1$$

Dans la pratique, le programme d'identification sépare dans chaque produit la partie qui contient des F_i. Par exemple:

$$(* \ F1 \ F0) \ \text{Donne: } ((F1 \ F0)1)$$

$$(+(* \ A \ 12 \ 2 \ F1 \ A00 \ F0)(* \ A22 \ 2 \ F1 \ B1 \ F0)) \ \text{Donne:}$$

$$(+((F1 \ F0) \ B1 \ 2 \ A22)) \ ((F1 \ F0)(A00 \ 2 \ A12))) \ .$$

Cela facilite évidemment l'identification. On remarquera que le fait de commuter les termes de la somme ou l'ordre des coefficients n'a pas d'importance. Il faut surtout prendre garde de ne pas commuter les F_i à l'intérieur d'un produit.

Dans le cas $p = 3$, qui nous a servi d'exemple jusqu'ici, nous aurons les équations:

$$B2 = 1$$

$$(B1 \ 2 \ A22 + A00 \ 2 \ A12) = 1$$

$$(A00 \ 2 \ A11 \ 3 \ A22) = 1$$

$$(B1 \ B1 \ 3 \ A22 + A00 \ A00 \ 3 \ A12) = 1$$

TRÉSOR DES INDICES

```
(
(11 2)
(111 12 3)
(1111 112 (13 22) 4)
(11111 1112 (113 122) (14 23) 5)
(111111 11112 (1113 1122) (114 123 222) (15 24 33) 6)
(1111111 111112 (11113 11122) (1114 1123 1222) (115 124 133 223)
            (16 25 34) 7)
(11111111 1111112 (111113 111122) (11114 11123 11222)
            (1115 1124 1133 1223 2222)
            (116 125 134 224 233) (17 26 35 44) 8)....)
```

TRÉSOR DES COEFFICIENTS

```
(
(1 1)
(1 2 1)
(1 3 (2 1) 1)
(1 4 (3 3) (2 2) 1)
(1 5 (4 6) (3 6 1) (2 2 1) 1)
(1 6 (5 10) (4 12 4) (3 6 3 3) (2 2 2) 1)
(1 7 (6 15) (5 20 10) (4 12 6 12 1) (3 6 6 3 3) (2 2 2 1) 1)....)
```

ORGANIGRAMME GÉNÉRAL

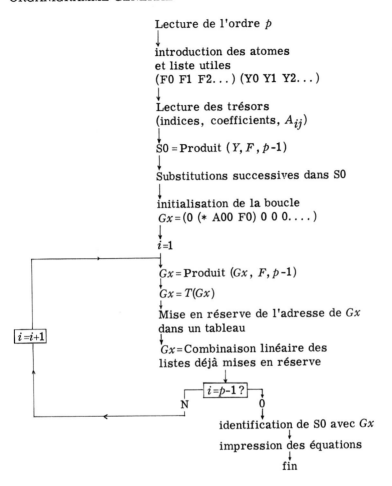

Lecture de l'ordre p

introduction des atomes
et liste utiles
(F0 F1 F2...) (Y0 Y1 Y2...)

Lecture des trésors
(indices, coefficients, A_{ij})

S0 = Produit $(Y, F, p-1)$

Substitutions successives dans S0

initialisation de la boucle
$Gx = (0\ (*\ A00\ F0)\ 0\ 0\ 0....)$

$i = 1$

Gx = Produit $(Gx, F, p-1)$

$Gx = T(Gx)$

Mise en réserve de l'adresse de Gx
dans un tableau

Gx = Combinaison linéaire des
listes déjà mises en réserve

$i = i+1$

$i = p-1$?

N   0

identification de S0 avec Gx

impression des équations

fin

EQUATIONS DE RUNGE-KUTTA ORDRE 2, RANG 2

    B1 = A01 + A11

GROUPE 1
   (B1)
    =
    1
GROUPE 2
   (A00 2 A11)
    =
    1

EQUATIONS DE RUNGE-KUTTA ORDRE 3, RANG 3

    B1 = A01 + A11
    B2 = A02 + A12 + A22

GROUPE 1
    (B2)
    =
    1

GROUPE 2
    (A00 2 A12 + B1 2 A22)
    =
    1

GROUPE 3
    (A00 2 A11 3 A22)
    =
    1
    (A00 A00 3 A12 + B1 B1 3 A22)
    =
    1

9. RÉSULTATS

On trouvera ci-dessus à titre d'exemple les équations pour les rangs 2 et 3, telles qu'on les obtient en machine, d'après l'organigramme précédent. Pour les ordres supérieurs, 4, 5, il est préférable de procéder autrement:

- obtention à priori de la liste S0 jusqu'à un ordre élevé (*annexe* 1)
- obtention de la combinaison linéaire pour le rang étudié (*Gx*) (*annexe* 2)
- identification jusqu'à l'ordre voulu de *Gx* avec S0 (*annexe* 3)
  ce qui donne les équations.

Cela permet de scinder le programme. Pour les ordres élevés, on procèdera donc "par morceaux".

Remarques.

Résultats théoriques - En comptant le nombre de groupements F_i apparaissant dans S0 (cf. annexe 1), on a le nombre d'équations à satisfaire pour un rang donné, ceci pour un *système canonique général*, car si on n'a qu'une seule équation $y' = f(x, y)$ donnant le système

$$\begin{vmatrix} y' \\ x' \end{vmatrix} = \begin{vmatrix} f(x, y) \\ 1 \end{vmatrix} ,$$

ce nombre se réduit; mais cela sort du cadre de l'algorithme (Ceschino et Kuntzmann [1963], p. 37, §16.3).

On a le tableau suivant:

rang de la méthode	1	2	3	4	5	6	7	8	9	.....	13	.....	20
nombre de coefficients A_{ij}	1	3	6	10	15	21	28	36	45		91		210
nombre d'équations à satisfaire pour un ordre égal au rang donné	1	2	4	8	17	37	85	201					

A partir du rang 5, on voit que le nombre d'inconnues est inférieur au nombre d'équations. Pour satisfaire les équations d'un ordre m, il faudra prendre une méthode de rang $r > m$ (Ceschino et Kuntzmann [1963]). Dans l'algorithme, il n'y a que le nombre des combinaisons linéaires qui soit augmenté. Les produits de jets ne se font que jusqu'à l'ordre m. Le cas de dégénérescence signalé au dessus a permis à Huta [1956, 1957] de déterminer à la main les équations pour l'ordre 6 avec 8 substitutions. On sait dans ce cas, que les 37 équations pour cet ordre se réduisent à 31. Cela peut se retrouver également par l'étude théorique (cf. également Sarafyan [1966]).

10. CONCLUSION

Les résultats obtenus sont conformes aux résultats connus. Le nombre impressionnant des équations de rang 9 et d'ordre 6 montre qu'il est inutile d'aller plus loin. Cependant, cette méthode peut s'appliquer à la détermination des équations pour des méthodes particulières de Runge-Kutta ou même des méthodes mixtes.

Nous devons aussi insister sur le fait que la méthode pour réaliser les différentes opérations est liée au traitement des listes en Algol. En LISP on aurait procédé autrement, au moins dans tout ce qui a rapport avec la représentation des atomes. Le lecteur non directement intéressé par la programmation ne retiendra que l'aspect démonstratif de la possibilité de faire automatiquement, grâce à une machine, certains calculs formels. Ce genre de travail montre en effet toute l'aide qu'on peut attendre d'une machine, dans les cas de méthodes bien formalisées et dans lesquelles les procédés constructifs interviennent constamment.

Nous espérons avoir montré que la machine est un outil à la disposition du mathématicien, qui peut le libérer des calculs ennuyeux et l'aider dans ses recherches grâce à certains résultats intermédiaires qu'il peut toujours demander.

RÉFÉRENCES

Abrahams, P.W., E.C.Berkeley, F.Black, D.G.Bobrow et T.G.Evans, 1964, The programming language Lisp. Its operation and applications (Information International, Inc., Cambridge, Mass.).

Bourbaki, N., Algèbre, chapitre 3, nouv. éd. (à paraître chez Hermann, Paris).

Ceschino, F. et J.Kuntzmann, 1963, Problèmes différentiels de conditions initiales (Dunod, Paris).

Cohen, J. et Nguyen-Huu Dung, 1965, Chiffres 8, 271-293.

Ehresmann, C., 1953, Introduction à la théorie des structures infinitésimales et des pseudo-groupes de Lie. *In*: Géométrie différentielle. Colloques Internationaux du C.N.R.S., Strasbourg, 1953 (C.N.R.S., Paris) pp. 97-110.

Huta, A., 1956, Acta Fac. Nat. Univ. Comenian. Math. 1, 201-224.

Huta, A., 1957, Acta Fac. Nat. Univ. Comenian. Math. 2, 21-24.

McCarthy, J., P.W.Abrahams, D.J.Edwards, T.P.Hart et M.I.Levin, 1962, Lisp 1.5. Programmer's Manual (M.I.T. Press, Cambridge).

Sarafyan, D., 1966, Improvements in the Derivation of Runge-Kutta Formulas and Computer Implementation (Louisiana State University).

ANNEXE 1 (SERIE DE TAYLOR)

```
(
    F0

( * F1 F0 )

( + ( * F1 F1 F0 ) ( * F2 F0 F0 ) )

( + ( * F1 F1 F1 F0 ) ( * F1 F2 F0 F0 ) ( * 2 F2 F1 F0 F0 ) ( * F3 F0 F0
  F0 ) )

( + ( * F1 F1 F1 F1 F0 ) ( * F1 F1 F2 F0 F0 ) ( * F1 2 F2 F1 F0 F0 ) ( *
  F1 F3 F0 F0 F0 ) ( * F2 F1 F0 F1 F0 ) ( * 2 F2 F1 F1 F0 F0 ) ( * 2 F2 F
  2 F0 F0 F0 ) ( * 3 F3 F1 F0 F0 F0 ) ( * F4 F0 F0 F0 F0 ) )

( + ( * F1 F1 F1 F1 F1 F0 ) ( * F1 F1 F1 F2 F0 F0 ) ( * F1 F1 2 F2 F1 F0
  F0 ) ( * F1 F1 F3 F0 F0 F0 ) ( * F1 F2 F1 F0 F1 F0 ) ( * F1 2 F2 F1 F1
  F0 F0 ) ( * F1 2 F2 F2 F0 F0 F0 ) ( * F1 3 F3 F1 F0 F0 F0 ) ( * F1 F4 F0
  F0 F0 F0 ) ( * 2 F2 F1 F1 F0 F1 F0 ) ( * 2 F2 F2 F0 F0 F1 F0 ) ( * 2 F2
  F1 F1 F1 F0 F0 ) ( * 2 F2 F1 F2 F0 F0 F0 ) ( * 2 F2 2 F2 F1 F0 F0 F0 )
  ( * 2 F2 F3 F0 F0 F0 F0 ) ( * 3 F3 F1 F0 F1 F0 F0 ) ( * 3 F3 F1 F1 F0 F0
  F0 ) ( * 3 F3 F2 F0 F0 F0 F0 ) ( * 4 F4 F1 F0 F0 F0 F0 ) ( * F5 F0 F0 F
  0 F0 F0 ) )

( + ( * F1 F1 F1 F1 F1 F1 F0 ) ( * F1 F1 F1 F1 F2 F0 F0 ) ( * F1 F1 F1 2
  F2 F1 F0 F0 ) ( * F1 F1 F1 F3 F0 F0 F0 ) ( * F1 F1 F2 F1 F0 F1 F0 ) ( *
  F1 F1 2 F2 F1 F1 F0 F0 ) ( * F1 F1 2 F2 F2 F0 F0 F0 ) ( * F1 F1 3 F3 F1
  F0 F0 F0 ) ( * F1 F1 F4 F0 F0 F0 F0 ) ( * F1 2 F2 F1 F1 F0 F1 F0 ) ( *
  F1 2 F2 F2 F0 F0 F1 F0 ) ( * F1 2 F2 F1 F1 F1 F0 F0 ) ( * F1 2 F2 F1 F2
  F0 F ) F0 ) ( * F1 2 F2 2 F2 F1 F0 F0 F0 ) ( * F1 2 F2 F3 F0 F0 F0 F0 ) (
  * F1 3 F3 F1 F0 F1 F0 F0 ) ( * F1 3 F3 F1 F1 F0 F0 F0 ) ( * F1 3 F3 F2
  F0 F0 F0 F0 ) ( * F1 4 F4 F1 F0 F0 F0 F0 ) ( * F1 F5 F0 F0 F0 F0 F0 ) (
  * F2 F1 F1 F0 F1 F1 F0 ) ( * F2 F1 F1 F0 F2 F0 F0 )
      ( * F2 F2 F0 F0 F2 F0 F0 ) ( * F2 F1 F1 F1 F0 F1 F0 ) ( * 2 F2
  F1 F2 F0 F0 F1 F0 ) ( * 2 F2 2 F2 F1 F0 F0 F1 F0 ) ( * 2 F2 F3 F0 F0 F0
  F1 F0 ) ( * 2 F2 F1 F1 F1 F1 F0 F0 ) ( * 2 F2 F1 F1 F2 F0 F0 F0 ) ( * 2
```

```
F2 F1 2 F2 F1 F0 F0 F0 ) ( * 2 F2 F1 F3 F0 F0 F0 F0 ) ( * 2 F2 F2 F1 F0
F1 F0 F0 ) ( * 2 F2 2 F2 F1 F1 F0 F0 F0 ) ( * 2 F2 2 F2 F2 F0 F0 F0 F0 )
 ( * 2 F2 3 F3 F1 F0 F0 F0 F0 ) ( * 2 F2 F4 F0 F0 F0 F0 F0 ) ( * F3 F1 F
0 F1 F0 F1 F0 ) ( * 6 F3 F1 F1 F0 F1 F0 F0 ) ( * 6 F3 F2 F0 F0 F1 F0 F0
 ) ( * 3 F3 F1 F1 F1 F0 F0 F0 ) ( * 3 F3 F1 F2 F0 F0 F0 F0 ) ( * 3 F3 2 F
2 F1 F0 F0 F0 F0 ) ( * 3 F3 F3 F0 F0 F0 F0 F0 ) ( * 6 F4 F1 F0 F1 F0 F0
F0 ) ( * 4 F4 F1 F1 F0 F0 F0 F0 ) ( * 4 F4 F2 F0 F0 F0 F0 F0 ) ( * 5 F5
F1 F0 F0 F0 F0 F0 ) ( * F6 F0 F0 F0 F0 F0 F0 ) )


( + ( * F1 F1 F1 F1 F1 F1 F1 F0 ) ( * F1 F1 F1 F1 F1 F2 F0 F0 ) ( * F1 F
1 F1 F1 2 F2 F1 F0 F0 ) ( * F1 F1 F1 F1 F3 F0 F0 F0 ) ( * F1 F1 F1 F2 F1
F0 F1 F0 ) ( * F1 F1 F1 2 F2 F1 F0 F0 ) ( * F1 F1 F1 2 F2 F2 F0 F0 F
0 ) ( * F1 F1 F1 3 F3 F1 F0 F0 F0 ) ( * F1 F1 F1 F4 F0 F0 F0 F0 ) ( * F1
 F1 2 F2 F1 F1 F0 F1 F0 ) ( * F1 F1 2 F2 F2 F0 F0 F1 F0 ) ( * F1 F1 2 F2
F1 F1 F1 F0 F0 ) ( * F1 F1 2 F2 F1 F2 F0 F0 F0 ) ( * F1 F1 2 F2 2 F2 F1
F0 F0 F0 ) ( * F1 F1 2 F2 F3 F0 F0 F0 F0 ) ( * F1 F1 3 F3 F1 F0 F1 F0 F
0 ) ( * F1 F1 3 F3 F1 F1 F0 F0 F0 ) ( * F1 F1 3 F3 F2 F0 F0 F0 F0 ) ( *
F1 F1 4 F4 F1 F0 F0 F0 F0 ) ( * F1 F1 F5 F0 F0 F0 F0 F0 ) ( * F1 F2 F1 F
1 F0 F1 F1 F0 ) ( * F1 F2 F1 F1 F0 F2 F0 F0 )
     ( * F1 F2 F2 F0 F0 F2 F0 F0 ) ( * F1 2 F2 F1 F1 F1 F0 F1 F0 ) ( * F1
 2 F2 F1 F2 F0 F0 F1 F0 ) ( * F1 2 F2 2 F2 F1 F0 F0 F1 F0 ) ( * F1 2 F2
F3 F0 F0 F0 F1 F0 ) ( * F1 2 F2 F1 F1 F1 F1 F0 F0 ) ( * F1 2 F2 F1 F1 F2
 F0 F0 F0 ) ( * F1 2 F2 F1 2 F2 F1 F0 F0 ) ( * F1 2 F2 F1 F3 F0 F0 F0
F0 ) ( * F1 2 F2 F2 F1 F0 F1 F0 F0 ) ( * F1 2 F2 2 F2 F1 F1 F0 F0 F0 )
( * F1 2 F2 2 2 F2 F2 F0 F0 F0 F0 ) ( * F1 2 F2 3 F3 F1 F0 F0 F0 F0 ) ( *
F1 2 F2 F4 F0 F0 F0 F0 F0 ) ( * F1 F3 F1 F0 F1 F0 F1 F0 ) ( * F1 6 F3 F1
F1 F0 F1 F0 F0 ) ( * F1 6 F3 F2 F0 F0 F1 F0 F0 ) ( * F1 3 F3 F1 F1 F1 F
0 F0 ) ( * F1 3 F3 F1 F2 F0 F0 F0 ) ( * F1 3 F3 2 F2 F1 F0 F0 F0 F
0 ) ( * F1 3 F3 F3 F0 F0 F0 F0 ) ( * F1 6 F4 F1 F0 F1 F0 F0 F0 ) ( *
F1 4 F4 F1 F1 F0 F0 F0 F0 ) ( * F1 4 F4 F2 F0 F0 F0 F0 F0 ) ( * F1 5 F5
F1 F0 F0 F0 F0 F0 ) ( * F1 F6 F0 F0 F0 F0 F0 F0 ) ( * 2 F2 F1 F1 F1 F0 F
1 F1 F0 ) ( * 2 F2 F1 F2 F0 F0 F1 F1 F0 ) ( * 2 F2 2 F2 F1 F0 F0 F1 F1 F
0 ) ( * 2 F2 F3 F0 F0 F0 F1 F1 F0 ) ( * 2 F2 F1 F1 F1 F0 F2 F0 F0 ) ( *
2 F2 F1 F2 F0 F0 F2 F0 F0 ) ( * 2 F2 2 F2 F1 F0 F0 F2 F0 F0 ) ( * 2 F2 F
3 F0 F0 F0 F2 F0 F0 ) ( * 2 F2 F1 F1 F1 F0 F1 F0 ) ( * 2 F2 F1 F1 F2
F0 F0 F1 F0 ) ( * 2 F2 F1 2 F2 F1 F0 F0 F1 F0 ) ( * 2 F2 F1 F3 F0 F0
F1 F0 ) ( * 2 F2 F2 F1 F0 F1 F0 F1 F0 ) ( * 2 F2 2 F2 F1 F1 F0 F0 F1 F0
) ( * 2 F2 2 F2 F2 F0 F0 F0 F1 F0 ) ( * 2 F2 3 F3 F1 F0 F0 F0 F1 F0 ) (
* 2 F2 F4 F0 F0 F0 F0 F1 F0 ) ( * 2 F2 F1 F1 F1 F1 F0 F0 ) ( * 2 F2 F
1 F1 F1 F2 F0 F0 F0 ) ( * 2 F2 F1 2 F2 F1 F0 F0 F0 ) ( * 2 F2 F1 F1 F
3 F0 F0 F0 F0 ) ( * 2 F2 F1 F2 F1 F0 F1 F0 F0 ) ( * 2 F2 F1 2 F2 F1 F1 F
0 F0 F0 ) ( * 2 F2 F1 2 F2 F2 F0 F0 F0 F0 ) ( * 2 F2 F1 3 F3 F1 F0 F0 F0
 F0 ) ( * 2 F2 F1 F4 F0 F0 F0 F0 F0 ) ( * 2 F2 2 F2 F1 F1 F0 F0 F0 ) (
( * 2 F2 2 F2 F2 F0 F0 F1 F0 F0 ) ( * 2 F2 2 F2 F1 F1 F1 F0 F0 F0 ) ( *
2 F2 2 F2 F1 F2 F0 F0 F0 F0 ) ( * 2 F2 2 F2 2 F2 F1 F0 F0 F0 F0 ) ( * 2
F2 2 F2 F3 F0 F0 F0 F0 F0 ) ( * 2 F2 3 F3 F1 F0 F1 F0 F0 F0 ) ( * 2 F2 3
F3 F1 F1 F0 F0 F0 F0 ) ( * 2 F2 3 F3 F2 F0 F0 F0 F0 ) ( * 2 F2 4 F4
F1 F0 F0 F0 F0 F0 ) ( * 2 F2 F5 F0 F0 F0 F0 F0 F0 ) ( * 3 F3 F1 F1 F0 F1
F0 F1 F0 ) ( * 3 F3 F1 F1 F0 F2 F0 F0 ) ( * 3 F3 F1 F1 F0 F1 F1 F0 F
0 ) ( * 3 F3 F1 F1 F0 F2 F0 F0 F0 ) ( * 6 F3 F1 F1 F1 F0 F1 F0 F0 ) ( * 6 F3 F1
F2 F0 F0 F1 F0 F0 ) ( * 6 F3 2 F2 F1 F0 F0 F1 F0 F0 ) ( * 6 F3 F3 F0 F0
F0 F1 F0 F0 ) ( * 3 F3 F1 F1 F1 F1 F0 F0 F0 ) ( * 3 F3 F1 F2 F0 F0 F0 F0
F0 ) ( * 3 F3 F1 2 F2 F1 F0 F0 F0 F0 ) ( * 3 F3 F1 F3 F0 F0 F0 F0 ) (
( * 3 F3 F2 F1 F0 F1 F0 F0 F0 ) ( * 3 F3 2 F2 F1 F1 F0 F0 F0 ) ( * 3
F3 2 F2 F2 F0 F0 F0 F0 F0 ) ( * 3 F3 3 F3 F1 F0 F0 F0 F0 ) ( * 3 F3 F
4 F0 F0 F0 F0 F0 F0 ) ( * 4 F4 F1 F1 F0 F1 F0 F0 ) ( * 12 F4 F1 F1 F0
F1 F0 F0 F0 ) ( * 12 F4 F2 F0 F0 F1 F0 F0 F0 ) ( * 4 F4 F1 F1 F1 F0 F0
F0 F0 ) ( * 4 F4 F1 F2 F0 F0 F0 F0 F0 ) ( * 4 F4 2 F2 F1 F0 F0 F0 F0 F0
) ( * 4 F4 F3 F0 F0 F0 F0 F0 ) ( * 10 F5 F1 F0 F1 F0 F0 F0 F0 ) ( * 5
F5 F1 F1 F0 F0 F0 F0 F0 ) ( * 5 F5 F2 F0 F0 F0 F0 F0 F0 ) ( * 6 F6 F1 F
0 F0 F0 F0 F0 F0 ) ( * F7 F0 F0 F0 F0 F0 F0 F0 ) )
  )
```

ANNEXE 2

Eléments de la dernière combinaison linéaire pour R-K 4,4

(* B3 F0)

(+(* A13 2 F1 A00 F0) (* A23 2 F1 B1 F0) (* A33 2 F1 B2 F0))

(+(* A13 3 F2 A00 F0 A00 F0) (* A23 3 F1 A11 2 F1 A00 F0)
  (* A23 3 F2 B1 F0 B1 F0) (* A33 3 F1 A12 2 F1 A00 F0)
  (* A33 3 F1 A22 2 F1 B1 F0) (* A33 3 F2 B2 F0 B2 F0))

(+(* A13 4 F3 A00 F0 A00 F0 A00 F0) (* A23 4 F1 A11 3 F2 A00 F0 A00 F0)
  (* A23 4 2 F2 A11 2 F1 A00 F0 B1 F0) (* A23 4 F3 B1 F0 B1 F0 B1 F0)
  (* A33 4 F1 A12 3 F2 A00 F0 A00 F0) (* A33 4 F1 A22 3 F1 A11 2 F1
   A00 F0) (* A33 4 F1 A22 3 F2 B1 F0 B1 F0) (* A33 4 2 F2 A12 2 F1
   A00 F0 B2 F0) (* A33 4 2 F2 A22 2 F1 B1 F0 B2 F0) (* A33 4 F3 B2
   F0 B2 F0 B2 F0))

ANNEXE 3

ÉQUATIONS DE RUNGE-KUTTA ORDRE 4, RANG 4

    B1 = A01 + A11
    B2 = A02 + A12 + A22
    B3 = A03 + A13 + A23 + A33

GROUPE 1
  (B3 =1)

GROUPE 2
  (B2 2 A33 + B1 2 A23 + A00 2 A13)
  =
  1

GROUPE 3
  (B1 2 A22 3 A33 + A00 2 A12 3 A33 + A00 2 A11 3 A23)
  =
  1
  (B2 B2 3 A33 + B1 B1 3 A23 + A00 A00 3 A13)
  =
  1

GROUPE 4
  (A00 2 A11 3 A22 4 A33)
  =
  1
  (B1 B1 3 A22 4 A33 + A00 A00 3 A12 4 A33 + A00 A00 3 A11 4 A23)
  =
  1

(B2 B1 2 A22 2 4 A33 + B2 A00 2 A12 2 4 A33 + B1 A00 2 A11 2 4 A23)

=

2

(B2 B2 B2 4 A33 + B1 B1 B1 4 A23 + A00 A00 A00 4 A13)

=

1

RK RANG 6 ORDRE 5

GROUPE 1

(B5 =1)

GROUPE 2

(B4 2 A55 + B3 2 A45 + B2 2 A35 + B1 2 A25 + A00 2 A15)

=

1

GROUPE 3

(B3 2 A44 3 A55 + B2 2 A34 3 A55 + B1 2 A24 3 A55 + A00 2 A14 3 A55 + B2
2 A33 3 A45 + B1 2 A23 3 A45 + A00 2 A13 3 A45 + B1 2 A22 3 A35 +
A00 2 A12 3 A35 + A00 2 A11 3 A25)

=

1

(B4 B4 3 A55 + B3 B3 3 A45 + B2 B2 3 A35 + B1 B1 3 A25 + A00 A00 3
A15)

=

1

GROUPE 4

(B2 2 A33 3 A44 4 A55 + B1 2 A23 3 A44 4 A55 + A00 2 A13 3 A44 4 A55 +
B1 2 A22 3 A34 4 A55 + A00 2 A12 3 A34 4 A55 + A00 2 A11 3 A24 4 A55
+ B1 2 A22 3 A33 4 A45 + A00 2 A12 3 A33 4 A45 + A00 2 A11 3 A23 4
A45 + A00 2 A11 3 A22 4 A35)

=

1

(B3 B3 3 A44 4 A55 + B2 B2 3 A34 4 A55 + B1 B1 3 A24 4 A55 + A00 A00
3 A14 4 A55 + B2 B2 3 A33 4 A45 + B1 B1 3 A23 4 A45 + A00 A00 3 A13
4 A45 + B1 B1 3 A22 4 A35 + A00 A00 3 A12 4 A35 + A00 A00 3 A11 4
A25)

=

1

(B4 B3 2 A44 2 4 A55 + B4 B2 2 A34 2 4 A55 + B4 B1 2 A24 2 4 A55 + B4
A00 2 A14 2 4 A55 + B3 B2 2 A33 2 4 A45 + B3 B1 2 A23 2 4 A45 + B3
A00 2 A13 2 4 A45 + B2 B1 2 A22 2 4 A35 + B2 A00 2 A12 2 4 A35 + B1
A00 2 A11 2 4 A25)

=

2

(B4 B4 B4 4 A55 + B3 B3 B3 4 A45 + B2 B2 B2 4 A35 + B1 B1 B1 4 A25 +
A00 A00 A00 4 A15)

=

1

GROUPE 5

(B1 2 A22 3 A33 4 A44 5 A55 + A00 2 A12 3 A33 4 A44 5 A55 + A00 2 A11
3 A23 4 A44 5 A55 + A00 2 A11 3 A22 4 A34 5 A55 + A00 2 A11 3 A22 4
A33 5 A45)

=

1

(B2 B2 3 A33 4 A44 5 A55 + B1 B1 3 A23 4 A44 5 A55 + A00 A00 3 A13 4 A44
5 A55 + B1 B1 3 A22 4 A34 5 A55 + A00 A00 3 A12 4 A34 5 A55 + A00 A00
3 A11 4 A24 5 A55 + B1 B1 3 A22 4 A33 5 A45 + A00 A00 3 A12 4 A33 5 A45
+ A00 A00 3 A11 4 A23 5 A45 + A00 A00 3 A11 4 A22 5 A35)

=

1

(B3 B2 2 A33 2 4 A44 5 A55 + B3 B1 2 A23 2 4 A44 5 A55 + B3 A00 2 A13 2
4 A44 5 A55 + B2 B1 2 A22 2 4 A34 5 A55 + B2 A00 2 A12 2 4 A34 5 A55 +
B1 A00 2 A11 2 4 A24 5 A55 + B2 B1 2 A22 2 4 A33 5 A45 + B2 A00 2 A12
2 4 A33 5 A45 + B1 A00 2 A11 2 4 A23 5 A45 + B1 A00 2 A11 2 4 A22 5 A35)

=

2

(B3 B3 B3 4 A44 5 A55 + B2 B2 B2 4 A34 5 A55 + B1 B1 B1 4 A24 5 A55 +
A00 A00 A00 4 A14 5 A55 + B2 B2 B2 4 A33 5 A45 + B1 B1 B1 4 A23 5 A45
+ A00 A00 A00 4 A13 5 A45 + B1 B1 B1 4 A22 5 A35 + A00 A00 A00 4 A12
5 A35 + A00 A00 A00 4 A11 5 A25)

=

1

(B3 2 A44 B3 2 A44 5 A55 + B2 2 A34 B3 2 A44 5 A55 + B1 2 A24 B3 2 A44
5 A55 + A00 2 A14 B3 2 A44 5 A55 + B3 2 A44 B2 2 A34 5 A55 + B2 2 A34
B2 2 A34 5 A55 + B1 2 A24 B2 2 A34 5 A55 + A00 2 A14 B2 2 A34 5 A55 +
B3 2 A44 B1 2 A24 5 A55 + B2 2 A34 B1 2 A24 5 A55 + B1 2 A24 B1 2 A24
5 A55 + A00 2 A14 B1 2 A24 5 A55 + B3 2 A44 A00 2 A14 5 A55 + B2 2 A34
A00 2 A14 5 A55 + B1 2 A24 A00 2 A14 5 A55 + A00 2 A14 A00 2 A14 5 A55
+ B2 2 A33 B2 2 A33 5 A45 + B1 2 A23 B2 2 A33 5 A45 + A00 2 A13 B2 2
A33 5 A45 + B2 2 A33 B1 2 A23 5 A45 + B1 2 A23 B1 2 A23 5 A45 + A00 2
A13 B1 2 A23 5 A45 + B2 2 A33 A00 2 A13 5 A45 + B1 2 A23 A00 2 A13 5
A45 + A00 2 A13 A00 2 A13 5 A45 + B1 2 A22 B1 2 A22 5 A35 + A00 2 A12
B1 2 A22 5 A35 + B1 2 A22 A00 2 A12 5 A35 + A00 2 A12 A00 2 A12 5 A35
+ A00 2 A11 A00 2 A11 5 A25)

=

1

(B4 B2 2 A33 3 A44 2 5 A55 + B4 B1 2 A23 3 A44 2 5 A55 + B4 A00 2 A13 3
A44 2 5 A55 + B4 B1 2 A22 3 A34 2 5 A55 + B4A00 2 A12 3 A34 2 5 A55 +
B4 A00 2 A11 3 A24 2 5 A55 + B3 B1 2 A22 3 A33 2 5 A45 + B3 A00 2 A12
3 A33 2 5 A45 + B3 A00 2 A11 3 A23 2 5 A45 + B2 A00 2 A11 3 A22 2 5
A35)
=
2

(B4 B3 B3 3 A44 2 5 A55 + B4 B2 B2 3 A34 2 5 A55 + B4 B1 B1 3 A24 2 5
A55 + B4 A00 A00 3 A14 2 5 A55 + B3 B2 B2 3 A33 2 5 A45 + B3 B1 B1 3
A23 2 5 A45 + B3 A00 A00 3 A13 2 5 A45 + B2 B1 B1 3 A22 2 5 A35 + B2
A00 A00 3 A12 2 5 A35 + B1 A00 A00 3 A11 2 5 A25)
=
2

(B4 B4 B3 2 A44 3 5 A55 + B4 B4 B2 2 A34 3 5 A55 + B4 B4 B1 2 A24 3 5
A55 + B4 B4 A00 2 A14 3 5 A55 + B3 B3 B2 2 A33 3 5 A45 + B3 B3 B1 2
A23 3 5 A45 + B3 B3 A00 2 A13 3 5 A45 + B2 B2 B1 2 A22 3 5 A35 + B2
B2 A00 2 A12 3 5 A35 + B1 B1 A00 2 A11 3 5 A25)
=
3

(B4 B4 B4 B4 5 A55 + B3 B3 B3 B3 5 A45 + B2 B2 B2 B2 5 A35 + B1 B1
B1 B1 5 A25 + A00 A00 A00 A00 5 A15)
=
1

A METHOD FOR COMPUTING
THE CHARACTER TABLE OF A FINITE GROUP

J. K. S. McKAY
University of Edinburgh

1. INTRODUCTION

The goal of mechanised mathematics has intrigued men from the Ancients to the present day. Much effort and thought in the last decade has been given to theorem proving by computer but the initial optimism of many workers in this field has waned, giving way to a more realistic assessment of the difficulties encountered and the methods needed to overcome them. If we look at the published literature we see that we have learnt very little in terms of the significance of results proved.

Theorem proving is still in its infancy and cannot be said to have come of age until theorems can routinely be proved mechanically for which human proofs are either difficult or lacking.

A less idealistic, but more immediately rewarding, project is to provide facilities for mathematicians and others with access to computers to obtain information relating to their field of interest, for example, in terms of specific examples or counter-examples of conjectures. A combination of this idea with theorem proving of the mechanical or the human kind should prove to be a powerful practical aid in some branches of mathematics. Multiple access computing with its private consoles should stimulate more pure mathematicians into using a computer an an aid to their work. One branch which seems well suited for such treatment is the theory of finite groups. This subject has the merit that the theory of representations of finite groups has been studied in great detail which means that methods suitable for representing a group in a computer have already been investigated; furthermore, crystallographers and solid-state physicists require explicit representations of groups for their work.

2. THE PROBLEM

It will be assumed that the reader is familiar with the basic concepts of group theory such as may be found in Ledermann [1964]. A useful introduction to the theory of representations is Burrow [1965].

We may treat, for a finite group $G = \{x_1, x_2, \ldots, x_g\}$, a representation, R, of G as the set of non-singular matrices $R(x_1), R(x_2), \ldots, R(x_g)$ with the property

$$x_i x_j = x_k \text{ implies } R(x_i)R(x_j) = R(x_k) \text{ for all } i, j = 1, 2, \ldots, g .$$

(It will be assumed throughout that the groups considered are finite and that the matrices have elements over the complex field.) Once we are given a representation, R, we can form another by transforming it by a constant non-singular matrix T to give $T^{-1}R\,T$. Two such representations are said to be equivalent and are not usually considered to be distinct.

If a non-singular matrix T exists such that

$$T^{-1}RT = \frac{\begin{array}{c|c} R_1 & 0 \end{array}}{\begin{array}{c|c} 0 & R_2 \end{array}} \quad (\text{written } R_1 \oplus R_2)$$

with R_1 and R_2 square non-singular matrices then R_1 and R_2 are themselves representations and R is said to be completely reducible. Otherwise R is irreducible.

This process may be repeated until

$$R = k_1 R_1 \oplus k_2 R_2 \oplus \ldots k_\gamma R_\gamma \quad (\text{where } k_i R_i \text{ means } \underbrace{R_i \oplus R_i \oplus \ldots \oplus R_i}_{k_i \text{ terms}})$$

with each of the R_i irreducible.

It can be proved that, given R, the multiplicity and dimension of these irreducible components are, up to order and equivalence, unique. More remarkable is the result known to Burnside that the number of inequivalent irreducible representations of a group is the number of conjugacy classes it possesses.

With the method described here the multiplicity of each irreducible representation in the decomposition of any given representation can be determined. This is done by the construction of a table known as the character table of the group.

The character table is a table of the traces of the matrices representing the group elements for each irreducible representation. A great deal of information about the structure of the group may be read from the table. An account of some uses to which character tables may be put can be found in Littlewood [1940]. We determine the character table from a definition of the group in terms of its generators and defining relations.

3. GENERATING A REPRESENTATION

A description of an efficient algorithm for coset enumeration is given in Leech [1963]. This algorithm forms a table of cosets from which a permutation representation of generators can be found since for each generator, a, we have its effect as a permutation on the cosets of some subgroup H; thus,

$$Hx_i a = Hx_{\pi_i} \qquad i = 1, 2, \ldots, g/h \, .$$

We see that the permutation $\pi : i \to \pi_i$ is a representation of a which is faithful if and only if the kernel of the homomorphism from G onto the group of representing permutation is the identity. We have a faithful representation of the factor group G/N with

$$N = \bigcap_{x \in G} x^{-1} H x$$

which is faithful to G if $N = I$. For groups whose order is known a check on the fidelity of the representation is given by enumerating the elements. One way of doing this is as follows. Suppose that we can enumerate the elements of the subgroup H; we generate G by forming all the distinct cosets of H in G. This is done without repetitions by making use of the table of cosets provided by the coset enumeration algorithm. From the method of construction of this table, it is seen that, for $i \neq 1$, each ith row of the coset table will contain an entry less than i, i.e., we can always find a generator, a, or its inverse, such that $Hx_i a = Hx_j$ and $j < i \, (\neq 1)$, so that we can build the group from the first coset upwards once we have a faithful representation for H and compatible representing matrices for the generators of G.

For large groups storage space is frequently at a premium. In this case it is convenient to store elements of G as ordered pairs (s, t) of integers indicating that the element is formed from the product of the sth element of H and the tth coset representative. All that is needed to resurrect the element of G is an enumeration of H and the coset representatives of G. It is apparent that this process may be continued by splitting H in the same manner and then storing each element as an ordered triple. It should be noted that the method described is tantamount to having a faithful representation of G available. Although this process reduces the space needed to store the group it does so at the expense of the time, in the form of multiplications, needed to regenerate the elements.

4. DETERMINATION OF CONJUGACY CLASSES AND CLASS ALGEBRA

The elements are assumed to be accessible, either explicitly in the form of permutations or matrices, or as the product of elements as described above. The elements are best ordered according to some easily computable weaker partitioning than is induced by the equivalence classes of the conjugacy relation. The exact equivalence relations to be chosen which will yield most informative partitioning are dependent on the type of element representation used. Suggestions are partitions by traces of elements and by periods. The latter is fast when the elements are stored as permutations since the period is the lowest common multiple of the disjoint cycle lengths of the permutation which, of course, themselves constitute a partition. Each additional partitioning refines the previous one, thus for each element we might store its trace and the trace of its square. All elements of one conjugacy class will be found in the same refined partition. If any indication of the success of this operation is required, then the additional fact that the order of a conjugacy class divides the order of the group is useful. The coefficients of the characteristic polynomial are the most informative class invariants and can be obtained for each element in a representation of degree n in $O(n^3)$ multiplications.

The exact procedure for determining the conjugacy classes is largely dependent on the method of element storage and the amount of fast store available to contain the group. Prior knowledge, such as the number and order of conjugacy classes can be extremely time-saving. The method described here assumes the representation of the elements of the group to take sufficiently little space as to be easily stored within the fast store.

The elements are first sorted into weak classes as described above. For each weak class its order and a representative are stored. If the inverse of the representative belongs to a distinct weak class it, too, is stored as the representative of its weak class. For each representative element, x, the elements $x_i^{-1} x \, x_i$ are formed and record made of the distinct elements of this form and the number of repetitions of each element. The conjugacy class is complete as soon as the number of distinct elements reaches the order of the weak class or the product of the largest number of repetitions and the number of distinct elements reaches g, whichever is the first to arise. If the conjugacy class is not self-inverse, the inverse class may be formed as the class of the inverse elements. The procedure is continued until all the weak classes have been dealt with. We are left with residual classes for which the weak equivalence is inadequate. We take a weak class, having order greater than the conjugacy class it contains, and remove the conjugacy class. An element is taken from the remainder and its conjugacy class formed as before. This is continued until all classes are determined. All elements are tagged with their class and each class with its inverse. The r classes are ordered so that the self-inverse are the first r_1 followed by the remaining r_2 (an even integer) which are arranged so that each class and its inverse are $\frac{1}{2} r_2$ apart.

5. THE CLASS ALGEBRA

The group algebra of G is the algebra of the formal sums

$$\xi = \sum_{i=1}^{g} \gamma_i x_i \, ,$$

where γ_i is a complex number. Addition and multiplication are $\xi + \eta = \sum \gamma_i x_i + \sum \delta_i x_i = \sum (\gamma_i + \delta_i) x_i$ and $\xi \eta = \sum_{i,j} \gamma_i \delta_j x_i x_j$.

Any representation of the algebra clearly forms a representation of the group and any representation of the group can be extended by linearity to form a representation of the algebra.

This algebra is semi-simple (for a proof see Burrow [1965]), i.e., it can be expressed as a direct sum of simple matrix algebras. Thus, to each element of the group there corresponds a matrix in each simple matrix algebra. Consider now the subalgebra of the group algebra which has as its basis the formal sums

$$c_i = \sum_{x \in C_i} x$$

with C_i a conjugacy class of order h_i. No ambiguity should arise if we use the same symbol, C_i, in its usual sense as the union of elements of the group belonging to the same conjugacy class and also as the formal sum of the group elements as elements in the group algebra. Let the multiplication table be

$$C_i C_j = \sum_{k=1}^{r} \alpha_{ijk} C_k \qquad i,j = 1,2,\ldots,r .\tag{1}$$

The α_{ijk} are termed the structure constants of the algebra and may be interpreted as the number of solutions of $x \cdot y = z (x \in C_i, \ y \in C_j)$ for fixed $z \in C_k$.

The structure constants are determined by multiplying an element of the ith conjugacy class by all the elements of the jth then finding how many belong to the kth class.

Let those elements in the product $x_i C_j$ belonging to C_k be $y_1, y_2, \ldots, y_q$. So x_i can be expressed as a product of an element in C_k and one form $C_{j'}$, in precisely q distinct ways. Hence $q = h_{kj'i}$. From the above we see, too, that $h_k \alpha_{ijk} = h_i \alpha_{kj'i}$. By taking inverses of both sides of (1) we find $\alpha_{ijk} = \alpha_{i'j'k'}$. Further, classes commute and so $\alpha_{ijk} = \alpha_{jik}$. Taking C_1 to be the identity class we have also, $\alpha_{1jk} = \delta_{jk}$ and $\alpha_{ij'1} = h_i \delta_{ij}$.

We need not compute all the structure constants directly because in computing $x_i C_j$ for fixed i,j we find the r right-hand constants, α_{ijk}, anyhow and so we may consider only the symmetries of the first two indices generated by $ij \to i'j'$ and $ij \to ji$. The classes are ordered into two sets, first those which are self-inverse then the others. If there are r classes in all, r_1 of which are self-inverse and r_2 (an even integer) others stored as described previously then the domain over which to compute $x_i\,C_j$ is $r_1 + \frac{1}{2}r_2 \geqslant i \geqslant j$ and $i - \frac{1}{2}r_2 \geqslant j \geqslant r_1$. The area of this domain is $\frac{1}{2}(r_1 + \frac{1}{2}r_2)^2 + \frac{1}{8}r_2^2$. This, as a fraction of the number of constants required, varies from $\frac{1}{4}$ to $\frac{1}{2}$ as r_1 varies from 0 to g.

Now $x C_i x^{-1} = C_i$ and so $x C_i = C_i x$.
We have

$$\sum_{j=1}^{q} (\xi_j x_j) C_i = \sum_{j=1}^{q} \xi_j C_i x_j = C_i \sum_{j=1}^{q} \xi_j x_j ,$$

i.e. C_i commutes with every element of the group algebra. This algebra of the classes is the centre of the group algebra. We now find the irreducible representations of C_i.

We require a lemma due to Schur.

Lemma. If R_1, R_2 are irreducible representations of G and

$$R_1(x)T = T R_2(x) \quad \text{for all } x \in G \tag{2}$$

then either T is the zero matrix or T is square non-singular.

Writing T as the matrix $T = t_1, t_2, \ldots, t_n$, we have by comparing the jth column of both sides

$$R_1(x) t_j = \sum_{i=1}^{n} r_2(x)_{ij} t_i \ .$$

Thus, the spanning space of T is an invariant subspace of $R_1(x)$.

This invariant subspace is (because $R_1(x)$ is irreducible) either the carrier space of $R_1(x)$ in which case $m \le n$, or the null space. In the first case we can take the transposed equation of (2) and prove that $n \ge m$ and hence either $T = 0$ or T is square non-singular, Q. E. D.

In our case we have, for some irreducible representation R,

$$R(x) R(C_i) = R(C_i)R(x) \text{ for all } x \in G \ .$$

Let λ be an eigenvalue of $R(C_i)$. $R(C_i) - \lambda I$ is singular and therefore, by the above lemma, is the zero matrix. Thus, every C_i is represented in an irreducible representation by a multiple of the unit matrix. Let this multiple be m_i^s in the irreducible representation R_s.

Let $\chi(x)$ be the character of the element $x \in C_i$ in the irreducible representation R_j. The characteristic polynomial of a matrix is invariant under a similarity transformation and so the trace, being a coefficient of the polynomial, is also invariant. Thus the trace is constant on each conjugacy class. We can therefore replace $\chi_i^j(x)$ by χ_i^j without ambiguity.

From (1) we have for the irreducible representation R_s of degree n,

$$R_s(C_i) R_s(C_j) = \sum_{k=1}^{r} \alpha_{ijk} R_s(C_k) \ . \tag{3}$$

Let C_1 be the identity class. It is represented by the identity matrix I_n hence $n = \chi_1^s$ but we have $\mathrm{tr}(C_i) = n \cdot m_i^s$ and

$$\mathrm{tr}(C_i) = \mathrm{tr}(\Sigma_x) = \sum_{x \in C_i} \mathrm{tr}(x) = \sum_{x \in C_i} \chi_i^s(x) = h_i \chi_i^s$$

so

$$m_i^s = \frac{h_i \chi_i^s}{\chi_1^s} \ .$$

Substituting in (3) we find

$$m_i^s m_j^s I_n = \sum_{k=1}^{r} \alpha_{ijk} m_k^s I_n$$

to obtain, by equating coefficients,

$$m_i^S m_j^S = \sum_{k=1}^{r} \alpha_{ijk} m_k^S \qquad i,j = 1,2,\ldots,r .$$

6. THE EIGEN PROBLEM

The equations may be written more transparently as the set of r eigen equations

$$A^{(j)} m^S = m_j^S m^S \qquad j = 1,2,\ldots,r \tag{4}$$

where $[A_{ik}^{(j)}] = \alpha_{ijk}$.

They have the non-trivial solution $m_1^S = 1$ and so the eigenvalues of $A^{(j)}$ are $m_j^S (s = 1,2,\ldots,r)$ and the corresponding vectors are $m^S = (m_1^S, m_2^S, \ldots, m_r^S)'$. These vectors are determinate to within a constant factor provided the eigenvalues of $A^{(j)}$ are distinct. The factor is known since $m_1^S = 1$. The characters themselves can now be determined by using the row orthogonality relations:

$$\sum_{i=1}^{r} h_i \chi_i^j \overline{\chi}_i^k = g\delta_{jk} \text{ with } j = k .$$

The difficulty arises in the case of repeated eigenvalues. Instead of the eigenvectors being uniquely determinate we derive a linear subspace spanned by the eigenvectors.

I have satisfactorily used a method based on the following observation:

Any linear combination of the matrices, $A^{(i)}$, will have the appropriate eigenvectors. Let

$$\sum_{i=1}^{r} \theta_i A^{(i)}$$

have distinct eigenvalues, i.e., for all $p \neq q = 1,2,\ldots,r$

$$\sum_{i=1}^{r} \theta_i m_i^p \neq \sum_{i=1}^{r} \theta_i m_i^q . \tag{5}$$

The θ_i are at our disposal. Can we find a set of θ_i dependent only on the known order of the group and the order of its conjugacy classes with this property?

I find no reasonable solution to this question; motivated by the observation that there are only r^2 values, m_i^S, for any group we should be able to choose the θ_i at random from some distributions so that there is a good likelihood of satisfying (5). In practice this means satisfying for all $p \neq q = 1,2,\ldots,r$ the condition that $\mathrm{prob}\{|\theta . (m^p - m^q)| < \epsilon\} \ll 1$, for small ϵ dependent on the wordlength of the computer, and suitably distributed θ.

A full analysis of this method has not been carried out but the results given below indicate optimism. It has the advantage of reducing the problem to the solution of one eigen problem but has also the disadvantage of indeterminacy.

7. DERIVATION OF AN ALGEBRAIC FORM FOR THE CHARACTERS

We can derive the numerical values of the characters from the components of the eigenvectors as described above; however, the numerical values in themselves are of less interest than their algebraic values, e.g., we would prefer to know a character to be $2\cos(\pi/10)$ rather than to know it as 1.902112. To this end the numerical values are processed by a procedure which expresses them in terms of sums of roots of unity.

The characters are traces of matrices. For an element, x, of period p and a representation of degree n the character of x is expressible as the sum of n pth roots of unity. We may envisage the situation geometrically in the complex plane as a chain of n rods, each of length unity, reaching from the origin to the character with the proviso that each must lie at an angle which is a multiple of $2\pi/p$ to the horizontal. The rods may be ordered by magnitude of angle and a systematic search made for a fit. If

$$\chi = \sum_{j=1}^{n} \exp(2\pi i k_j/p) ,$$

we may reorder the rods, if necessary, to ensure that $0 \leqslant k_1 \leqslant k_2 \leqslant \ldots k_n \leqslant p-1$.

We now attempt to fit a chain of n rods by starting with $k_1 = k_2 = \ldots = k_n = 0$ and increasing the angles so that the monotonicity of the k_i is maintained. This works satisfactorily except occasionally when n is large (> 20, say). Two improvements have been made. We rotate the character and fit the rods to χ' where

$$\chi = \exp(2\pi i k/p)\chi' \text{ and } 0 \leqslant \arg(\chi') < 2\pi/p .$$

Secondly, we improve matters further, especially for large n, by noting that we may have, among the rods in the chain, some which would form a regular polygon if they were adjacent.

A polygon of q sides corresponds to the identity

$$\sum_{k=0}^{q-1} \exp(2\pi i k/q) = 0 .$$

The only polygons which can occur are those for which q is a factor of p. For each prime factor, q_i, of p we may attempt to fit a chain of $n - q_i$ rods since the remaining q_i rods can be arranged as a regular polygon of q_i

sides contributing nothing to the chain. In general we may try to fit $n - \sum_i c_i q_i$ (where the c_i are positive integers) knowing that to do so is equivalent to fitting a chain of n rods.

For co-prime, q_1, q_2 we may represent all integers not less than $(q_1 - 1)(q_2 - 1)$ by $c_1 q_1 + c_2 q_2$ for suitably chosen positive c_1, c_2 and so, if p has two or more distinct prime factors of which the two smallest are q_1 and q_2, we may try to fit chains of from 0 to $n - (q_1 - 1)(q_2 - 1)$ rods. This fact is of use only when $(q_1 - 1)(q_2 - 1) \leqslant n$; however if this is not the case we may still form all the sums $\sum c_i q_i$ not greater than n, and try to find the corresponding fit for each chain of length $n - \sum c_i q_i$.

8. RESULTS

The program has been tested with complete success on all the non-abelian groups of order $\leqslant 32$ and those of order 64 from definitions found in Coxeter and Moser [1965] and Hall and Senior [1964] respectively. A special program to test the method has successfully derived the characters of the new group discovered by Janko [1966] of degree 175,560 from its definition, as

$$a^2 = (ab)^2 = b^5 = 1, \quad b^{-1}cbc^2 = (ac)^3 = c^{11} = 1, \quad d^2 = dbdb^{-1} = (cd)^2 = (ad)^6 = (ac^2d)^5 = 1 \ .$$

Computation time is very large for dealing with such a group and it seems that recourse should be made to methods using a representation of elements as words in the generators for dealing with groups of this size in the future. In this way, it should eventually prove possible to investigate group structure mechanically without enumerating all elements explicitly.

A solution to the word problem which arises could be found by using a matrix representation of the generators to check identity.

REFERENCES

Burrow, M., 1965, Representation Theory of Finite Groups (Academic Press, New York).
Coxeter, H.S.M. and W.O.J.Moser, 1965. Generators and Relations for Discrete Groups, 2nd ed. (Springer Verlag, Berlin).
Hall, M. and J.K.Senior, 1964, Groups of Order $2^n (n \leqslant 6)$ (Macmillan, London).
Janko, Z., 1966, Journal of Algebra, 3, 147-186.
Ledermann, W., 1963, An Introduction to the Theory of Finite Groups (Oliver and Boyd, Edinburgh).
Leech, J., 1963, Coset Enumeration on Digital Computers, Proc. Camb. Phil. Soc., 59. 257-267.
Littlewood, D.E., 1940, The Theory of Group Characters (Oxford University Press).

PERIODIC FORESTS OF STUNTED TREES
THE IDENTIFICATION OF DISTINCT FORESTS

J. C. P. MILLER
University of Cambridge

1. INTRODUCTION

1.1. We are concerned in this paper with an infinite background of *nodes,* situated at the vertices of a plane tesselation of equilateral triangles of unit side. These nodes are of two kinds, called *live,* marked with a cross, and *vacant,* marked with a dot.

Permissible patterns of live nodes are determined thus: We start from a single straight line of nodes at unit distance apart (the *x*-axis, with $x = r$, $r = 0, \pm 1, \pm 2, \pm 3, \ldots$ giving the nodes). We shall consider this to be the *ground*, and the live nodes to be *roots*, of possible *trees* growing in the direction of increasing y; vacant nodes cannot give rise to growth. The pattern of roots is at the moment assumed to be arbitrary, but attention will be restricted almost immediately to *periodic patterns* only. If live nodes are indicated by 1's and vacant nodes by 0's, the root-pattern corresponds to an infinite binary sequence; periodic sequences of this kind are readily amenable to mathematical manipulation in terms of polynomials with coefficients in the Galois Field, GF(2), see §2 ‡.

Any live node, at any level $y = \frac{1}{2}s\sqrt{3}$, s an integer, may give rise to a branch to one or other or both of the two nearest nodes at the next higher level, $y = \frac{1}{2}(s+1)\sqrt{3}$, but this growth is *stunted* (i.e. not permitted) on any side where the neighbouring node on that side is also live and could provide a branch to the same higher-level node, if it were not reciprocally stunted. Thus from a complete, doubly infinite, system of root-nodes at ground level, the complete system of live nodes at all higher levels is determined uniquely. (The converse is not true, since a complementary line of nodes at level $\frac{1}{2}s\sqrt{3}$ (i.e. one with live and vacant nodes interchanged) yields the same line of live nodes as the original line at level $\frac{1}{2}(s+1)\sqrt{3}$.)

Figs. 1 and 2, starting from two different periodic patterns of root-nodes, each with period 7, show types of forest that can arise from this procedure.

1.2. There is an alternative way of deriving the same pattern. Let a_r denote

---

‡ In this theoretical treatment (×,.) becomes (1, 0); I also find it helpful in hand calculation to use (1,.) in place of (1, 0) when working with detached coefficients, the 1's are then relatively more prominent.

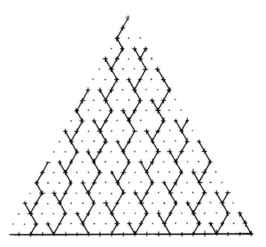

Fig. 1. Trees generated by a finite segment of root-line. Part of the forest generated by $1/(t^3+t^2+1)$; root-period 7.

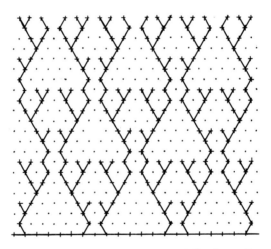

Fig. 2. Segment of (reflexive) forest generated by $1/(t^3+t^2+1)(t^3+t+1)$; root-period 7.

the character of the node at $x=r$, $y=0$, i.e. $a_r=1$ for a live node, $a_r=0$ for a vacant node. List the a_r in order of r increasing down a vertical column. Define differences

$$\Delta^{s+1}a_r = \left| \Delta^s a_{r+\frac{1}{2}} - \Delta^s a_{r-\frac{1}{2}} \right|$$

the absolute value of the difference between adjacent entries in the sth column to right of the first, and write this difference at horizontal level r. The entries are all 1 or 0 and form a triangular pattern, exactly matching the background of nodes obtained above, but turned through a right-angle clockwise. This difference method was, in fact, the manner in which the node diagram was first encountered.

Now, $\Delta^{s+1} a_r = 1$ if and only if just one of $\Delta^s a_{r+\frac{1}{2}}$ is 1, and the other zero. Thus each live node (or 1) in row (or column) $s+1$ can be connected to a unique nearest live node (or 1) in the previous row (or column) s and eventually to a unique root (or unit) at $s = 0$. The result is a *forest of stunted trees*.

1.3. At this stage we note a triangular symmetry of the arrangement of the complete system of live nodes. There are two kinds of triangles of adjacent nodes: B-triangles (growth- or Branch-triangles) with points downward (i.e. towards s diminishing), and C-triangles (stunt- or Check-triangles) with points upward (towards s increasing). B-triangles may have any num-

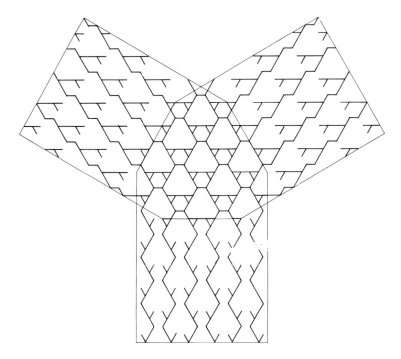

Fig. 3. Parts of the three forests generated by $1/f_i^*(t)$

$$f_1^*(t) = t^4 + t^3 + t^2 + t + 1 \qquad f_2^*(t) = t^4 + t^3 + 1 \qquad f_3^*(t) = t^4 + t + 1 .$$

These share a common background, which gives the R-tesselation in the centre,
$$n_1 = 5, \ n_2 = n_3 = 15.$$

ber 0, 1, 2, or 3 of live nodes, but C-*triangles always have* 0 *or* 2, *i.e.,*
0(*mod* 2) *live nodes*.

This property of C-triangles is triangularly symmetric and means that,
in any large triangle of nodes, the same system of live nodes arises
throughout whichever side of the large triangle we start with as ground,
with growth occurring towards the third vertex. (This assumes, of course,
that the sets of roots form a consistent trio.)

In each case then, the background of nodes gives rise to three forests,
with growth direction at $2\pi/3$ to one another. These forests may be either
congruent or distinct. Fig. 3 has three distinct forests; figs. 1 and 2 each
correspond to sets of congruent forests.

We shall normally regard forests as infinite (enclosed within a triangle
having all sides at infinite distance), semi-infinite (with two sides at infinite
distance), or in a sector (with one side at infinity). It is convenient also to
have a name for a set of trees enclosed within a finite equilateral triangle,
and generated from roots along one of its sides; we shall call this a *copse,*
see fig. 1. Note that the outer triangle has the orientation of a C-triangle.

1.4. In any background, adjacent nodes occur in three directions at $2\pi/3$
with another. For a forest, we choose one of these directions to give the
ground, and join all pairs of adjacent live nodes in the other two directions
by branches.

A *tesselation* is formed by joining pairs of adjacent live nodes in all three
directions, and is readily seen to result in a plane-filling of triangles, regular hexagons and alternate-sided hexagons of various sizes, all with triangular symmetry (see figs. 4 and 5). The tesselation as a whole may or
may not have axes of trigonal symmetry. For tesselations it is convenient
to replace cross and dot by dot and blank, i.e. $(\times, .)$ by $(. , \quad)$; this last is
the layout adopted for the production of backgrounds on the Titan (Atlas 2)

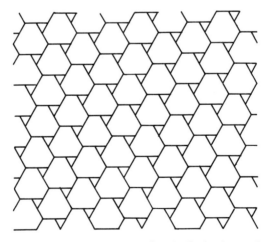

Fig. 4. The S-tesselation corresponding to the background of fig. 1.

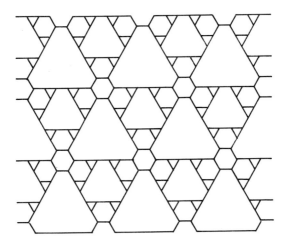

Fig. 5. The T-tesselation corresponding to the background of fig. 2.

at Cambridge, using a program prepared by S. R. Bourne. For the background of a copse, we shall use the term (*finite triangular*) *net*.

1.5. As already mentioned, the discussion in this paper is concerned with
periodic forests. This implies that the line of roots must also be periodic,
a necessary but not sufficient condition. Any row of minimum period n
leads to a minimum period n for the subsequent row if n is odd, but the
minimum period may be n or $\frac{1}{2}n$ if n is even. Since the number of distinct
rows of period n is bounded, repetition must eventually occur, and continue,
resulting in trees that are eventually periodic, with possible non-periodic
trunks (see fig. 6).

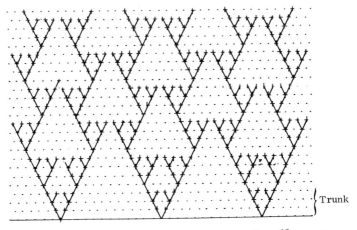

Fig. 6. Segment of forest, with trunk, generated by $1/(1+t^{12})$, $n = 12$.

We may remove the non-periodic trunk and complete an infinite *purely periodic forest* covering the whole plane, once the periodic part is established. We give a criterion in §3.2 for root-lines of least period n that lead to purely periodic forests without a trunk. Such forests have *root-period n*, and a *row-period m*; these are discussed in §§3.2 to 3.4.

1.6. Periodic binary sequences have been extensively studied in connection with communication theory and with computers. The best account is that of Selmer [1966], a comprehensive expansion of lecture notes with full references; this is not yet published.

We mention also Peterson [1961], a useful published account, and Zierler [1959], where the method we use in this paper is developed.

We quote results needed in the present paper in §2.

Forests of stunted trees have been defined mathematically and described in Miller [1966], which gives a theory of periodic forests in terms of sets of ratios of polynomials with coefficients in GF(2). Forests with $n \leqslant 48$ are enumerated in that paper. Various properties of periodic forests, and theorems needed subsequently are listed in §§3 and 4; §§5 and 6 deal with

Table 1
Number of Purely Periodic Forests
with Root-Period $n \leqslant 31$

n	m	N	R	n	m	N	R
				21	1	2	–
3	1	1	1		3	2	–
5	3	1	1		7	1	1
6	2	1	1		9	2	–
7	1	2	–		21	18	–
	7	1	1		63	786	16
9	7	4	2	22	62	768	16
10	6	4	2	23	89	2	–
11	31	3	1		2047	89	1
12	4	5	3	24	8	340	30
13	63	5	1	25	1023	656	4
14	2	4	–	26	126	5120	32
	14	20	4	27	511	4864	16
15	1	2	–	28	4	72	–
	3	3	1		28	21384	144
	15	72	8	29	16383	565	1
17	5	3	3	30	2	8	–
	15	256	16		6	63	7
18	14	259	17		30	298230	540
19	511	27	1	31	1	6	–
20	12	272	20		31	1117317	1057

n = root-period
m = row-period
N = total number of different forests
R = number of forests with reflexive symmetry

the identification of distinct individual forests in detail, and §7 includes some results obtained by examination of the various forests and tesselations so obtained.

We give in table 1 an extract from the enumerations given in Miller [1966].

2. PERIODIC BINARY SEQUENCES

2.1. Consider now a semi-infinite root-sequence along the ground, starting at the origin, with $r = 0$, and let a_r be 1 or 0 according as the node with coordinate r is live or vacant. Then

$$G(t) = \sum_0^\infty a_r t^r$$

is a generating function for the line of root nodes. We work subsequently in GF(2), i.e. modulo 2 for all coefficients, so that e.g. $1 + t^n$ and $1 - t^n$ are identical, and $(1 + t)^{2^j} = 1 + t^{2^j}$, etc.

If the sequence is ultimately periodic with root-period n, then clearly

$$(1 + t^n) \cdot G(t) = \sigma^*(t)$$

a finite polynomial in t. The degree of $\sigma^*(t)$ is less than n if, and only if, the sequence is purely periodic, without a non-periodic part at the start. Then

$$G(t) = \frac{\sigma^*(t)}{1 + t^n} \; .$$

If further

$$(\sigma^*(t), 1 + t^n) = F^*(t)$$

and

$$\sigma^*(t) = \phi^*(t) F^*(t) \qquad 1 + t^n = f^*(t) F^*(t)$$

then

$$G(t) = \frac{\phi^*(t)}{f^*(t)}$$

which is in its lowest terms, with $\phi^*(t)$ of lower degree than $f^*(t)$ when the sequence is purely periodic; we assume this to be the case below.

The notation is essentially that of Selmer [1966].

2.2. Each sequence corresponds to a unique co-prime pair $\phi^*(t), f^*(t)$.

However, sequences with the same periodic *cycle* of terms are not regarded as essentially distinct; they correspond to different starting points within the original sequence, i.e., they are *translates* of the original sequence, represented by

$$_sG(t) = {}_s\phi^*(t)/f^*(t)$$

where

$$_s\phi^*(t) = t^{-S}{}_s\phi^*(t) \quad (\text{mod } 1 + t^n) \ .$$

Thus each *cycle* corresponds to *n* sequences, if the minimum period is exactly *n*.

For a given polynomial $f^*(t)$ of degree k, there are $2^k - 1$ different non-zero polynomials $\phi^{*\prime}(t)$ of degree less than k. Each $\phi^{*\prime}(t)$ gives a distinct sequence, with period n or a submultiple of n, where n is the period for $\phi^{*\prime}(t) = 1$. Periods less than n, and possibly some sequences with period exactly n, correspond to cases where $\phi^*(t)$ and $f^*(t)$ are not co-prime. For $(\phi^*(t), f^*(t)) = 1$ - we drop the prime in this case - the least period is always n, and the number of corresponding sequences is a multiple of n, yielding an integral number of distinct cycles, all with minimal denominator $f^*(t)$.

2.3. Each *irreducible* polynomial $f^*(t)$ of degree k yields $(2^k - 1)/n$ cycles of the same length n. There is just one cycle if $n = 2^k - 1$, in which case the polynomial is called *primitive*. For example, with $k=4$, $t^4 + t + 1$, which we condense to 10011, is primitive with one cycle of period 15, but $t^4 + t^3 + t^2 + t + 1$ or 11111, though irreducible, is not primitive; it yields three cycles of period 5, for $\phi^*(t) = 1, 11, 101$ respectively.

For polynomials composite in GF(2) we can split $\phi^*(t)/f^*(t)$ into partial fractions with powers of irreducible polynomials as denominators. Generating functions may be added to provide a new generating function that corresponds to the sum sequence of the original sequences. Periods are then determined as the least common multiple of the periods of the sequences generated by the individual partial fractions. It remains only to add that if $f^*(t)$ is irreducible and $1/f^*(t)$ yields a sequence of period n (which is odd), then $1/\{f^*(t)\}^\lambda$ will yield a sequence of period $n. 2^j$, where $2^{j-1} < \lambda \leqslant 2^j$.

2.4. Enumeration of cycles is straightforward. For a given $f^*(t)$ of degree k, every $\phi^{*\prime}(t)$ of degree $< k$ yields a purely periodic sequence. We eliminate those for which $(\phi^{*\prime}(t)/f^*(t)) \neq 1$ by consideration of individual divisors of $f^*(t)$. There remain only the polynomials $\phi^*(t)$ prime to $f^*(t)$. The number of these must be a multiple of n since all least periods are exactly n; division by n yields the number of cycles corresponding to the denominator $f^*(t)$.

2.5. In any sequence or cycle (considered joined round a circle) we can define *runs* of successive similar digits between two of the opposite digits; they are *blocks* for a succession of 1's between two 0's, and *gaps* for a succession of 0's between two 1's.

We quote a theorem concerning numbers of runs when $1 + t \nmid f*(t)$:

Theorem A. *The totality of distinct non-zero cycles generated by a square-free polynomial $f*(t)$ of degree k has a combined length $2^k - 1$ and consists of 2^{k-1} runs. Half of these runs have length 1, one quarter have length 2, one-eight have length 3, and so on up to two runs of length $k - 2$, for each of these lengths there are equally many blocks and gaps. Finally there is one gap of length $k - 1$ and one block of length k.*

We can extend this to runs of length zero, i.e., to pairs of consecutive 1's or 0's; there are 2^{k-2} such pairs of 1's, but only $2^{k-2} - 1$ pairs of 0's (with one also in the zero sequence, which we disregard).

This theorem is due to Golomb for the single cycle of length $2^k - 1$ obtained from a primitive $f*(t)$; the extension to other polynomials was given by Selmer. Slight modification is needed when $1 + t \mid f*(t)$, irrelevant here.

3. FORESTS

3.1. Consider now a forest confined to the sector $r \geq \frac{1}{2}s$, $s \geq 0$, with root-generating function

$$G_0(t) = \sum_0^\infty a_{0,r} t^r = \frac{\sigma_0^*(t)}{1 + t^n} = \frac{\phi_0^*(t)}{f*(t)}$$

and having the sequence at growth-level s above the ground given by

$$t^{\frac{1}{2}s} G_s(t) = \sum^\infty a_{s,r} t^{r+\frac{1}{2}s} = t^{\frac{1}{2}s} \frac{\sigma_s^*(t)}{1 + t^n} = t^{\frac{1}{2}s} \frac{\phi_s^*(t)}{f*(t)}$$

(it may be shown that $f*(t)$ is independent of s in a purely periodic forest without a non-periodic trunk).

It is readily seen that

$$\left. \begin{aligned} t^{\frac{1}{2}s}\sigma_s^*(t) &= t^{\frac{1}{2}(s-1)}(t^{-\frac{1}{2}} + t^{\frac{1}{2}})\sigma_{s-1}^*(t) \\ &= (t^{-\frac{1}{2}} + t^{\frac{1}{2}})^s \sigma_0^*(t) \end{aligned} \right\} \pmod{2, \ 1 + t^n}$$

or

$$\sigma_s^*(t) = (t^{-1} + 1)^s \sigma_0^*(k) \pmod{2, \ 1 + t^n}$$

since this implies

$$a_{s,r} = a_{s-1,r} + a_{s-1,r-1} \pmod 2$$

which is precisely equivalent to the stunting rule of §1.1.

3.2. It is now evident that each root-periodic forest also has a row-period, since the number of polynomials of degree less than k and prime to $f^*(t)$ is finite, so that $\sigma_S^*(t)$ must eventually be periodic (mod $2, 1 + t^n$), possibly with an initial non-periodic trunk.

In fact, if $n = 2^j \cdot q$ with q odd, then $1 + t^{2^j} = (1 + t)^{2^j}$ (mod 2) exactly divides $1 + t^n$, and for a purely periodic forest we must have

$$(1 + t)^{2^j} \mid \sigma_0^*(t)$$

without a trunk or non-periodic part.

The *row-period* is the number m of distinct rows, not congruent even under translation. We then have

$$\sigma_{S+m}^*(t) = t^u \sigma_S^*(t) \quad (\text{mod } 2, f^*(t))$$

for some u, m being the least integer for which this is so.

3.3. We also define the S-period, S, which is the least integer such that row S is brought into congruence with row 0 by a translation $\frac{1}{2}n$, half the root-period.

Finally the T-period is the least common period, the least common multiple of n, m and S, or of the root- and row-periods, of all three forests generated by the background.

A single background may give three root-periods n_i, three row-periods m_i, three S-periods S_i, but has only one T-period T. We have $n_1 m_1 = n_2 m_2 = n_3 m_3 = C$ a submultiple of T^2, and the S_i are submultiples of T. The n_i can be all different.

A complete purely-periodic forest or tesselation can be divided into congruent *cells*. This can be done in a variety of ways; the smallest such cells have $2C$ unit triangles.

3.4. The determination of root- and row-periods is, in the last resort, a matter for trial. We have seen, however, that for an irreducible denominator $f^*(t)$ of degree k, the period n divides $2^k - 1$, and that the period n is progressively doubled as the denominator becomes higher powers of $f^*(t)$. For composite $f^*(t)$ the period is given by an appropriate least common multiple.

In Miller [1966] corresponding rules are developed for row periods. They are more complicated than for root-periods, and we shall state only the following results:

If a forest has root-period $n = 2^j \cdot q$, q odd and if e is the least integer such that $q \mid 2^e \pm 1$, i.e. $q \mid 2^{2e} - 1$, then the row-period m divides $(2^e - 1)2^j$. For many forests this gives the shortest row-period, but examination of table 1 demonstrates that submultiple periods are not uncommon. The least common multiple process does not, however, apply in general, for composite $f^*(t)$. It does so if all periods m are S-periods, but not usually if one or more m_i are proper submultiples of S_i.

4. CLEARINGS

4.1. It is evident on examination of individual tesselations or forests (see fig. 2), that vacant nodes tend to occur in triangular clusters. These clusters, or *clearings,* are surrounded by complete sets of adjacent live nodes.

The *size of a clearing* is defined as the length of the longest gap contained in the clearing. Thus a clearing of size 1 gives a regular hexagon in a tesselation, and we include triangles of three live nodes as clearings of size 0. Fig. 2 contains clearings of sizes 5, 3, 1 and 0.

We shall use clearings for the identification of individual forests.

4.2. Consider first a single cycle, represented by $\sigma^*(t)$, with period n. The n sequences are represented by

$$\frac{s^{\sigma^*(t)}}{1+t^n} \ (\text{mod } 2)$$

with

$$s\sigma^*(t) = t^{-s}\sigma^*(t) \ (\text{mod } 2, \ 1+t^n)$$

all of degree at most $k-1$. Any one of these that is not divisible by t, and is of degree n', has a gap of length $n-n'-1$ at its high-degree end, and so corresponds to one row in a clearing of size $\geq n'-n-1$, uniquely.

Unless the gap is in the bottom row of a clearing, the previous row has a longer gap, and $s_{-1}\sigma^*(t)$ is in this case of degree $n'-1$, and so divisible by a lower power of $1+t$. In a purely periodic forest, however, all $p\sigma_q^*(t)$ are divisible by $(1+t)^{2^j}$ at least; the longest gap is a clearing is characterized by having the corresponding $p\sigma_q^*(t)$ *exactly divisible* by $(1+t)^{2^j}$.

4.3. Each cycle gives in this way a unique $p\sigma_q^*(t)$ corresponding to each live node in the sequence. Conversely, each polynomial $p\sigma_q^*(t)$ with constant term 1 corresponds to a distinct *gap* as defined in 2.5, including zero gaps. We may then use Theorem A to give the numbers of clearings of each size in all the set of forests generated by $f^*(t)$.

The forests generated by $f^*(t)$ (which is never divisible by $1+t$) include all sequences generated by $f^*(t)$, each once, and so include all the gaps. If the degree of $f^*(t)$ is k, there are 1 gap $k-1$, 1 gap $k-2$, 2 gaps $k-3$, etc. to 2^{k-2} gaps 0. Now, a clearing of size k' includes one gap of each size $0(1)k'$, whence the forests generated by $f^*(t)$ include 1 clearing of size $k-1$, 1 of size $k-3$, 2 of size $k-4$, and so on to 2^{k-3} unit triangles or clearings of size zero.

4.4. We can concentrate on the longest gap in each clearing for this is the only one for which the corresponding $s\sigma^*(t)$ is exactly divisible by $(1+t)^{2^j}$ when $n=2^jq$, q odd. This factor thus divides out to give

$$\frac{s\sigma^*(t)}{1+t^n} = \frac{s\phi^{*"}(t)}{f^{*"}(t)} = \frac{s\phi^{*'}(t)}{f^*(t)}$$

in which neither $\phi*''(t)$ nor $f*''(t)$ is divisible by a factor $1+t$. The further factor common to $_s\phi*''(t)$ and $f*''(t)$, if present, is present for all s in any one forest, and is divided out to yield $_s\phi*'(t)/f*(t)$.

In this case $\phi*'(t)$ runs through all polynomials of degree less than k, *without factor* $1+t$, and also *without factor* t (since we have concentrated on cycles with non-zero constant term). *Thus $\phi*'(t)$ runs through polynomials of degree less than k, with a unit constant term, and with an odd number of non-zero coefficients.*

5. IDENTIFICATION OF DISTINCT FORESTS

5.1. We are now in a position to outline a procedure for identifying and listing distinct forests for a given denominator $f*(t)$.

We first list the polynomials $\phi*'(t)$ in a specific order (details are given in §6, where, in fact, it is shown to be more convenient to list $(1+t)^{2j}\phi*'(t)=\sigma*'(t)$ directly). The first few are

$$1,\ 111,\ 1101,\ 1011,\ 11001,\ 11111,\ 10101,\ 10011, \text{ etc.}$$

Here 1101, e.g. stands for t^3+t^2+1, and so on.

5.2. (a) We now choose the first unused $\phi*'(t)$ in this list, multiply by $(1+t)^{2j}$ to give the line of roots; the remaining lines of the forest may be constructed by successive multiplication by $1+t$ until a complete set of distinct rows is obtained.

(b) We must now examine *each* gap in the cycle for *each* row to determine (1) whether $(1+t)^{2j}$ *exactly* divides the corresponding $_s\sigma*(t)$, and (2) if it does, we must mark the corresponding $\phi*'(t)$ as having now been used, to prevent its use later for a supposedly new root-line.

These two processes (a) and (b) are repeated until all polynomials $\phi*'(t)$ are marked, and all distinct forests are obtained (their number is already known). Each forest is identified by the longest gap in the largest clearing corresponding to the earliest $\phi*'(t)$ in the initial list.

5.3. We need not record or count clearings of sizes 0, 1, 2, although the *counts* prove a useful check. This is because $n=3$ provides the unique forest with maximum clearing of size 1, and $n=7$, with $m=1$ (figs. 1, 4) provides the unique forest with maximum clearing of size 2.

On the other hand, when n is a multiple of 6, we can always construct forests with maximum clearings of size 4, by using the theory of alternation (decimation) described in Miller [1966].

It is not known whether forests with maximum clearing of size 3 are finite or infinite in number. Several are known, for $n=5, 6, 12, 14, 15, 17$ and 73(2). (But see note added in proof p. 167.)

In practice, then, we record clearings down to size 4 only, though all are counted.

6. ORGANISATION OF THE SEARCH

6.1. The required polynomials $\phi^{*\prime}(t)$ include all polynomials of low degree, up to $k-1$, with constant term 1, and not divisible by $1+t$. The difference of any two such polynomials will have factors t and $1+t$, i.e., the differences are multiples of 110 or t^2+t.

Let $\psi_1(t)=110$, $\psi_2(t)=1010$, $\psi_3(t)=10010,\ldots$, $\psi_r(t)=(t^r+1)t$. This set provides one polynomial of each degree $\geqslant 2$; all are divisible by 110. We set up an ordinary binary count, and represent the last non-zero digit by 2^{r-1}, the sequence of values starts

$$2^{r-1} \quad 1,2,1,4,1,2,1,8,1,2,1,4,1,2,1,16$$

corresponding to

$$r \quad 1,2,1,3,1,2,1,4,1,2,1,3,1,2,1,5$$

Then the $\phi^{*\prime}(t)$ are generated by starting with 1 and adding the successive $\psi_r(t)$ corresponding to the sequence of values of r generated by the binary count, i.e. we add $\psi_1, \psi_2, \psi_1, \psi_3, \psi_1, \psi_2, \psi_1, \psi_4$, etc. in turn. This yields the succession of values given in §5.1.

6.2. In fact, we need $\sigma^{*\prime}(t) = (1+t)2^j \phi^{*\prime}(t)$ and it is more convenient to generate this directly, starting with $1 + t^{2j}$ and adding, in appropriate order given by the binary count,

$$(1 + t^{2^j})\psi_1, \ (1 + t^{2^j})\psi_2, \ (1 + t^{2^j})\psi_3, \text{ etc.}$$

For example, for $j=2$, we start with 10001 and add appropriate terms from the sequence

1100110, 10101010, 100110010, 1000000010, 10001100010, etc.

The most frequent process is the marking of the $\phi^{*\prime}(t)$ as they occur; this process must be streamlined for a computer (and also for desk work). The simplest way to do this to be to record use, not of $\phi^{*\prime}(t)$ but of the leading digits of $\sigma^{*\prime}(t)$; the last digit is always 1, and the preceding 2^j digits can be recovered from earlier digits by use of the fact of divisibility by $1 + t^{2j}$. All possible arrangements of the digits before these 2^j+1 digits will occur (up to a maximum of $k-1$ digits in all) and can be used to give addresses in a computer (or paper) list.

When a new root line is needed (relatively infrequently) we may still pick out the first unused member, but in the list of leading digits (2^j+1 short of the whole root-line). We append a 1 to the right, reduce (uniquely) modulo $1 + t^{2j}$ to 2^j+1 digits, *with the last digit zero*; we then insert the 2^j digits left of the zero *between* the original leading digits and the appended 1.

Thus, with $j=1$, the last entry given in §5.1 corresponds to $101 \times 10011 = 1011111$. This would be listed as 1011

Append 1	10111
Reduce mod 101	110
Insert 11	1011111

giving the correct result.

6.3. The whole process of the search can readily be mechanised, but so far this has not been done. Instead, the Titan has been used at Cambridge to produce background diagrams of dots and blanks, with the root-cycle as input data.

The process described in §5.2 has been carried out by hand in conjunction with the production of individual backgrounds using a program prepared by S. R. Bourne. Of the two methods of listing mentioned in §6.2, the first has been found easier to implement (without many errors!) by hand, the second seems more convenient on a computer.

Complete sets of forests have been obtained for $n \leqslant 15$ and $n = 17, 18, 20, 24$. It may be noted that period $n = 2^j$ always results in a forest of finite height, that is, the forest terminates in the s-direction.

Table 2

Identification of Forests with $n = 14$

$(1+t^2)\psi_r$				Values of $\sigma^{*\prime}(t)$						
1	11110	101	1.	11110101	6.	111100101	10.	100010101	12.
2	100010	11011	2.	11101011	7.	111111011	(10.)	100001011	10.
3	1011010	111001	3.	11001001	8.	111011001	11.	100101001	13.
4	10101010	100111	(3.)	11010111	(7.)	111000111	2.	100110111	(11.)
5	101001010	1111101	4.	10001101	9.	110011101	11.	101101101	13.
		1100011	5.	10010011	(8.)	110000011	Per. 7	101110011	(11.)
		1000001	1.	10110001	(9.)	110100001	(10.)	101010001	(12.)
		1011111	(4.)	10101111	(6.)	110111111	10.	101001111	(10.)

$n=14$ Forest Number	$\sigma^{*\prime}(t)$	Numbers of Clearings											
		Size	0	1	2	3	4	5	6	7	8	9	10	11
1.	101 R	24	6	.	4	.	.	.	1	.	.	.	1
2.	11011 R	18	22	6	.	.	1	.	.	.	1		
3.	111001	25	9	9	3	1	.	.	.	1		
4.	1111101	26	10	4	5	2	.	.	1			
5.	1100011 R	26	10	4	5	2	.	.	1			
6.	11110101	24	15	4	3	3	.	1				
7.	11101011	25	12	7	2	3	.	1				
8.	11001001	25	12	7	2	3	.	1				
9.	10001101	25	12	7	2	3	.	1				
10.	111100101	25	12	7	3	.	3					
11.	111011001	24	14	8	4	.	2					
12.	100010101	4	1	.	.	.	1					
13.	100101001 R	24	14	8	4	.	2					
14.	11010110111	3	3	1	1							
Also $n=7$	11 R	6	4	.	1	.	1					
	10111	1	.	1								

6.4. The case $n = 14$ may be taken as an example. Here $j = 1$, the degree of $1 + t^{14}$ is even and we have the largest clearing of size 11. In table 2 we list $(1 + t^2)\psi_r$ to $r = 5$, and $\sigma^{*'}(t)$ to degree 8, and below this, individual forests, with counts of clearings for $n = 14$, and $n = 7$ since $7 \mid 14$.

We start with $\sigma^{*'}(t) = 101$, construct the forest, and mark off the two values of $\sigma^{*'}(t)$ that occur, the second being 1000001 for a clearing of size 7. We follow similarly with $\sigma^{*'}(t) = 11011$.

The next forest, for $\sigma^{*'}(t) = 111001$ is not reflexive, so we mark off its mirror image, arising from 100111, as well. Mirror images are indicated by parentheses.

We proceed in this way, marking clearings of size $\geqslant 5$, straightforwardly until Forest no. 10, with $\sigma^{*'}(t) = 111100101$ is reached; here we mark off six values of $\sigma^{*'}(t)$, three with 10, and three with (10), corresponding to three clearings of size 5 in each of the two mirror-image forests.

We note that $\sigma^{*'}(t) = 110000011$ corresponds to a forest of period 7, which must also be included in the count of clearings.

Finally, Forest no. 14 arises from a simple denominator 1011^2, and has largest clearing of size 3. The $\sigma^{*'}(t)$ table is not extended this far because small denominators are worth separate study, and this forest had, in fact, already turned up. Similarly the simple forest for $n = 7$ (fig. 2) had also appeared earlier. In other words, forests with largest clearing of size 3 apparently tend to have relatively simple denominators.

In totalling the numbers of clearings, each forest with reflexive symmetry, counts once, each of the others twice, to allow for the (distinct) mirror image.

The total for all forests listed, including those for $n = 7$ is, as expected:

Size	0	1	2	3	4	5	6	7	8	9	10	11
Number	512	256	128	64	32	16	8	4	2	1	.	1

This applies to the denominator $f^*(t) = 1101^2 . 1011^2$.

The denominator $1101^2 . 1011$, comprising forests 3, 6, 12, 14 and "Per 7", gives, using one forest of each type (except for "Per 7", where both 1011 and 1101 divide $1011^2 . 1101$) since the mirror image gives a polynomial dividing a different $f^*(t)$:

Size	0	1	2	3	4	5	6	7	8
Number	64	32	16	8	4	2	1	.	1

These denominators thus provide useful checks, as does 1011^2. The pattern also applies to $1011 . 1011$ and 1011, but here the period is $n = 7$.

7. SYMMETRY PROPERTIES OF TESSELATIONS AND OTHER TOPICS

7.1. As mentioned in §6.3, a combined hand and computer operation was

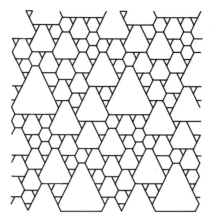

Fig. 7. One of the U-tesselations with minimum T-period, $T = 14$. Generated by $\phi_i^*(t)/f^*(t)$, with $f^*(t) = 1011^2 . 1101^2$

$$\phi_1^*(t) = 100101 \qquad \phi_2^*(t) = 111101 \qquad \phi_3^*(t) = 111011 .$$

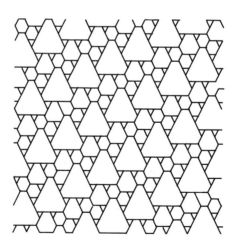

Fig. 8. The U-tesselation with minimum cell-size. Generated by $1/f_i^*(t)$, $n_i = 31$.

$$f_1^*(t) = 101001 \qquad f_2^*(t) = 110111 \qquad f_3^*(t) = 10111 .$$

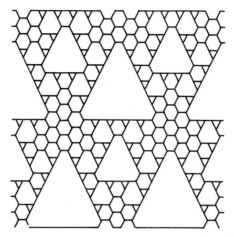

Fig. 9. An attractive T-tesselation generated by $111/1011^2 . 1101^2$, $n = 14$.

used to obtain a complete collection of distinct forests (mirror images excluded) for $n = 17, 18, 20, 24$; these number respectively 138, 138, 146 and 185. Those for $n \leqslant 15$ were obtained entirely by hand.

The purpose of these collections is to study properties of individual forests that are not apparent in the mathematical development. It was also of interest to carry out complete enumerations and identifications whilst developing processes for this purpose.

7.2. A particularly interesting study is that concerning the relationship of forests given by a single background.

Forests may be reflexive, or they may be unsymmetric, with a distinct mirror-image. A background gives three forests, which may be put into one of four groups, as listed below, with the corresponding tesselation type:

(a) Distinct unsymmetric forests or a U-tesselation

(b) One reflexive forest, and a
pair of mirror-images of
unsymmetric forests   or an R-tesselation

(c) Three identical unsymmetric
forests   or an S-tesselation

(d) Three identical reflexive
forests   or a T-tesselation

(U = Unsymmetric, R = Reflexive, S = Skew-symmetric, T = Triangularly-
symmetric.)

Thus fig. 1 gives an S-forest, fig. 2 a T-forest, fig. 3 (centre) gives an R-tesselation, fig. 4 an S-tesselation, fig. 5 a T-tesselation, fig. 6 also

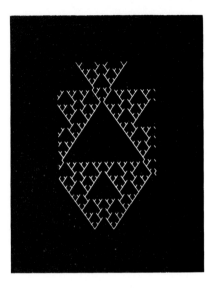

Fig. 10. Part of a forest produced by display on PDP-7; generated by $(t^5 + 1)/(t^{31} + 1)$,
$n = 31$.

gives a T-forest for its periodic part, fig. 7 gives an example of a U-tesselation with minimum T-period, $T = 14$, while fifth degree primitive polynomials provide (fig. 8) another example of a U-tesselation, with $n = 31$ and minimum cell-size. Finally fig. 9 gives a T-tesselation of attractive appearance.

The theory of such symmetries is not yet completely developed; R-symmetries are relatively easy to cope with, but the triangular symmetries, whether S- or T- need more elaborate mathematical treatment of enumeration [‡]. It is therefore of interest to prepare full sets of forests where feasible to pick out the symmetric ones.

7.3. We can only quote a few counts here. Forests with S- and T-symmetry have been found and counted as follows

	3	6	7	12	14	15	21	24
S-	-	-	2	2	10	26	2	28
T-	1	1	1	3	2	4	1	12

[‡] Discussions at the Blaricum conference have yielded some helpful and successful ideas for further development, in particular, ideas provided by F.L.Bauer and A.van Wijngaarden. These investigations are reserved for a further paper.

They exist for $n = 28, 30, 31, 73, 85, 105$ and in other cases, e.g., whenever $m = 1$ it is possible to construct one.

7.4. Another use for computers is for the evaluation of m. It is relatively simple to find T- and S-periods, but when symmetry is not present, the only known method for irreducible polynomials is trial among submultiples of S or T. A useful program for this purpose was made for the PDP-7 display table at Cambridge by J. S. Elliott. From the root-cycle as input this develops a section of the corresponding tree, with a facility for extending the display picture by shifting the last row into the root position. Fig. 10 shows a photograph of one of these displays.

7.5. The whole subject is capable of development in several directions, though not many of them have the attractive pictorial aspect of these Periodic Forests of Stunted Trees.

REFERENCES

Miller, J. C. P., 1966, Periodic Forests of Stunted Trees (unpublished).
Peterson, W. W., 1961, Error-Correcting Codes (M.I.T. Press, Cambridge, Mass.).
Selmer, E. S., 1966, Linear Recurrence Relations over Finite Fields (Dept. of
    Mathematics, University of Bergen, Norway).
Zierler, N., 1959, J. Soc. Indust. Appl. Math. 7, 31-48.

NOTE ADDED IN PROOF

Since this paper was first written, Dr. H. ApSimon has proved that the number of tesselations with maximum clearings of size 3 is finite, and has constructed all ten of them. Two are R-tesselations with $n = 5$ or 15 and $n = 17$ or 85, two are T-tesselations with $n = 6$, 12 and six are S-tesselations with $n = 14, 28, 56, 73(2), 273$.

COMPUTATIONS ON
CERTAIN BINARY BRANCHING PROCESSES

S. M. ULAM
University of California, Los Alamos

The following will present an account of some computations performed this year on a combinatorial problem suggested by certain schematized and over-simplified models of evolution. The first calculations dealt with pure branching processes. The subsequent ones with a generalization of such processes to the cases when, in each generation, a binary "collision" or "mating" takes place and in which each pair of points produces a number of offspring. This work was performed on electronic computers (the "Stretch") in the Los Alamos Scientific Laboratory, in collaboration with J. C. Everett and R. Schrandt.

In a simple branching process, starting with one or several particles, these particles each produce independently and with given probabilities: p_0, $p_1, \ldots, p_m$ $0, 1, 2 \ldots n$ new particles in the next generation - and the process continues. Any special outcome or course of such a process can be pictured as a graph which has the appearance of a tree, i.e., there are no loops in it. In a binary branching process we again start with one or more initial points; say N initial individuals. We then assume a pairing between them. This pairing we assume, in the first instance, to be effected at random with uniform probability, i.e., if N is even we select one-half of the individuals and attach to each of them, with uniform probability, indices of the remaining one-half. (If N should be odd, we omit one of the particles and pair the rest). For each of the pairs, we may assume, say with probabilities which do not vary from pair to pair, a production of $0, 1, 2 \ldots n$ new particles. These constitute the next generation and the process continues. If one wants to represent the history of such a process by a graph, this graph will not appear anymore as a tree but will have, in each generation, loops given by the outcome of the random mating. Such a graph might be called a "pair tree". For the ordinary branching process there exist satisfactory mathematical descriptions. In particular, the notion of a *measure* can be defined for the space of all possible graphs extending to infinity. Such measures permit one to formulate, in a concise form, asymptotic laws governing the behavior of multiplicative processes (cf. Everett and Ulam [1948a]; also Everett and Ulam [1948b]).

In this article we want to present the results of a numerical study of a very special process and we shall give first an account of the calculations referring to processes involving only mitosis, i.e., the pure branching cases. Later on, we will discuss our calculations concerning the *binary* branching processes.

The setup is the following: Given is a set of N points ("organisms") each of which can, in any given generation, receive with a given probability α an "improvement" (a favorable mutation). For orientation, we give the numerical values of these numbers as used in our calculation. N was of the order of 500, α is a small number, typically $\alpha = \frac{1}{50}$ or $\frac{1}{100}$ so that, on the average, in any given generation only a few, say five or ten, of the individuals will receive an improvement. We assume that each individual will produce, for certain, a new one for the next generation but those individuals that acquire a number of improvements will produce with some probability, which we denote by k, one additional progeny. As time goes on and the number of generations increases, more and more individuals will acquire these improvements and there will be a number of improvements which will vary from individual to individual. Denote by l_i the number of improvements possessed by the ith individual. (All improvements of an individual are inherited by its descendants.) We operate with the following recipe: Let $L(n)$ denote the *average* number of improvements possessed by the individuals of the nth generation. We assume that every individual will produce one child for certain but with the probability $k(l_i - L)$ it will produce another one. If $l - L$ is negative we take this probability as 0. The population will increase as time goes on and whenever, in a given generation, it surpasses twice the number of the original population, i.e., it becomes greater or equal to $2N$, we normalize it back to N by cutting down the number of particles with any given number of improvements to one-half of the number present. If such a number should be less than 2, we omit it altogether. It is clear that in this process the average number of improvements present in the population will increase and there will be a distribution of the number of individuals possessing a given quantity of these improvements. The random appearance of the improvements is supposed to imitate in this simple-minded way only the favorable mutations coming to the population. Our recipe for production of new particles is schematizing the "advantages" accruing from possession of such "improvements", relative to the average present in the population and therefore expresses in this over-simplified way a "survival of the fittest".

Presumably, the possession of just a few of our "advantages" has but small additional value. We have assumed in our calculations various values for k. For example, $k - \frac{1}{20}$, or $\frac{1}{10}$, etc. It turned out that the distribution of the number of advantages, at any given time, possessed by the population was such that the difference between the maximum number present and the minimal one never exceeded $1/k$ so that, according to our recipe, only single additional children were appearing in a generation. We assume, of course, that the progeny inherits the total number of "advantages" possessed by the parents.

We have varied from problem to problem the constant α, k and the results have shown invariably that the number L varied linearly with time (i.e., with n, the number of generations). This result, of course, was expected and is quite simple to justify - more interesting and not at all obvious is the slope of the curve (i.e., the line representing L as a function of n), as a function of our parameters α and k. This turns out to be a rather complicated matter. Despite the sizeable number of our experiments, no definite formulation is sufficiently suggested. An analytical solution of the problem is, of course, not at all obvious - in our problem we introduce the normalization and also our formulation for dependence of the number of additional children as a function of the number of advantages possessed by an individual relative to the average in the population as linear. This cannot be justified in a continuum treatment of the problem since it would lead to some individuals possessing an arbitrarily large number of progeny. Obviously, however, the slope was greater, the greater α and the greater k, but the dependence on α and k was not at all of the same kind. Other combinatorial properties of such a branching process can be studied, statistically by our "Monte Carlo" i.e., given individuals in the nth generation, one can examine the average number of generations necessary for finding a common ancestor in the past (i.e., the nearest such), etc., etc.

What we mainly want to report on, here, is the process where one has "mating" between pairs of individuals and a different rule of inheritance of "advantages" from the two parents by the offspring. Our calculations were performed on models of the following type: We assumed again a large number of individuals - typically of the order of 500 or 1,000; for α we took values such as in the single branching process and then assumed, in each generation, a random pairing of our particles. Given such a pairing and given parents who possess a certain number of improvements, say, l_i and l_i', we assume that the offspring of such (*there are two for certain*), inherit with probability one-half, each of the advantages of the parents. The expected number of inherited advantages is thus: $\frac{1}{2}(l_i + l_i')$. However, with certain probabilities, the offspring may inherit more or less than that number. It is the fluctuations in this process that, as we shall see later, accelerate very greatly the process of "evolution", i.e., provide for a much quicker rise of $L(n)$ as a function of n. Again, we assume that a pair possessing more than the average number of improvements present in the population will produce additional offspring with probabilities depending on the number $L(n) - \frac{1}{2}(l_i + l_i')$ with a constant of proportionality k just as in our simple problems. The result of computations (carried over many hundreds of generations) shows a growth of $L(n)$ which is faster than quadratic and, in fact, of almost exponential character. This result is, of course, quite natural and expected qualitatively by genetics; we are interested in its dependence on the parameters α and k. The recipes used are obviously not realistic; for one thing, some of the advantages accruing from the parents are, after some generations, identical i.e., when, through the process of mutations determined by our α the population acquires new favorable characteristics - in our recipe for inheritance it will be so that *the same* improvement is inherited from both parents and should not be counted twice as our recipe would allow.

The next batch of problems, therefore, involved identifying by indices the improvements coming into the population as a whole and keeping track of this index when an offspring of a pair inherits them from both parents. One then took care of counting only once an improvement of a given type which came by our lottery process from both parents. This series of calculations have still shown a very fast growth of $L(n)$ but slower than in the previous class of problems. The difference between the two ways of schematizing our "evolution" depends on the number of individuals in the population. If it is very large, then in the beginning, for a number of generations, there will be no difference between the two treatments; i.e., between the one where the improvements are not specified and the one when one keeps track of which improvements are present in various individuals. This is because it is extremely unlikely that two individuals will possess the same favorable mutations if their number is very large and if they mate at random. After a sufficient number of generations, assuming that the population is more or less constant, this will begin to happen increasingly. In the "asymptotic" behavior, the situation is this: single individuals acquire, after a number of generations, practically all the improvements which come at random into the population as a whole - the process of this acquisition cannot, of course, go any faster than that limit. The number of generations in which this takes place is roughly according to the logarithm of the total number of mutations coming to the population - it is *several* times larger than this logarithm. The results of our numerical work show a rather less sensitive dependence on k than one would have perhaps expected a priori.

Again, one can examine combinatorial questions like that of the probability of having a common ancestor or several ancestors a number of generations back. One can define a degree of relationship, i.e., the genealogical proximity, etc., etc. It is intended to present the results of our statistical samplings of such "pair trees" in a future report.

REFERENCES

Everett, C.J. and S.M.Ulam, 1948a, Proc. Nat. Acad. Sci. USA 34, 403-405.
Everett, C.J. and S.M.Ulam, 1948b, Multiplicative Systems in Several Variables, AECD-2164, AECD-2165, AECD-2532 (Technical Information Branch, Oak-Ridge, Tenn.).

BIBLIOGRAPHY ON THE USE OF COMPUTERS
IN MATHEMATICAL RESEARCH

This bibliography is intended to cover all published papers involving the use of electronic computers as an aid in mathematical research, with the following exceptions:

> Papers published in 1967 or later,
> Papers of restricted circulation,
> Papers on boolean function minimization, error-correcting codes, experimental testing of numerical methods, construction of function tables, studies in "automatic proving".

Whenever the machine used is mentioned in the paper, its name appears within parentheses after the author's name.

The transliterations and abbreviations are taken from *Mathematical Reviews*.

Abdel Karim, A. I. (Z 22), 1966
    The stability of the fourth order Runge-Kutta method for the solution of systems of differential equations, Comm. ACM 9, 113–116.
Alanen, J. D. and D. E. Knuth, 1964
    Tables of finite fields, Sankhyā Ser. A 26, 305–328.
Altmann, S. L. and C. J. Bradley, 1962
    On the symmetries of spherical harmonics, Philos. Trans. Roy. Soc. London Ser. A 255, 199–215.
Anderson, D. W., E. H. Brown Jr. and F. P. Peterson (IBM 7094), 1966
    Spin cobordism, Bull. Amer. Math. Soc. 72, 256–260.
Andree, R. V. *et al.* (IBM 650), 1962
    A table of indices and power residues for all primes and prime powers below 2000. W. W. Norton and Co Inc., New York.
Arai, K. (Musasino - 1), 1960
    On the generation of prime numbers using the Eratosthenes' sieve by the Musasino-1, Rev. Elec. Comm. Lab. 8, 189–193.
Backstrom, R. P., 1966
    On the determination of the zeros of the Fibonacci sequence, Fibonacci Quart. 4, 313–322.
Bang, T., 1954
    Store Primtal, Nordisk Mat. Tidskr. 2, 157–168, 191.
Barra, J. R. and R. Guérin (IBM 7094), 1963
    Utilisation pratique de la méthode de Yamamoto pour la construction systématique de carrés gréco-latins, Publ. Inst. Statist. Univ. Paris 12, 131–136.
Barrodale, I. (IBM 1620), 1966
    A note on equal sums of like powers, Math. Comp. 20, 318–322.
Bateman, P. T. and R. A. Horn (ILLIAC), 1962
    A heuristic asymptotic formula concerning the distribution of prime numbers, Math. Comp. 16, 363–367.

Bateman, P. T. and R. A. Horn (CDC 1604), 1965
Primes represented by irreducible polynomials in one variable. *In*: Proc. Symp. Pure Math. VIII (Amer. Math. Soc., Providence) pp. 119-132.

Baumert, L., S. W. Golomb and M. Hall Jr. (IBM 7090), 1962
Discovery of an Hadamard matrix of order 92, Bull. Amer. Math. Soc. 68, 237-238.

Berg, M. (IBM 1401), 1966
Phi, the golden ratio (to 4599 decimal places), and Fibonacci numbers, Fibonacci Quart. 4, 157-162.

Bergmann, G., 1966
Beispiel numerischer Einheitenbestimmung, Math. Ann. 167, 143-168.

Birch, B. J. (EDSAC), 1965
Conjectures concerning elliptic curves - *In*: Proc. Symp. Pure Math. VIII (Amer. Math. Soc., Providence) pp. 106-112.

Birch, B. J. and H. P. F. Swinnerton-Dyer (EDSAC 2), 1963
Notes on elliptic curves, I, J. Reine Angew. Math. 212, 7-25.

Birch, B. J. and H. P. F. Swinnerton-Dyer (EDSAC 2), 1965
Notes on elliptic curves, II, J. Reine Angew. Math. 218, 79-108.

Bivins, R. L., N. Metropolis, P. R. Stein and M. B. Wells (MANIAC), 1954
Characters of the symmetric groups of degree 15 and 16, MTAC 8, 212-216.

Boas, R. P. Jr and V. C. Klema (IBM 709), 1964
A constant in the theory of trigonometric series, Math. Comp. 18, 674.

Bose, R. C., I. M. Chakravarti and D. E. Knuth, 1960,
On methods of constructing sets of mutually orthogonal latin squares using a computer, I, Technometrics, 2, 507.

Bose, R. C., I. M. Chakravarti and D. E. Knuth, 1961
On methods of constructing sets of mutually orthogonal latin squares using a computer, II, Technometrics, 3, 111-117.

Bouwkamp, C. J., A. J. W. Duijvestijn and P. Medema (IBM 650), 1960
Tables relating to simple squared rectangles of order nine through fifteen (Technische Hogeschool, Eindhoven).

Brady, A. H., 1965
Solutions of restricted cases of the halting problems used to determine particular values of a non-computable function, Notices Amer. Math. Soc. 12, 476-477.

Brenner, C. and J. L. Brenner (Burroughs 220), 1962
The popularity of small integers as primitive roots, Numer. Math. 4, 336-342.

Brillhart, J. (IBM 701), 1962
Concerning the numbers $2^{2p}+1$, p prime, Math. Comp. 16, 424-430.

Brillhart, J. (IBM 701 *et al.*), 1963
Some miscellaneous factorizations, Math. Comp. 17, 447-450.

Brillhart, J. (IBM 7090), 1964
On the factors of certain Mersenne numbers, II, Math. Comp. 18, 87-92.

Brillhart, J. and G. D. Johnson (IBM 701), 1960
On the factors of certain Mersenne numbers, Math. Comp. 14, 365-369.

Brillhart, J., D. H. Lehmer and E. Lehmer (IBM 7090), 1964
Bounds for pairs of consecutive seventh and higher power residues, Math. Comp. 18, 397-407.

Brjuno, A. D. (Strela), 1964
Razloženie algebraičeskih čisel v cepnye drobi, Ž. Vyčisl. Mat. i Mat. Fiz. 4, 211-221.

Bruck, R. H., 1956
Computational aspects of certain combinatorial problems. *In*: Proc. Symp. Appl. Math. VI (Amer. Math. Soc., Providence), pp. 31-43.

Brudno, S. (IBM 709), 1964
A further example of $A^4 + B^4 + C^4 + D^4 = E^4$, Proc. Cambridge Philos. Soc. 60, 1027-1028.

De Bruijn, N. G. (IBM 1620), 1964
Some direct decomposition of the set of integers, Math. Comp. 18, 537-546.

Cairns, S. S., 1954
    Computational attacks on discrete problems. *In*: Proc. Symp. spec. top. in appl.
    math., Northw. Univ., 1953, Amer. Math. Monthly 61, no. 7, part II, 29-31.
Cantor, D. G., G. Estrin, A. S. Fraenkel and R. Turn (IBM 7090), 1962
    A very high-speed digital number sieve, Math. Comp. 16, 141-154.
Carlitz, L., 1962
    The coefficients of the lemniscate function, Math. Comp. 16, 475-478.
Carlitz, L., 1963
    A sequence of integers related to the Bessel function, Proc. Amer. Math. Soc.,
    14, 1-9.
Cavior, S. R., 1963
    A note on octic permutation polynomials, Math. Comp. 17, 450-452.
Cheema, M. S. (IBM 7072), 1964
    Vector partitions and combinatorial identities, Math. Comp. 18, 414-420.
Chikawa, K., K. Iséki and T. Kusakabe (IBM 602-A), 1961
    On a problem by H. Steinhaus, Acta Arith. 7, 251-252.
Chikawa, K., K. Iséki, T. Kusakabe and K. Shibamura (Facom 128-B and IBM 602-A),
    1961
    Computation of cyclic parts of Steinhaus problem for power 5, Acta Arith. 7,
    253-254.
Church, R. (CDC 1604), 1965
    Enumeration by rank of the elements of the free distributive lattice with seven
    generators, Notices Amer. Math. Soc. 12, 724.
Cohen, A. M. (Mercury), 1962
    Numerical determination of lattice constants, J. London Math. Soc. 37, 185-188.
Cohn, H. (EDVAC), 1954 a
    A periodic algorithm for cubic forms. II, Amer. J. Math. 76, 904-914.
Cohn, H. (MIDAC), 1954 b
    Numerical study of signature rank of cubic cyclotomic units, MTAC 8, 186-188.
Cohn, H. (UNIVAC), 1955 a
    A numerical study of quintics of small discriminant, Comm. Pure Appl. Math. 8,
    377-385.
Cohn, H. (MIDAC), 1955 b
    Some experiments in ideal factorization on the MIDAC, J. ACM 2, 111-116.
Cohn, H. (IBM 701), 1956
    Stability configurations of electrons on a sphere, MTAC 10, 117-120.
Cohn, H. (SEAC), 1957
    A numerical study of Dedekind's cubic class number formula, J. Res. Nat. Bur.
    Standards, 59, 265-271.
Cohn, H. (IBM 650), 1958
    A computation of some biquadratic class numbers, MTAC 12, 213-217.
Cohn, H. (GEORGE), 1959
    Numerical study of the representation of a totally positive quadratic integer as the
    sum of quadratic integral squares, Numer. Math. 1, 121-134.
Cohn, H. (GEORGE), 1960
    A numerical study of Weber's real class number calculation, I. Numer. Math. 2,
    347-362.
Cohn, H. (GEORGE), 1961
    Proof that Weber's normal units are not perfect powers, Proc. Amer. Mat. Soc.
    12, 964-966.
Cohn, H. (GEORGE), 1962 a
    A numerical study of the relative class numbers of real quadratic integral do-
    mains, Math. Comp. 16, 127-140.
Cohn, H., 1962 b
    Number theory: Some illustrative computations in algebraic number theory. *In*:
    Survey of numerical analysis (Mc Graw Hill, New York), pp. 543-549.

Cohn, H. (CDC 3600), 1965
  A numerical survey of the floors of various Hilbert fundamental domains, Math.
  Comp. 19, 594-605.
Cohn, H. (CDC 3600), 1966
  Computation concerning the shape of a Hilbert modular domain. *In*: Proceedings
  of IFIP Congress 65, New York City, May 24-29, 1965 (Spartan Books, Washington), vol. 2, p. 494.
Cohn, H. and S.Gorn (EDVAC), 1957
  A computation of cyclic cubic units, J. Res. Nat. Bur. Standards 59, 155-168.
Comét, S. (BARK), 1954
  On the machine calculation of characters of the symmetric group. *In*: Tolfte Skandinaviska Matematikerkongressen, Lund (1953), pp. 18-23.
Comét, S. (BARK and BESK), 1955
  Notations for partitions, MTAC 9, 143-146.
Comét, S. (BESK), 1960
  Improved methods to calculate the characters of the symmetric group, Math.
  Comp. 14, 104-117.
Dade, E.C. and H.Zassenhaus (IBM 7090), 1963
  How programming difficulties can lead to theoretical advances. *In*: Proc. Symp.
  Appl. Math. XV (Amer. Math. Soc., Providence), pp. 87-94.
Davis, P. and P.Rabinowitz (SEAC), 1956a
  Abscissas and weights for Gaussian quadrature of high order, J. Res. NBS 56,
  35-37.
Davis, P. and P.Rabinowitz (SEAC), 1956b
  Numerical experiments in potential theory using orthonormal functions, J. Wash.
  Acad. Sci. 46, 12-17.
Davis, P. and P.Rabinowitz (SEAC and WEIZAC), 1958
  Additional abscissas and weights for Gaussian quadrature of high order: values
  for $n=64$, 80, 96, J. Res. NBS 60, 613-614.
Deily, G.R., 1966
  Terminal digit coincidences between Fibonacci numbers and their indices, Fibonacci Quart. 4, 151-156.
Dresel, L.A.G. and D.E.Daykin (Elliott 803), 1965
  Factorization of 36 Fibonacci numbers F_n with $n > 100$, Fibonacci Quart. 3, 232-233.
Duijvestijn, A.J.W.(PASCAL), 1962
  Electronic computation of squared rectangles (thesis Technological University
  Eindhoven), 92 pp.
Dunton, M., 1965
  Bounds for pairs of cubic residues, Proc. Amer. Math. Soc. 16, 330-332.
Ehlich, H. (Siemens 2002), 1965
  Zur Pillaischen Vermutung, Arch. Math. 16, 223-226.
Fehlberg, E. (IBM 7094), 1966.
  New high-order Runge-Kutta formulas with an arbitrarily small truncation error,
  Z. Angew. Math. Mech. 46, 1-16.
Fell, H., M.Newman and E.Ordman (IBM 7090), 1963
  Tables of genera of groups of linear fractional transformations, J. Res. Nat. Bur.
  Standards Sect. B, 67B, 61-68.
Felsch, H. (Z 22), 1961
  Programmierung der Restklassenabzählung einer Gruppe nach Untergruppen,
  Numer. Math. 3, 250-256.
Fletcher, J.G. (IBM 7094), 1965
  A program to solve the pentomino problem by the recursive use of macros, Comm.
  ACM 8, 621-623.
Forsythe, G.E. (SWAC), 1955
  SWAC computes 126 distinct semigroups of order 4, Proc. Amer. Math. Soc. 6,
  443-447.

Fraenkel, A. and B.Reuter (CDC 1604-A), 1966
  On certain sequences of integers and prime numbers. *In*: Proc. 2nd National Con-
  ference on Data Processing, Rehovoth, Israel, Jan. 1966 (Information Processing
  Assoc., Jerusalem), pp. 437-450.
Fraser, W. and C.C.Gotlieb (IBM 650), 1962
  A calculation of the number of lattice points in the circle and sphere, Math. Comp.
  16, 282-290.
Fröberg, C.E. (SMIL), 1958
  Some computations of Wilson and Fermat remainders, MTAC 12, 281.
Fröberg, C.E. (SMIL), 1961, On the sum of inverses of primes and of twin primes,
  BIT 1, 15-20.
Fröberg, C.E. (SMIL), 1963
  Investigation of the Wilson remainders in the interval $3 \leqslant p \leqslant 50,000$, Ark. Mat. 4,
  479-499.
Fröberg, C.E. (CDC 3600), 1966
  Numerical studies of the Möbius power series, BIT 6, 191-211.
Gardiner, V., R.Lazarus, N.Metropolis and S.Ulam, 1956
  On certain sequences of integers defined by sieves, Math. Mag. 29, 117-122.
Gardiner, V.L., R.B.Lazarus and P.R.Stein (IBM Stretch and MANIAC II), 1964
  Solutions of the Diophantine equation $x^3 + y^3 = z^3 - d$, Math. Comp. 18, 408-413.
Genuys, F. (IBM 704), 1958
  Dix mille décimales de π, Chiffres 1, 17-22.
Gerhards, L. and W.Lindenberg (IBM 7090), 1965
  Ein Verfahren zur Berechnung des vollständigen Untergruppenverbandes endlicher
  Gruppen auf Dualmaschinen, Numer. Math. 7, 1-10.
Gilbert, E.N. (IBM 7090), 1964
  Randomly packed and solidly packed spheres, Canad. J. Math. 16, 286-298.
Gilbert, E.N. (IBM 7090), 1965
  Latin squares which contain no repeated digrams, SIAM Rev. 7, 189-198.
Gillies, D.B. (ILLIAC II), 1964
  Three new Mersenne primes and a statistical theory, Math. Comp. 18, 93-97.
Gloden, A., 1965
  New primes of the form $n^4 + 1$, Math. Comp. 19, 144-145.
Godwin, H.J. and P.A.Samet (DEUCE), 1959
  A table of real cubic fields, J. London Math. Soc. 34, 108-110.
Goldberg, K. (SEAC), 1953
  A table of Wilson quotients and the third Wilson prime, J. London Math. Soc. 28,
  252-256.
Gotusso, L. (USS 90 Remington), 1964
  Studio dell'andamento del resto nel problema dei divisori, Atti Sem. Mat. Fis.
  Univ. Modena 13, 209-220.
Grace, D.W. (Burroughs 220), 1963
  Search for largest polyhedra, Math. Comp. 17, 197-199.
Hall, M. Jr. (SWAC), 1956
  A survey of difference sets, Proc. Amer. Math. Soc. 7, 975-986.
Hall, M. Jr. (SWAC), 1962
  Discrete variable problems. *In*: Survey of numerical analysis (McGraw Hill,
  New York), pp. 518-542.
Hall, M. Jr., 1966
  Numerical analysis of finite geometries. *In*: Proceedings of the IBM Scientific
  Computing Symposium on combinatorial problems, March 16-18, 1964 (IBM Data
  Processing Division, White Plains, New York), pp. 11-22.
Hall, M. Jr. and D.E.Knuth, 1964
  Groups of exponent 4, Notices Amer. Math. Soc. 11, 120-121.
Hall, M. Jr. and D.E.Knuth, 1965
  Combinatorial analysis and computers, Amer. Math. Monthly 72 no. 2 part II,
  21-28.

Hall, M. Jr. and J.D.Swift (SWAC), 1955
Determination of Steiner triple systems of order 15, MTAC 9, 146-152.
Hall, M. Jr., J.D.Swift and R.Killgrove (SWAC), 1959
On projective planes of order nine, MTAC 13, 233-246.
Hall, M. Jr., J.D.Swift and R.J.Walker (SWAC), 1956
Uniqueness of the projective plane of order eight, MTAC 10, 186-194.
Haselgrove, C.B. (EDSAC 1 and Manchester University Mark I), 1958
A disproof of a conjecture of Pólya, Mathematika 5, 141-145.
Haselgrove, C.B. and J.C.P.Miller (EDSAC and Manchester University Mark I), 1960
Tables of the Riemann Zeta function, Roy. Soc. Math. Tables, Vol. 6 (Cambridge Univ. Press).
Hayashi, H.S. (CDC 1604 A), 1965
Computer investigation of difference sets, Math. Comp. 19, 73-78.
Heap, B.R. and M.J.Lynn (KDF 9), 1965
On a linear Diophantine problem of Frobenius, Num. Math. 7, 226-231.
Horowitz, M. (IBM 1620), 1964
Mean random path across a square, Notices Amer. Math. Soc., 11, 55.
Hurwitz, A. (IBM 7090), 1962
New Mersenne primes, Math. Comp. 16, 249-251.
Inkeri, K. and S.Hyyrö (Wegematic 1000), 1961
On the congruence $3^{p-1} \equiv 1 \pmod{p^2}$ and the Diophantine equation $x^2 - 1 = y^p$, Ann. Univ. Turku Ser. A I no. 50, 4 pp.
Isemanger, K.R. (SILLIAC), 1960
The complete factorization of $2^{132} + 1$, Math. Comp. 14, 73-74.
Karst, E. (IBM 650), 1961a
Faktorzerlegung Mersennescher Zahlen mittels programmgesteuerter Rechengeräte, Numer. Math. 3, 79-86.
Karst, E., 1961b
New factors of Mersenne numbers, Math. Comp. 15, 51.
Karst, E. (IBM 1620), IBM 1410 and OSAGE), 1963
List of all prime divisors $q = 2Kp + 1$ of $2^p - 1$, $K < 10$, $p < 15000$, BIT 3, 222-228.
Keedwell, A.D. (Mercury), 1965
A search for projective planes of a special type with the aid of a digital computer, Math. Comp. 19, 317-322.
Keller, H.B. and J.R.Swanson (IBM 7090), 1963
Experiments in the lattice problem of Gauss, Math. Comp. 17, 223-230.
Killgrove, R.B. (SWAC), 1960
A note on the non-existence of certain projective planes of order nine, Math. Comp. 14, 70-71.
Killgrove, R.B. (IBM 7090 and SWAC), 1965
Completions of quadrangles in projective planes, II, Canad. J. Math. 17, 155-165.
Killgrove, R.B. and K.E.Ralston (SWAC), 1959
On a conjecture concerning the primes, MTAC 13, 121-122.
Kleinfeld, E. (SWAC), 1960
Techniques for enumerating Veblen-Wedderburn systems, J. ACM 7, 330-337.
Kloss, K.E. (NBS PILOT), 1965
Some number-theoretic calculations, J. Res. NBS 69 B, 335-336.
Knuth, D.E. (Burroughs 220), 1962
Euler's constant to 1271 places, Math. Comp. 16, 275-281.
Knuth, D.E., 1964
Addition chains and the evaluation of nth powers, Notices Amer. Math. Soc. 11, 230-231.
Knuth, D.E., 1965a
A class of projective planes, Amer. Math. Soc. Trans. 115, 541-549.
Knuth, D.E. (Burroughs 220), 1965b
Finite semifields and projective planes, J. Algebra 2, 182-217.

Korfhage, R.R. (IBM 7090), 1964
    On a sequence of prime numbers, Notices Amer. Math. Soc. 11, 376.
Kravitz, S. (IBM 650), 1960
    The congruence $2^{p-1} \equiv 1 \pmod{p^2}$ for $p < 100,000$, Math. Comp. 14, 378.
Kravitz, S. (IBM 650), 1961
    Divisors of Mersenne numbers $10,000 < p < 15,000$, Math. Comp. 15, 292-293.
Kravitz, S. and M.Berg (IBM 7090), 1964
    Lucas' test for Mersenne numbers, $6000 < p < 7000$, Math. Comp. 18, 148-149.
Lal, M. and W.J.Blundon (IBM 1620), 1966
    Solutions of the Diophantine equations $x^2 + y^2 = l^2$, $y^2 + z^2 = m^2$, $z^2 + x^2 = n^2$, Math.
    Comp. 20, 144-147.
Lal, M., M.F.Jones and W.J.Blundon, 1966
    Numerical solutions of the Diophantine equation $y^3 - x^2 = k$, Math. Comp. 20, 322-
    325.
Lander, L.J. and T.R.Parkin (CDC 3200), 1966
    Equal sums of biquadrates, Math. Comp. 20, 450-451.
Lander, L.J. and T.R.Parkin (CDC 6600), 1966
    A counterexample to Euler's conjecture on sums of like powers, Bull. Amer.
    Math. Soc. 72, 1079.
Leech, J. (EDSAC), 1957a
    Note on the distribution of prime numbers, J. London Math. Soc. 32, 56-58.
Leech, J. (EDSAC $1\frac{1}{2}$), 1957b
    Some solutions of Diophantine equations, Proc. Cambridge Philos. Soc. 58, 778-
    780.
Leech, J. (EDSAC II), 1958
    On $A^4 + B^4 + C^4 + D^4 = E^4$, Proc. Cambridge Philos. Soc. 54, 554-555.
Leech, J., 1963
    Coset enumeration on digital computers, Proc. Cambridge Philos. Soc. 59, 257-
    267.
Leech, J. (KDF 9), 1965
    Generators for certain normal subgroups of (2, 3, 7), Proc. Cambridge Philos.
    Soc. 61, 321-332.
Leech, J. (KDF 9), 1966
    Note on the abstract group (2, 3, 7; 9), Proc. Cambridge Philos. Soc. 62, 7-10.
Lehman, R.S. (IBM 704), 1960
    On Liouville's function, Math. Comp. 14, 311-320.
Lehman, R.S. (IBM 7090), 1966
    Separation of zeros of the Riemann zeta-function, Math. Comp. 20, 523-541.
Lehmer, D.H. (SWAC), 1953
    The sieve problem for all-purpose computers, MTAC 7, 6-14.
Lehmer, D.H. (SWAC), 1954
    A sieve problem on "pseudo-squares", MTAC 8, 241-242.
Lehmer, D.H. (SWAC), 1956a
    Extended computation of the Riemann zeta function, Mathematika 3, 102-108.
Lehmer, D.H. (SWAC), 1956b
    On the roots of the Riemann zeta function, Acta Math. 95, 291-298.
Lehmer, D.H. (SWAC), 1959a
    Combinatorial problems with digital computers. *In*: Proc. 4th Canad. Math. Con-
    gress, Banff, 1957 (Univ. Toronto Press, Toronto) pp. 160-178.
Lehmer, D.H., 1959b
    On a problem of Hardy and Littlewood, J. London Math. Soc. 36, 395-396, 485.
Lehmer, D.H. (IBM 701), 1959c
    On the exact number of primes less than a given limit, Illinois J. Math. 3, 381-
    388.
Lehmer, D.H. (IBM 701), 1960
    Discrete variable methods in numerical analysis. *In*: Proceedings of the Interna-
    tional Congress of Mathematicians 1958 (Cambridge University Press), pp. 545-
    552.

Lehmer, D. H., 1963 a
A note on primitive roots, Scripta Math. 26, 117-119.

Lehmer, D. H., 1963 b
Some high-speed logic. *In*: Proc. Symp. Appl. Math. XV (Amer. Math. Soc., Providence), pp. 141-145.

Lehmer, D. H. (IBM 704), 1964
On a problem of Störmer, Illinois J. Math., 8, 57-79.

Lehmer, D. H., 1965 a
On certain chains of primes, Proc. London Math. Soc. (3) 14 a, 183-186.

Lehmer, D. H. (IBM 7090), 1965 b
The primality of Ramanujan's tau-function, Amer. Math. Monthly 72, no. 2, part II, 15-18.

Lehmer, D. H., 1965 c
The prime factors of consecutive integers, Amer. Math. Monthly 72, no. 2 part II, 19-20.

Lehmer, D. H. and E. Lehmer (SWAC and IBM 7090), 1962
On sums of residues, Proc. Amer. Math. Soc. 13, 102-106.

Lehmer, D. H., E. Lehmer and W. M. Mills (IBM 701 and 704), 1963
Pairs of consecutive power residues, Canad. J. Math. 15, 172-177.

Lehmer, D. H., E. Lehmer, W. H. Mills and J. L. Selfridge (IBM 701, 704, 709 and 7090), 1962
Machine proof of a theorem on cubic residues, Math. Comp. 16, 407-415.

Lehmer, D. H., E. Lehmer and H. S. Vandiver (SWAC), 1954
An application of high-speed computing to Fermat's last theorem, Proc. Nat. Acad. Sci. USA 40, 25-33.

Lehmer, D. H. and S. Selberg (IBM 701), 1960
A sum involving the function of Möbius, Acta Arith. 6, 111-114.

Lehmer, E., 1954
On cyclotomic numbers of order sixteen, Canad. J. Math. 6, 449-454.

Lehmer, E. (SWAC), 1955
On the number of solutions of $u^k + D = w^2$ (mod p), Pacific J. Math. 5, 103-118.

Lehmer, E. (SWAC), 1956 a
Number theory on the SWAC. *In*: Proc. Symp. Appl. Math. VI (Amer. Mat. Soc., Providence), pp. 103-108.

Lehmer, E. (SWAC), 1956 b
On the location of Gauss sums, MTAC 10, 194-202.

Lehmer, E. (IBM 7040), 1966
Artiads characterized, J. Math. Anal. Appl. 15, 118-131.

Lehmer, E. and H. S. Vandiver (SWAC), 1957
On the computation of the number of solutions of certain trinomial congruences, J. ACM 4, 505-510.

Levine, J. and R. E. Dalton (IBM 650), 1962
Minimum periods, modulo p, of first-order Bell exponential integers, Math. Comp. 16, 416-423.

Lindenberg, W. (ER 56), 1962
Über eine Darstellung von Gruppenelementen in digitalen Rechenautomaten, Numer. Math. 4, 151-153.

Lippmann, R. A. (IBM 650), 1963
Note on irregular discriminants, J. London Math. Soc. 38, 385-386.

Lochs, G. (Datatron 205), 1963
Die ersten 968 Kettenbruchnenner von π, Monatsh. Math. 67, 311-316.

von Lockemann, W. (Siemens 2002), 1960
Ein Rechnerprogramm zur Erzeugung von lateinischen Quadraten, Elektronische Rechenanlagen 2, 129-130.

Love, C. H., 1966
Abscissas and weights for Gaussian quadrature for $N = 2$ to 100, and $N = 125$, 150, 175 and 200, J. Res. NBS 70 B, 249-256.

Low, M. E. (IBM 7094), 1965
    Real zeros of real Dirichlet L-series, Notices Amer. Math. Soc. 12, 93.
Ludeke, C. A. and J. E. Cornett, 1966
    A computer investigation of a subharmonic bifurcation point in the Duffing equa-
    tion, SIAM J. Appl. Math. 14, 1298-1306.
Luke, Y. L., W. Fair, G. Coombs and R. Moran (IBM 1620), 1965
    On a constant in the theory of trigonometric series, Math. Comp. 19, 501-502.
Lunelli, L. (ELEA 6001), 1966
    Procedimenti per la costruzione di piani di esperimenti incompleti, Calcolo 3,
    313-338.
Lunelli, L. and M. Lunelli (CRC 102 A/P), 1960
    Tavola di congruenze $a^n = 1$ (mod K) per $a = 2, 5, 10$, Atti Sem. Mat. Fis. Univ.
    Modena 10, 219-223.
Lunelli, L. and M. Sce (CRC 102 A/P), 1958
    Sulla ricerce dei k-archi completi mediante una calcolatrice electronica. In:
    Convegno intern.: Reticoli i geometrie proiettive, Palermo, 25-29 Oct. 1957,
    Messina 30 Oct. 1957 (Cremonese, Rome), pp. 81-86.
Mapes, D. C. (IBM 709), 1963
    Fast method for computing the number of primes less than a given limit, Math.
    Comp. 17, 179-185.
Martin, J. L. (ACE), 1962
    The exact enumeration of self-avoiding walks on a lattice, Proc. Cambridge
    Philos. Soc. 58, 92-101.
Maurer, W. D. (IBM 7094), 1966
    Computer experiments in finite algebra, Comm. ACM 9, 598-603, 643.
Mayoh, B. H. (GIER), 1966
    On the second Goldbach conjecture, BIT 6, 48-50.
McLaren, A. D. (EDSAC II), 1963
    Optimal numerical integration on a sphere, Math. Comp. 17, 361-383.
Mendelsohn, N. J., A. L. Dulmage, D. M. Johnson and E. T. Parker (Univac M-460),
    1960
    Construction of mutually orthogonal latin squares, Notices Amer. Math. Soc. 7,
    208.
Michels, H. H. (IBM 7090), 1963
    Abscissas and weights coefficients for Lobatto quadrature, Math. Comp. 17,
    237-244.
Miller, J. C. P. (EDSAC), 1951
    Large primes, Eureka 14, 10-11.
Miller, J. C. P. and M. F. C. Woollett (EDSAC), 1955
    Solutions of the Diophantine equation $x^3 + y^3 + z^3 = k$, J. London Math. Soc. 30, 101-
    110.
Mills, W. H. (CDC 1604), 1965
    Bounded consecutive residues and related problems. In: Proc. Symp. Pure Math.
    VIII (Amer. Math. Soc., Providence), pp. 170-174.
Mitchell, W. C. (IBM 7094), 1966
    The number of lattice points in a k-dimensional hypersphere, Math. Comp. 20,
    300-310.
Mullin, A. A. (IBM 7094), 1966
    Another estimate of the pi-function, Notices Amer. Math. Soc. 13, 376.
Muskat, J. B. (IBM 7070 and 7090), 1966
    On divisors of odd perfect numbers, Math. Comp. 20, 141-144.
Neubauer, G. (Siemens 2002), 1963
    Eine empirische Untersuchung zur Mertensschen Funktion, Numer. Math. 5, 1-13.
Neubüser, J. (Z 22), 1960
    Untersuchungen des Untergruppenverbandes endlicher Gruppen auf einer pro-
    grammgesteuerten elektronischen Dualmaschine, Numer. Math. 2, 280-292.

Neubüser, J. (Z 22), 1961
Bestimmung der Untergruppenverbände endlicher p-Gruppen auf einer programmierten elektronischen Dualmaschine, Numer. Math. 3, 271-278.

von Neumann, J. and H.H.Goldstine (IAS computer), 1953
A numerical study of a conjecture of Kummer, MTAC 7, 133-134.

von Neumann, J. and B.Tuckerman (IAS computer), 1955
Continued fraction expansion of $2^{\frac{1}{3}}$, MTAC 9, 23-24.

Newman, M. (SEAC), 1956
A table of the coefficients of the powers of $\eta(\tau)$, Nederl. Akad. Wetensch. Proc. Ser. A 59 = Indag. Math. 18, 204-216.

Newman, M. (IBM 704), 1958
Further identities and congruences for the coefficients of modular forms, Canad. J. Math. 10, 577-586.

Newman, M. (IBM 704), 1959
Construction and application of a class of modular functions, Proc. London Math. Soc. (3) 9, 334-350 and 373-387.

Nicholson, S.C. and J.Jeenel (NORC), 1955
Some comments on a NORC computation of π, MTAC 9, 161-164.

Nicol, C.A., 1966
Some Diophantine equations involving arithmetic functions, J. Math. Anal. Appl. 15, 154-161.

Nikolai, P.J. (UNIVAC 1103 A), 1960
Permanents of incidence matrices, Math. Comp. 14, 262-266.

Norton, K.K. (ILLIAC), 1961
Remarks on the number of factors of an odd perfect number, Acta Arith. 6, 365-374.

Ockert, R. (TR 4), 1961
Ein Verfahren zur Primfaktorzerlegung grosser Zahlen mit Hilfe binärer quadratischer Formen, Computing 1, 256-263.

Osborn, R. (IBM 650), 1961
Tables of all primitive roots of odd primes less than 1000 (Univ. Texas Press, Austin).

Ostrowski, R.T. and K.D.Van Duren (UNIVAC M-460), 1961
On a theorem of Mann on Latin squares, Math. Comp. 15, 293-295.

Paige, L.J. and C.B.Tompkins (SWAC), 1960
The size of the 10×10 orthogonal latin square problem. In: Proc. Symp. Appl. Math. X (Amer. Math. Soc., Providence), pp. 71-83.

Parker, E.T. (UNIVAC M-460), 1959
A computer search for latin squares orthogonal to latin squares of order ten, Notices Amer. Math. Soc. 6, 798.

Parker, E.T. (UNIVAC M-460), 1962
On orthogonal latin swuares. In: Proc. Symp. Pure Math. VI (Amer. Math. Soc., Providence), pp. 43-46.

Parker, E.T. (UNIVAC 1206), 1963
Computer investigation of orthogonal latin squares of order ten. In: Proc. Symp. Appl. Math. XV (Amer. Math. Soc., Providence) pp. 73-81.

Parker, E.T. and R.B.Killgrove (UNIVAC 1206 and SWAC), 1964
A note on projective planes of order nine, Math. Comp. 18, 506-508.

Parker, E.T. and P.J.Nikolai (UNIVAC 1103 A), 1958
A search for analogues of the Mathieu groups, MTAC 12, 38-43.

Pasta, J.R. and S.Ulam (MANIAC), 1959
Heuristic numerical work in some problems of hydrodynamics, MTAC 13, 1-12.

Paxson, G.A. (IBM 7090), 1961
The compositeness of the thirteenth Fermat number, Math. Comp. 15, 420.

Pearson, E.H. (CDC 1604), 1963
On the congruences $(p-1)! \equiv -1$ and $2^{p-1} \equiv 1 \pmod{p^2}$, Math. Comp. 17, 194-195.

Rabinowitz, P. (WEIZAC), 1960
    Abscissas and weights for Lobatto quadrature of high order, Math. Comp. 14,
    47-52.
Rebolia, L. (IBM 1620), 1966
    Formule di quadratura di tipo Gaussiano con valori delle derivate dell' inte-
    grando, Calcolo 3, 351-369.
Reitwiesner, G.W. (ENIAC), 1950
    An ENIAC determination of π and e to more than 2000 decimal places, MTAC 4,
    11-15.
Richtmyer, R.D., M.Devaney and N.Metropolis (MANIAC I), 1962
    Continued fraction expansions of algebraic numbers, Numer. Math. 4, 68-84.
Riesel, H. (BESK), 1956
    A note on the prime numbers of the forms $N = (6a+1)2^{2n-1} - 1$ and $M = (6a-1)2^{2n} - 1$,
    Ark. Mat. 3, 245-253.
Riesel, H. (BESK), 1958 a
    A new Mersenne prime, MTAC 12, 60.
Riesel, H. (BESK), 1958 b
    Mersenne numbers, MTAC 12, 207-213.
Riesel, H. (BESK), 1962
    All factors $q < 10^8$ in all Mersenne numbers $2p - 1$, p prime $< 10^4$, Math. Comp.
    16, 478-482.
Riesel, H. (BESK), 1963
    A factor of the Fermat number F_{19}, Math. Comp. 17, 458.
Riesel, H. (BESK), 1964
    Note on the congruence $a^{p-1} = 1 \pmod{p^2}$, Math. Comp. 18, 149-150.
Robinson, R.M. (SWAC), 1954
    Mersenne and Fermat numbers, Proc. Amer. Math. Soc. 5, 842-846.
Robinson, R.M. (SWAC), 1957 a
    Factors of Fermat numbers, MTAC 11, 21-22.
Robinson, R.M. (IBM 701), 1957 b
    Some factorization of numbers of the form $2^n \pm 1$, MTAC 11, 265-268.
Robinson, R.M. (SWAC), 1958
    A report on primes of the form $k \cdot 2^n + 1$ and on factors of Fermat numbers, Proc.
    Amer. Math. Soc. 9, 673-681.
Robinson, R.M. (IBM 7090), 1965
    Some conjectures about cyclotomic integers, Math. Comp. 19, 210-217.
Rogers, K., 1964
    The Schnirelmann density of the squarefree integers, Proc. Amer. Math. Soc. 15,
    515-516.
Rosser, J.B., 1963
    Unexpected dividends in the theory of prime numbers. In: Proc. Symp. Appl. Math.
    XV (Amer. Math. Soc., Providence), pp. 259-268.
Rosser, J.B. and L.Schoenfeld (IBM 650), 1962
    Approximate formulas for some functions of prime numbers, Illinois J. Math. 6,
    64-94.
Salié, H. (ZRA 1), 1965
    Über die kleinste Primzahl, die eine gegebene Primzahl als kleinsten positiven
    quadratischen Nichtrest hat, Math. Nachr. 29, 113-114.
Salzer, H.E. and N.Levine (ERA 1103 and IBM 704), 1958
    Table of integers not exceeding 10 00000 that are not expressible as the sum of
    four tetrahedral numbers, MTAC 12, 141-144.
Sarafyan, D., 1965
    Improvements in the derivation of Runge-Kutta type formulas and computer im-
    plementation, Notices Amer. Math. Soc. 12, 340.
Scheffler, D. and R.Ondrejka (IBM 709), 1960
    The numerical evaluation of the eighteenth perfect number, Math. Comp. 14,
    199-200.

Schinzel, A. and A. Wakulicz (XYZ), 1959
Sur l'équation $\varphi(x+k)=\varphi(x)$. II. Acta Arith. 5, 425-426.

Segal, S. L. (IBM 1620), 1962
On $\pi(x+y) \leqslant \pi(x) + \pi(y)$, Trans. Amer. Math. Soc. 104, 523-527.

Selfridge, J. L. (SWAC), 1953
Factors of Fermat numbers, MTAC 7, 274-275.

Selfridge, J. L. and A. Hurwitz (IBM 7090), 1964
Fermat numbers and Mersenne numbers, Math. Comp. 18, 146-148.

Selfridge, J. L., C. A. Nicol and H. S. Vandiver (SWAC), 1955
Proof of Fermat's last theorem for all prime exponents less than 4002, Proc. Nat. Acad. Sci. USA 41, 970-973.

Selfridge, J. L., C. A. Nicol and H. S. Vandiver (SWAC), 1956
On Diophantine equations which have no solutions, Proc. Nat. Acad. Sci. USA 42, 264-266.

Selfridge, J. L. and B. W. Pollack (IBM 7090), 1964
Fermat's last theorem is true for any exponent up to 25,000, Notices Amer. Math. Soc. 11, 97.

Selmer, E. A. (IAS computer), 1954 a
A conjecture concerning rational points on cubic curves, Math. Scand. 2, 49-54.

Selmer, E. A. (IAS Computer), 1954 b
The diophantine equation $ax^3 + by^3 + cz^3 = 0$. Completion of the tables, Acta Math. 92, 191-197.

Shanks, D. (IBM 704), 1959 a
A sieve method for factoring numbers of the form $n^2 + 1$, MTAC 13, 78-84.

Shanks, D. (IBM 704), 1959 b
Quadratic residues and the distribution of primes, MTAC 13, 272-284.

Shanks, D. (IBM 704), 1960
On the conjecture of Hardy and Littlewood concerning the number of primes of the form $n^2 + a$, Math. Comp. 14, 320-332.

Shanks, D., 1963
Supplementary data and remarks concerning a Hardy-Littlewood conjecture, Math. Comp. 17, 188-193.

Shanks, D. (IBM 7090), 1964
The second-order term in the asymptotic expansion of B(x), Math. Comp. 18, 75-86.

Shanks, D. and L. P. Schmid, 1966
Use of a computer to correct and suggest theoretical studies of binary quadratic forms. *In*: Proceedings of IFIP Congress 65, New York City, May 24-29, 1965 (Spartan Books, Washington) vol. 2, pp. 586-587.

Shanks, D. and J. W. Wrench Jr. (IBM 7090), 1962
Calculation of π to 100,000 decimals, Math. Comp. 16, 76-99.

Shen Lin and T. Rado, 1965
Computer studies of Turing machine problems, J. ACM 12, 196-212.

Shen Mok-Kong (PERM and TR-4), 1964
On checking the Goldbach conjecture, BIT 4, 243-245.

Smith, H. F. (IBM 701 and IBM 650), 1957
On a generalization of the prime pair problem, MTAC 11, 249-254.

Spira, R., 1966 a
Approximate functional approximations and the Riemann hypothesis, Proc. Amer. Math. Soc. 17, 314-317.

Spira, R., 1966 b
Zeros of sections of the zeta function, I, Math. Comp. 20, 542-550.

Starynkevitch, D. (CAB 500), 1963
Recherche des nombres premiers élevés sur une calculatrice binaire, Rev. Fr. Tr. Inf., 6, 171-173.

Stein, M. L. and P. R. Stein, 1965 a
Experimental results on additive 2-bases, Math. Comp. 19, 427-434.

Stein, M. L. and P.R.Stein (MANIAC II), 1965b
    New experimental results on the Goldbach conjecture, Math. Mag. 38, 72-80.
Stemmler, R.M. (IBM 7090), 1964
    The ideal Waring theorem for exponents 401 - 200,000, Math. Comp. 18, 144-146.
Sweeney, D.W. (IBM 7094), 1963
    On the computation of Euler's constant, Math. Comp. 17, 170-178.
Swift, J.D. (SWAC), 1960a
    Construction of Galois fields of characteristic two and irreducible polynomials,
    Math. Comp. 14, 94-103.
Swift, J.D., 1960b
    Isomorph rejection in exhaustive search techniques. In: Proc. Symp. Appl. Math.
    X (Amer. Math. Soc., Providence), pp. 195-200.
Swinnerton-Dyer, H.P.F., 1966
    Applications of computers to pure mathematics. In: Numerical Analysis, an intro-
    duction (Academic Press, London and New York), pp. 159-164.
Taussky, O. (SEAC), 1956
    Some computational problems in algebraic number theory. In: Proc. Symp. Appl.
    Math. VI (Amer. Math. Soc., Providence), pp. 187-193.
Taussky, O., 1962
    Number theory: Some computational problems in algebraic number theory. In:
    Survey of numerical analysis (Mc Graw Hill, New York), pp. 549-557.
Taussky, O. and J.Todd (SEAC), 1960
    Some discrete variable computations. In: Proc. Symp. Appl. Math. X (Amer. Math.
    Soc., Providence), pp. 201-209.
Tompkins, C. (SWAC), 1956
    Machine attacks on problems whose variables are permutations. In: Proc. Symp.
    Appl. Math. VI (Amer. Math. Soc., Providence), pp. 195-211.
Trotter, H.F. (IBM 7094), 1964
    A machine program for coset enumeration, Canad. Math. Bull. 7, 357-368.
Turing, A.M. (Manchester Univ. Mark I Computer), 1953
    Some calculations of the Riemann zeta function, Proc. London Math. Soc. (3), 3,
    99-117.
Tuškina, T.A. (M-20), 1965
    Čislennyi eksperiment po vyčisleniju invarianta Hasse dlja nekotoryh krivyh, Izv.
    Akad. Nauk SSSR Ser. Mat. 29, 1203-1204.
Tutte, W.T., 1965
    The quest of the perfect square, Amer. Math. Monthly 72 no. 2 part II, 29-35.
Ulam, S.M., 1960
    A collection of mathematical problems (Intersc. Publ., New York).
Ulam, S.M., 1963
    Electronic computers and scientific research (part 1), Computers and Automation
    12, 20-24.
Vaida, D. (CIFA-1), 1959
    Calculul polinoamelor ireductible modulo 2, cu masina electronică de calcul
    CIFA-1, Acad. R.P.Romîne, Stud. Cerc. Mat. 10, 447-458.
Vandiver, H.S. (SWAC), 1954a
    Examination of methods of attack in the second case of Fermat's last theorem,
    Proc. Nat. Acad. Sci. USA 40, 732-735.
Vandiver, H.S. (SWAC), 1954b
    The relation of some data obtained from rapid computing machines to the theory
    of cyclotomic fields, Proc. Nat. Acad. Sci. USA 40, 474-480.
Vandiver, H.S. (SWAC), 1958
    The rapid computing machine as an instrument in the discovery of new relations
    in the theory of numbers, Proc. Nat. Acad. Sci. USA 44, 459-464.
Walker, R.J. (SWAC), 1960
    An enumerative technique for a class of combinatorial problems. In: Proc. Symp.
    Appl. Math. X (Amer. Math. Soc., Providence) pp. 91-94.

Walker, R. J. (CDC 1604), 1963
Determination of division algebras with 32 elements. *In*: Proc. Symp. Appl. Math. XV (Amer. Math. Soc.; Providence), pp. 83-85.
Walkup, D. W., 1963
On a result of Heineken, Notices Amer. Math. Soc. 10, 578.
Watson, E. J. (Mercury), 1962
Primitive polynomials (mod 2), Math. Comp. 16, 368-369.
White, M. E. (IBM 1620), 1965
Modular arithmetic for finite groups, Notices Amer. Math. Soc. 12, 52.
Wilf, H. S. (ILLIAC), 1963
Calculations relating to a conjecture of Pólya and Schoenberg, Math. Comp. 17, 200-201.
Williams, H. C., R. A. Germon and C. R. Zarnke (IBM 7040 and 1620 II), 1965
Solution of the cattle problem of Archimedes, Math. Comp. 19, 671-674.
Wrathall, C. P. (IBM 709, IBM 7090 and SWAC), 1964
New factors of Fermat numbers, Math. Comp. 18, 324-325.
Wrench, J. W. Jr. (UNIVAC), 1954
A new approximation to the reciprocal of π, MTAC 8, 49-51.
Wrench, J. W. Jr., 1961
Evaluating Artin's constant and the twin-prime constant, Math. Comp. 15, 396-398.
Wunderlich, M. (CDC 1604), 1962
Certain properties of pyramidal and figurate numbers, Math. Comp. 16, 482-486.
Wunderlich, M. (IBM 709), 1963
On the non-existence of Fibonacci squares, Math. Comp. 17, 455-457.
Yamabe, H. and D. Pope (UNIVAC 1103), 1961
A computational approach to the four-color problem, Math. Comp. 15, 250-253.
Yamamoto, K., 1965 a
On Gaussian sums with biquadratic residue characters, J. Reine Angew. Math. 219, 200-213.
Yamamoto, K. (OKITAC 5090 H), 1965 b
On the Diophantine equation $4/n = 1/x + 1/y + 1/z$, Mem. Fac. Sci. Kyushu Univ. Ser. A 19, 37-47.
Zahn, C. T. Jr. (IBM 704), 1962
Black box maximization of circular coverage, J. Res. Nat. Bur. Standards Sect. B 66 B, 181-216.

ADDED IN PROOF

Dekkers, A. J. and A. J. W. Duijvestijn (PASCAL), 1962
Solving a chessboard puzzle with the PASCAL, Philips Tech. Rev. 24, 157-163.
Heap, B. R. (KDF 9), 1966
The enumeration of homeomorphically irreducible star graphs, J. Mathematical Phys. 7, 1582-1587.
Iwasawa, K. and C. C. Sims (IBM 7094), 1966
Computation of invariants in the theory of cyclotomic fields, J. Math. Soc. Japan 18, 86-96.
Krishnamurthy, V. (IBM 7094), 1966
On the number of topologies on a finite set, Amer. Math. Monthly 73, 154-157.
Lehman, R. S. (IBM 7090), 1966
On the difference $\pi(x)$-li(x), Acta Arith. 11, 397-410.
Miller, J. C. P. and D. J. Wheeler (EDSAC), 1951
Large prime numbers, Nature 168, 838.
Stein, P. R. and S. M. Ulam (STRETCH, MANIAC II and IBM 7090), 1966
Non-linear transformation studies on electronic computers, Rozprawy Matematyczne XXXIX (Warsaw).